Pitman Research Notes in Mathematics Series

Submission of proposals for consideration
Suggestions for publication, in the form of outlines and representative samples, are invited by the Editorial Board for assessment. Intending authors should approach one of the main editors or another member of the Editorial Board, citing the relevant AMS subject classifications. Alternatively, outlines may be sent directly to the publisher's offices. Refereeing is by members of the board and other mathematical authorities in the topic concerned, throughout the world.

Preparation of accepted manuscripts
On acceptance of a proposal, the publisher will supply full instructions for the preparation of manuscripts in a form suitable for direct photo-lithographic reproduction. Specially printed grid sheets can be provided and a contribution is offered by the publisher towards the cost of typing. Word processor output, subject to the publisher's approval, is also acceptable.

Illustrations should be prepared by the authors, ready for direct reproduction without further improvement. The use of hand-drawn symbols should be avoided wherever possible, in order to maintain maximum clarity of the text.

The publisher will be pleased to give any guidance necessary during the preparation of a typescript, and will be happy to answer any queries.

Important note
In order to avoid later retyping, intending authors are strongly urged not to begin final preparation of a typescript before receiving the publisher's guidelines. In this way it it hoped to preserve the uniform appearance of the series.

Longman Scientific & Technical
Longman House
Burnt Mill
Harlow, Essex, UK
(tel (0279) 426721)

Titles in this series

1 Improperly posed boundary value problems
A Carasso and A P Stone
2 Lie algebras generated by finite dimensional ideals
I N Stewart
3 Bifurcation problems in nonlinear elasticity
R W Dickey
4 Partial differential equations in the complex domain
D L Colton
5 Quasilinear hyperbolic systems and waves
A Jeffrey
6 Solution of boundary value problems by the method of integral operators
D L Colton
7 Taylor expansions and catastrophes
T Poston and I N Stewart
8 Function theoretic methods in differential equations
R P Gilbert and R J Weinacht
9 Differential topology with a view to applications
D R J Chillingworth
10 Characteristic classes of foliations
H V Pittie
11 Stochastic integration and generalized martingales
A U Kussmaul
12 Zeta-functions: An introduction to algebraic geometry
A D Thomas
13 Explicit *a priori* inequalities with applications to boundary value problems
V G Sigillito
14 Nonlinear diffusion
W E Fitzgibbon III and H F Walker
15 Unsolved problems concerning lattice points
J Hammer
16 Edge-colourings of graphs
S Fiorini and R J Wilson
17 Nonlinear analysis and mechanics: Heriot-Watt Symposium Volume I
R J Knops
18 Actions of fine abelian groups
C Kosniowski
19 Closed graph theorems and webbed spaces
M De Wilde
20 Singular perturbation techniques applied to integro-differential equations
H Grabmüller
21 Retarded functional differential equations: A global point of view
S E A Mohammed
22 Multiparameter spectral theory in Hilbert space
B D Sleeman
24 Mathematical modelling techniques
R Aris
25 Singular points of smooth mappings
C G Gibson
26 Nonlinear evolution equations solvable by the spectral transform
F Calogero
27 Nonlinear analysis and mechanics: Heriot-Watt Symposium Volume II
R J Knops
28 Constructive functional analysis
D S Bridges
29 Elongational flows: Aspects of the behaviour of model elasticoviscous fluids
C J S Petrie
30 Nonlinear analysis and mechanics: Heriot-Watt Symposium Volume III
R J Knops
31 Fractional calculus and integral transforms of generalized functions
A C McBride
32 Complex manifold techniques in theoretical physics
D E Lerner and P D Sommers
33 Hilbert's third problem: scissors congruence
C-H Sah
34 Graph theory and combinatorics
R J Wilson
35 The Tricomi equation with applications to the theory of plane transonic flow
A R Manwell
36 Abstract differential equations
S D Zaidman
37 Advances in twistor theory
L P Hughston and R S Ward
38 Operator theory and functional analysis
I Erdelyi
39 Nonlinear analysis and mechanics: Heriot-Watt Symposium Volume IV
R J Knops
40 Singular systems of differential equations
S L Campbell
41 N-dimensional crystallography
R L E Schwarzenberger
42 Nonlinear partial differential equations in physical problems
D Graffi
43 Shifts and periodicity for right invertible operators
D Przeworska-Rolewicz
44 Rings with chain conditions
A W Chatters and C R Hajarnavis
45 Moduli, deformations and classifications of compact complex manifolds
D Sundararaman
46 Nonlinear problems of analysis in geometry and mechanics
M Atteia, D Bancel and I Gumowski
47 Algorithmic methods in optimal control
W A Gruver and E Sachs
48 Abstract Cauchy problems and functional differential equations
F Kappel and W Schappacher
49 Sequence spaces
W H Ruckle
50 Recent contributions to nonlinear partial differential equations
H Berestycki and H Brezis
51 Subnormal operators
J B Conway

52 Wave propagation in viscoelastic media
F Mainardi
53 Nonlinear partial differential equations and their applications: Collège de France Seminar. Volume I
H Brezis and J L Lions
54 Geometry of Coxeter groups
H Hiller
55 Cusps of Gauss mappings
T Banchoff, T Gaffney and C McCrory
56 An approach to algebraic K-theory
A J Berrick
57 Convex analysis and optimization
J-P Aubin and R B Vintner
58 Convex analysis with applications in the differentiation of convex functions
J R Giles
59 Weak and variational methods for moving boundary problems
C M Elliott and J R Ockendon
60 Nonlinear partial differential equations and their applications: Collège de France Seminar. Volume II
H Brezis and J L Lions
61 Singular systems of differential equations II
S L Campbell
62 Rates of convergence in the central limit theorem
Peter Hall
63 Solution of differential equations by means of one-parameter groups
J M Hill
64 Hankel operators on Hilbert space
S C Power
65 Schrödinger-type operators with continuous spectra
M S P Eastham and H Kalf
66 Recent applications of generalized inverses
S L Campbell
67 Riesz and Fredholm theory in Banach algebra
B A Barnes, G J Murphy, M R F Smyth and T T West
68 Evolution equations and their applications
K Kappel and W Schappacher
69 Generalized solutions of Hamilton-Jacobi equations
P L Lions
70 Nonlinear partial differential equations and their applications: Collège de France Seminar. Volume III
H Brezis and J L Lions
71 Spectral theory and wave operators for the Schrödinger equation
A M Berthier
72 Approximation of Hilbert space operators I
D A Herrero
73 Vector valued Nevanlinna Theory
H J W Ziegler
74 Instability, nonexistence and weighted energy methods in fluid dynamics and related theories
B Straughan
75 Local bifurcation and symmetry
A Vanderbauwhede
76 Clifford analysis
F Brackx, R. Delanghe and F Sommen
77 Nonlinear equivalence, reduction of PDEs to ODEs and fast convergent numerical methods
E E Rosinger
78 Free boundary problems, theory and applications. Volume I
A Fasano and M Primicerio
79 Free boundary problems, theory and applications. Volume II
A Fasano and M Primicerio
80 Symplectic geometry
A Crumeyrolle and J Grifone
81 An algorithmic analysis of a communication model with retransmission of flawed messages
D M Lucantoni
82 Geometric games and their applications
W H Ruckle
83 Additive groups of rings
S Feigelstock
84 Nonlinear partial differential equations and their applications: Collège de France Seminar, Volume IV
H Brezis and J L Lions
85 Multiplicative functionals on topological algebras
T Husain
86 Hamilton-Jacobi equations in Hilbert spaces
V Barbu and G Da Prato
87 Harmonic maps with symmetry, harmonic morphisms and deformations of metrics
P Baird
88 Similarity solutions of nonlinear partial differential equations
L Dresner
89 Contributions to nonlinear partial differential equations
C Bardos, A Damlamian, J I Díaz and J Hernández
90 Banach and Hilbert spaces of vector-valued functions
J Burbea and P Masani
91 Control and observation of neutral systems
D Salamon
92 Banach bundles, Banach modules and automorphisms of C^*-algebras
M J Dupré and R M Gillette
93 Nonlinear partial differential equations and their applications: Collège de France Seminar. Volume V
H Brezis and J L Lions
94 Computer algebra in applied mathematics: an introduction to MACSYMA
R H Rand
95 Advances in nonlinear waves. Volume I
L Debnath
96 FC-groups
M J Tomkinson
97 Topics in relaxation and ellipsoidal methods
M Akgül
98 Analogue of the group algebra for topological semigroups
H Dzinotyiweyi
99 Stochastic functional differential equations
S E A Mohammed

100 Optimal control of variational inequalities
V Barbu
101 Partial differential equations and dynamical systems
W E Fitzgibbon III
102 Approximation of Hilbert space operators Volume II
C Apostol, L A Fialkow, D A Herrero and D Voiculescu
103 Nondiscrete induction and iterative processes
V Ptak and F-A Potra
104 Analytic functions - growth aspects
O P Juneja and G P Kapoor
105 Theory of Tikhonov regularization for Fredholm equations of the first kind
C W Groetsch
106 Nonlinear partial differential equations and free boundaries. Volume I
J I Díaz
107 Tight and taut immersions of manifolds
T E Cecil and P J Ryan
108 A layering method for viscous, incompressible L_p flows occupying R^n
A Douglis and E B Fabes
109 Nonlinear partial differential equations and their applications: Collège de France Seminar. Volume VI
H Brezis and J L Lions
110 Finite generalized quadrangles
S E Payne and J A Thas
111 Advances in nonlinear waves. Volume II
L Debnath
112 Topics in several complex variables
E Ramírez de Arellano & D Sundararaman
113 Differential equations, flow invariance and applications
N H Pavel
114 Geometrical combinatorics
F C Holroyd and R J Wilson
115 Generators of strongly continuous semigroups
J A van Casteren
116 Growth of algebras and Gelfand-Kirillov dimension
G R Krause and T H Lenagan
117 Theory of bases and cones
P K Kamthan and M Gupta
118 Linear groups and permutations
A R Camina and E A Whelan
119 General Wiener-Hopf factorization methods
F-O Speck
120 Free boundary problems: applications and theory. Volume III
A Bossavit, A Damlamian and M Fremond
121 Free boundary problems: applications and theory. Volume IV
A Bossavit, A Damlamian and M Fremond
122 Nonlinear partial differential equations and their applications: Collège de France Seminar. Volume VII
H Brezis and J L Lions
123 Geometric methods in operator algebras
H Araki and E G Effros
124 Infinite dimensional analysis-stochastic processes
S Albeverio
125 Ennio de Giorgi Colloquium
P Krée
126 Almost-periodic functions in abstract spaces
S Zaidman
127 Nonlinear variational problems
A Marino, L. Modica, S. Spagnolo and M Degiovanni
128 Second-order systems of partial differential equations in the plane
L K Hua, W Lin and C-Q Wu
129 Asymptotics of high-order ordinary differential equations
R B Paris and A D Wood
130 Stochastic differential equations
R Wu
131 Differential geometry
L A Cordero
132 Nonlinear differential equations
J K Hale and P Martinez-Amores
133 Approximation theory and applications
S P Singh
134 Near-rings and their links with groups
J D P Meldrum
135 Estimating eigenvalues with *a posteriori/a priori* inequalities
J R Kuttler and V G Sigillito
136 Regular semigroups as extensions
F J Pastijn and M Petrich
137 Representations of rank one Lie groups
D H Collingwood
138 Fractional calculus
G F Roach and A C McBride
139 Hamilton's principle in continuum mechanics
A Bedford
140 Numericalanalysis
D F Griffiths and G A Watson
141 Semigroups, theory and applications. Volume I
H Brezis, M G Crandall and F Kappel
142 Distribution theorems of L-functions
D Joyner
143 Recent developments in structured continua
D De Kee and P Kaloni
144 Functional analysis and two-point differential operators
J Locker
145 Numerical methods for partial differential equations
S I Hariharan and T H Moulden
146 Completely bounded maps and dilations
V I Paulsen
147 Harmonic analysis on the Heisenberg nilpotent Lie group
W Schempp
148 Contributions to modern calculus of variations
L Cesari
149 Nonlinear parabolic equations: qualitative properties of solutions
L Boccardo and A Tesei
150 From local times to global geometry, control and physics
K D Elworthy

151 A stochastic maximum principle for optimal control of diffusions
U G Haussman
152 Semigroups, theory and applications. Volume II
H Brezis, M G Crandall and F Kappel
153 A general theory of integration in function spaces
P Muldowney
154 Oakland Conference on partial differential equations and applied mathematics
L R Bragg and J W Dettman
155 Contributions to nonlinear partial differential equations. Volume II
J I Díaz and P L Lions
156 Semigroups of linear operators: an introduction
A C McBride
157 Ordinary and partial differential equations
B D Sleeman and R J Jarvis
158 Hyperbolic equations
F Colombini and M K V Murthy
159 Linear topologies on a ring: an overview
J S Golan
160 Dynamical systems and bifurcation theory
M I Camacho, M J Pacifico and F Takens
161 Branched coverings and algebraic functions
M Namba
162 Perturbation bounds for matrix eigenvalues
R Bhatia
163 Defect minimization in operator equations: theory and applications
R Reemtsen
164 Multidimensional Brownian excursions and potential theory
K Burdzy
165 Viscosity solutions and optimal control
R J Elliott
166 Nonlinear partial differential equations and their applications. Collège de France Seminar. Volume VIII
H Brezis and J L Lions
167 Theory and applications of inverse problems
H Haario
168 Energy stability and convection
G P Galdi and B Straughan
169 Additive groups of rings. Volume II
S Feigelstock
170 Numerical analysis 1987
D F Griffiths and G A Watson
171 Surveys of some recent results in operator theory. Volume I
J B Conway and B B Morrel
172 Amenable Banach algebras
J-P Pier
173 Pseudo-orbits of contact forms
A Bahri
174 Poisson algebras and Poisson manifolds
K H Bhaskara and K Viswanath
175 Maximum principles and eigenvalue problems in partial differential equations
P W Schaefer
176 Mathematical analysis of nonlinear, dynamic processes
K U Grusa
177 Cordes' two-parameter spectral representation theory
D F McGhee and R H Picard
178 Equivariant K-theory for proper actions
N C Phillips
179 Elliptic operators, topology and asymptotic methods
J Roe
180 Nonlinear evolution equations
J K Engelbrecht, V E Fridman and E N Pelinovski
181 Nonlinear partial differential equations and their applications. Collège de France Seminar. Volume IX
H Brezis and J L Lions
182 Critical points at infinity in some variational problems
A Bahri
183 Recent developments in hyperbolic equations
L Cattabriga, F Colombini, M K V Murthy and S Spagnolo
185 Optimization and identification of systems governed by evolution equations on Banach space
N U Ahmed
185 Free boundary problems: theory and applications. Volume I
K H Hoffmann and J Sprekels
186 Free boundary problems: theory and applications. Volume II
K H Hoffmann and J Sprekels
187 An introduction to intersection homology theory
F Kirwan
188 Derivatives, nuclei and dimensions on the frame of torsion theories
J S Golan and H Simmons
189 Theory of reproducing kernels and its applications
S Saitoh
190 Volterra integrodifferential equations in Banach spaces and applications
G Da Prato and M Iannelli
191 Nest algebras
K R Davidson
192 Surveys of some recent results in operator theory. Volume II
J B Conway and B B Morrel
193 Nonlinear variational problems. Volume II
A Marino and M K Murthy
194 Stochastic processes with multidimensional parameter
M E Dozzi
195 Prestressed bodies
D Iesan
196 Hilbert space approach to some classical transforms
R H Picard
197 Stochastic calculus in application
J R Norris
198 Radical theory
B J Gardner
199 The C^*-algebras of a class of solvable Lie groups
X Wang

200 Stochastic analysis, path integration and dynamics
K D Elworthy and J C Zambrini
201 Riemannian geometry and holonomy groups
S Salamon
202 Strong asymptotics for extremal errors and polynomials associated with Erdös type weights
D S Lubinsky
203 Optimal control of diffusion processes
V S Borkar
204 Rings, modules and radicals
B J Gardner
205 Two-parameter eigenvalue problems in ordinary differential equations
M Faierman
206 Distributions and analytic functions
R D Carmichael and D Mitrović
207 Semicontinuity, relaxation and integral representation in the calculus of variations
G Buttazzo
208 Recent advances in nonlinear elliptic and parabolic problems
P Bénilan, M Chipot, L Evans and M Pierre
209 Model completions, ring representations and the topology of the Pierce sheaf
A Carson
210 Retarded dynamical systems
G Stepan
211 Function spaces, differential operators and nonlinear analysis
L Paivarinta
212 Analytic function theory of one complex variable
C C Yang, Y Komatu and K Niino
213 Elements of stability of visco-elastic fluids
J Dunwoody
214 Jordan decompositions of generalized vector measures
K D Schmidt
215 A mathematical analysis of bending of plates with transverse shear deformation
C Constanda
216 Ordinary and partial differential equations. Volume II
B D Sleeman and R J Jarvis
217 Hilbert modules over function algebras
R G Douglas and V I Paulsen
218 Graph colourings
R Wilson and R Nelson
219 Hardy-type inequalities
A Kufner and B Opic
220 Nonlinear partial differential equations and their applications. Collège de France Seminar. Volume X
H Brezis and J L Lions
221 Workshop on dynamical systems
E Shiels and Z Coelho
222 Geometry and analysis in nonlinear dynamics
H W Broer and F Takens
223 Fluid dynamical aspects of combustion theory
M Onofri and A Tesei
224 Approximation of Hilbert space operators. Volume I. 2nd edition
D Herrero
225 Operator Theory: Proceedings of the 1988 GPOTS-Wabash conference
J B Conway and B B Morrel
226 Local cohomology and localization
J L Bueso Montero, B Torrecillas Jover and A Verschoren
227 Nonlinear waves and dissipative effects
D Fusco and A Jeffrey
228 Numerical analysis. Volume III
D F Griffiths and G A Watson
229 Recent developments in structured continua. Volume III
D De Kee and P Kaloni
230 Boolean methods in interpolation and approximation
F J Delvos and W Schempp
231 Further advances in twistor theory. Volume I
L J Mason and L P Hughston
232 Solvability and bifurcations of nonlinear equations
P Drabek
233 Geometry in the neighborhood of invariant manifolds of maps and flows and linearization
U Kirchgraber and K Palmer
234 Quantales and their applications
K I Rosenthal
235 Integral equations and inverse problems
V Petkov and R Lazarov
236 Pseudo-differential operators
S R Simanca
237 A functional analytic approach to statistical experiments
I M Bomze
238 Quantum mechanics, algebras and distributions
D Dubin and M Hennings
239 Hamilton flows and evolution semigroups
J Gzyl
240 Topics in controlled Markov chains
V S Borkar
241 Invariant manifold theory for hydrodynamic transition
S Sritharan
242 Lectures on the spectrum of $L^2(\Gamma\backslash G)$
F L Williams
243 Progress in variational methods in Hamiltonian systems and elliptic equations
M Girardi, M Matzeu and F Pacella

P Drábek
University of West Bohemia, Plzeň, Czechoslovakia

Solvability and bifurcations of nonlinear equations

Longman Scientific & Technical
Copublished in the United States with
John Wiley & Sons, Inc., New York

Longman Scientific & Technical
Longman Group UK Limited
Longman House, Burnt Mill, Harlow
Essex CM20 2JE, England
and Associated Companies throughout the world.

Copublished in the United States with
John Wiley & Sons Inc., 605 Third Avenue, New York, NY 10158

First published 1992

AMS Subject Classification: 34B15, 35J65, 47H15

ISSN 0269-3674

British Library Cataloguing in Publication Data

A catalogue record for this book is
available from the British Library

Library of Congress Cataloging-in-Publication Data

A catalogue record for this book is available

Printed and Bound in Great Britain
by Biddles Ltd, Guildford and King's Lynn

Contents

PART II

STRONGLY NONLINEAR PROBLEMS

Preface

Nonlinear boundary value problems for both ordinary and partial differential equations have been studied very intensively during the last two decades. In this book we present some recent results which were obtained by the author (in some cases with co-authors) in the eighties. The book is divided into two parts. The first part deals with *weakly nonlinear problems*, the second part is devoted to the study of *strongly nonlinear problems*. The methods used to prove the main results of this book are based both on the classical results of mathematical analysis and on the recent results of nonlinear functional analysis. We use the basic properties of initial value problems for ordinary differential equations (see e.g. CODDINGTON and LEVINSON [64]), the basic properties of boundary value problems for ordinary and partial differential equations (see e.g. BERS, JOHN and SCHECHTER [28], FUČÍK [125], FUČÍK and KUFNER [128]), and the properties of function spaces (ADAMS [1], KUFNER, JOHN and FUČÍK [183]). We also use some results from the spectral theory of homogeneous operators (see FUČÍK, NEČAS, SOUČEK and SOUČEK [129]), the properties of the topological degree of the mappings $\mathbb{R}^n \to \mathbb{R}^n$, $X \to X$, $X \to X^*$ (see e.g. FUČÍK [125], DEIMLING [78], SKRYPNIK [276]), and some basic facts from the critical point theory.

The text is organized in a usual manner. Each of the 15 sections has its own numeration (both for the formulas and for the subsections). The end of a proof is marked by the sign □ .

I use the opportunity to express my gratitude to all who supported me and helped me to bring the manuscript to its final form. Above all, I want to mention Prof. Alois KUFNER who read the manuscript, Dr. Jiří JARNÍK who substantially improved my English, and Ms. Růžena PACHTOVÁ who carefully typed the text.

Plzeň, September 1991 P. D.

List of symbols

In this book we consider *real valued* functions of *real variables*. We indicate subsection in which the symbol is used for the first time.

BVP the boundary value problem, Subsection 1.1

IVP the initial value problem, 11.1

$\mathbb{N}$ the set of all positive integers, 1.1

$\mathbb{Z}$ the set of all integers, 9.1

$\mathbb{R}$ the set of all reals, 1.1

$\mathbb{R}^N$ the N-dimensional Euclidean space, 3.1

$|.|$ the modulus or the Euclidean norm in $\mathbb{R}^N$, 1.1, 9.1

$(.,.)_N$ the inner product in $\mathbb{R}^N$, 9.3

$(x_1,x_2,\dots,x_N)$ an element of $\mathbb{R}^N$, 9.1

(a,b) an open interval in $\mathbb{R}$, 1.1

$[a,b]$ a closed interval in $\mathbb{R}$, 1.1

for a.a. t for almost all t (in the sense of the Lebesgue measure), 1.1

a.e. in (a,b) almost everywhere in (a,b) (in the sense of the Lebesgue measure), 1.9

Ω a bounded domain in $\mathbb{R}^N$, 3.1

$\partial\Omega$ the boundary of Ω, 3.1

$L^p(a,b)$, $L^p(\Omega)$ the Lebesgue spaces, 1.1, 3.1

$\|.\|_p$ the norm in L^p

$(.,.)_2$ the inner product in L^2, 3.1

$C^k([a,b])$, $C^k(\bar{\Omega})$, $C^{k,\alpha}(\bar{\Omega})$, $C_0^\infty(0,\pi)$ the spaces of continuously differentiable functions, 1.1, 5.1

$\|.\|_{C^k}$ the norm in $C^k([a,b])$

$W^{k,p}(a,b)$, $W_0^{k,p}(a,b)$, $W^{k,p}(\Omega)$, $W_0^{k,p}(\Omega)$ the Sobolev spaces, 1.3, 3.1

$\|.\|_{k,p}$ the norm in $W^{k,p}$

$L^1_{loc}(\mathbb{R})$ the space of locally Lebesgue integrable fuctions in $\mathbb{R}$, 11.1

$L^\infty = L^\infty([0,T], \mathbf{R}^N)$ the space of vector functions $f = (f_1,\dots,f_N)$ such that $f_i \in L^\infty(0,T)$, 9.1

$W^{k,\infty}([0,T], \mathbf{R}^N)$ is defined analogously to L^∞ , 9.3

C_T^0 the space of all continuous and T-periodic functions, 8.1

u^+, u^- the positive and the negative part of u , i.e. $u^+ = \frac{1}{2}(|u| + u)$, $u^- = \frac{1}{2}(|u| - u)$, 1.5

$X \to Y$, $H \to H$, $u \mapsto F(u)$ symbols for operator, 1.3

$u_n \to u$ the strong convergence, 1.5

$u_n \rightharpoonup u$ the weak convergence, 1.4

Δ_d the d-th closed quadrant in $\mathbf{R}^2$, 2.12

B_R the ball centred at the origin with radius R , 1.5

∂B_R the sphere centred at the origin with radius R , 1.8

$B_\rho(x_0)$ the ball centred at x_0 with radius ρ , 4.10

$\overline{B_\rho(x_0)}$ the closure of the ball $B_\rho(x_0)$, 4.11

$B_r \setminus \overline{B_\rho(x_0)}$ the set $\{x \in B_r;\ x \notin \overline{B_\rho(x_0)}\}$, 4.11

meas E the Lebesgue measure of a set E , 1.8

Span $\{\cos mt, \sin mt\}$ the linear hull of the set $\{\cos mt, \sin mt\}$, 2.6

$\int_{v>0}$ the integral over the set where $v > 0$, 2.6

deg $[F;B_R,0]$ the Leray-Schauder degree of $F : X \to X$ with respect to the ball B_R and the point 0 , 1.5

$\deg_B[F;B_R,0]$ the Brouwer degree, 4.10

Deg $[F;B_R,0]$ the degree of $F : X \to X^*$ in the sense of SKRYPNIK [276] (see Section 14), 14.6

Ind (A,u_0) the index of the isolated critical point u_0 of a mapping A , 14.6

$|\alpha| = \alpha_1 + \dots + \alpha_N$ the length of a multiindex α , 3.1

$D^\alpha u = \dfrac{\partial^{|\alpha|}u}{\partial^{\alpha_1}x_1\partial^{\alpha_2}x_2\dots\partial^{\alpha_N}x_N}$ the partial derivative of order $|\alpha|$, 3.1

Ker L the kernel of an operator L , i.e. $\{u \in X;\ Lu = 0\}$, 3.1

dim V the dimension of the vector space V , 3.3

$V^{\perp}$	the orthogonal complement of V , 4.1
$V \oplus V^{\perp}$	the direct sum of V and $V^{\perp}$, 4.1
$L \mid V^{\perp}$	the restriction of an operator L to $V^{\perp}$, 4.5
dom(L)	the domain of an operator L , 5.2
Im(L)	the image of an operator L , 5.2
L^{-1}	the operator inverse to L , 3.1
L^*	the operator adjoint to L , 9.3
X^*	the space dual to X , 10.2
0_X	the zero element in a Banach space X , 10.1
$\\|\cdot\\|_X$	the norm in a Banach sapce X , 10.1
$(\cdot,\cdot)_X$	the duality between X^* and X , i.e. $(a,b)_X$, $a \in X^*$, $b \in X$, 10.2
$g'_s(x,s)$	the partial derivative of $g(x,s)$ with respect to s , 4.1
Δ	the Laplace operator, 3.6
Δ^2	the biharmonic operator, 3.10
∇	the gradient, 10.10
div	the divergence of a vector function, 10.10
$\frac{\partial u}{\partial \nu}$	the derivative of u with respect to the outer normal ν , 3.9
$\hookrightarrow$	a continuous imbedding, 10.1
$\hookrightarrow\hookrightarrow$	a compact imbedding, 1.4
$g^{-1}(\underline{G})$	the set $\{s \in \mathbf{R};\ g(s) = \underline{G}\}$, 8.1
$g(u(t))$	a vector function of the vector argument $u(t) = (u_1(t), u_2(t), \ldots, u_N(t))$, 9.1

Introduction

Using a suitable operator representation it is possible to write various *boundary value problems* (BVPs) for both ordinary and partial differential equations in the form of an *operator equation*

$$Lu + N(u) = f ,$$

where L is a linear Fredholm operator with a nontrivial kernel, N is a nonlinear compact operator and f is a given element. In literature such BVPs are called *weakly nonlinear problems* (or *semilinear problems*). We will mention here some books and papers published in the late sixties and early seventies which initiated a very intensive study of these problems.

Let us consider the Dirichlet BVP

$$u''(t) + m^2u(t) + g\big(u(t)\big) = f(t) , \quad t \in [0,\pi] , \tag{0.1}$$

$$u(0) = u(\pi) = 0 , \tag{0.2}$$

where $f \in C\big([0,\pi]\big)$, $m \geqq 0$ is an integer and $g : \mathbb{R} \to \mathbb{R}$ is a continuous and bounded function. The solvability of BVPs of the type (0.1), (0.2) was studied by LAZER and LEACH [186], LANDESMAN and LAZER [185], and WILLIAMS [296]. In a simpler form it is possible to formulate their result as follows.

Let us suppose that the limits

$$\lim_{s\to\infty} g(s) = g(\infty) \quad \textit{and} \quad \lim_{s\to-\infty} g(s) = g(-\infty) \tag{0.3}$$

exist and are finite.

Then BVP (0.1), (0.2) *has at least one solution for any* $f \in C\big([0,\pi]\big)$ *satisfying*

$$g(-\infty)\int_0^\pi (\sin mt)^+\,dt - g(\infty)\int_0^\pi (\sin mt)^-\,dt < \int_0^\pi f(t)\sin mt\,dt <$$

$$< g(\infty)\int_0^\pi (\sin mt)^+\,dt - g(-\infty)\int_0^\pi (\sin mt)^-\,dt . \tag{0.4}$$

Note that the condition (0.4) is also *necessary* for the solvability of BVP (0.1), (0.2) if g satisfies $g(-\infty) < g(s) < g(+\infty)$ for any $s \in \mathbb{R}$.

The proof of the above assertion may be found in FUČÍK [125].

The classical result of LANDESMAN and LAZER [185] has been generalized in various directions. Nonlinear BVPs with nonlinearities g which are more general than those in (0.1) - (0.4) have been studied. For instance, nonlinearities $g = g(t,s)$ which are unbounded in the second variable s were also considered. In the last case we distinguish the nonlinearities with *sublinear*, *linear* and *superlinear* growth with respect to s because this behaviour of g is very important in the proof of existence of a solution of the corresponding BVP (cf. FUČÍK [125]). Several authors also have considered nonlinear functions g which depend also on the derivatives of the solution (see Section 3). On the other hand, there are several results which generalize [185] considering other types of boundary conditions (e.g. *periodic* boundary conditions, *Neumann* boundary conditions, *mixed* boundary conditions, etc.) or other types of differential operators (BVPs for *elliptic partial differential equations*, for *systems of equations of Liénard type*, etc.).

Let us remark that in the case of BVPs for ordinary differential equations we get the existence results for more general nonlinearities g than in the case of BVP for partial differential equations. Let us mention also the result of AMBROSETTI and PRODI [11] which may be formulated for a simple BVP (0.1), (0.2) as follows.

Let $m = 1$ *and let* $g : \mathbb{R} \to \mathbb{R}$ *be a twice continuously differentiable function. Let us suppose that* $g(0) = 0$, $g''(s) > 0$ *for any* $s \in \mathbb{R}$,

$$-1 < \lim_{s \to -\infty} g'(s) < 0 , \quad 0 < \lim_{s \to \infty} g'(s) < 3 .$$

Then there exists a C^1*-manifold* M *of codimension* 1 *in* $C^{0,\alpha}([0,\pi])$ *such that* $C^{0,\alpha}([0,\pi]) \setminus M$ *is composed of two components* A_1, A_2 *with the following properties:*

a) *if* $f \in A_1$, *then BVP* (0.1), (0.2) *has no solution in* $C_0^{2,\alpha}([0,\pi])$;

b) *if* $f \in M$, *then BVP* (0.1), (0.2) *has precisely one solution in* $C_0^{2,\alpha}([0,\pi])$;

c) *if* $f \in A_2$, *then BVP* (0.1), (0.2) *has precisely two solutions in*

$C_0^{2,\alpha}([0,\pi])$.

This result shows how the relation between the rate of the growth of g at $\pm\infty$ and the spectrum of the linear differential operator in (0.1) impacts on the *existence* and *multiplicity* of solution of BVP (0.1), (0.2).

The bibliography which deals with weakly nonlinear problems is very extensive. Since in FUČÍK [125] the reader may find references up to 1979 *we concentrate our attention on works published in the eighties.*

The Landesman-Lazer type condition (0.4) does not offer any information about the solvability of BVP (0.1), (0.2) in the case $g(\infty) = g(-\infty) = 0$. Nonetheless, this BVP with $g \equiv 0$ is still solvable for any f satisfying *the orthogonality condition*

$$\int_0^\pi f(t) \sin mt \, dt = 0 . \tag{0.5}$$

It appears that the condition (0.5) is sufficient for the existence of a solution also in the case when $g \not\equiv 0$, $g(\infty) = g(-\infty) = 0$ and g has some "reasonable" asymptotic properties at $\pm\infty$ (e.g. $g(s)\cdot s \geqq 0$ for $|s|$ sufficiently large, etc.). Problems of this type were studied in FUČÍK [125], CAÑADA [36], DRÁBEK [86,87,88], DRÁBEK and TERSIAN [99], DRÁBEK and TOMICZEK [100], de FIGUEIREDO and NI [114], GUPTA [142], HOFER [159], IANNACCI, NKASHAMA and WARD [164].

When the limits (0.3) do not exist, it is possible to formulate a sufficient condition which is analogous to (0.4) by replacing $g(\infty)$ and $g(-\infty)$ by $\liminf_{s\to+\infty} g(s)$ and $\limsup_{s\to-\infty} g(s)$, respectively (see e.g. FUČÍK [125]). However, also this generalized condition provides no information about the solvability of BVP (0.1), (0.2) if e.g. $g(s) = \sin s$. Periodic BVPs for scalar equations (or for systems) which contain nonlinearities of this type were studied in FUČÍK [125], CARISTI [44], DANCER [74], DING [79,80], DRÁBEK and INVERNIZZI [96], FONDA and MAWHIN [120], FONDA and ZANOLIN [122], FOURNIER and MAWHIN [124], GUPTA, NIETO and SANCHES [143], KANNAN and ORTEGA [170,171], LAZER and Mc KENNA [196], MAWHIN [208,209,210], MAWHIN and WILLEM [217], NIETO and SANCHES [234], ORTEGA [249-251], RAMOS and SANCHES [262], WARD [289,293].

There is almost no difference (from the point of view of the methods of the proofs) between the case of a bounded nonlinearity and the nonlinearity having sublinear growth at $\pm\infty$ (cf. FUČÍK [125], DRÁBEK [92]). However, the situation is qualitatively different in the case when g has at least a linear growth at $\pm\infty$. Simple examples show that the existence results can be obtained when the rate of growth of g at $\pm\infty$ "is not too large". Let us mention in this connection the book by FUČÍK [125] and papers by AHMAD [3,4], AHMAD and LAZER [6], ARIAS [14], d'AUJOURD'HUI [16,17,18], BERESTYCKI and de FIGUEIREDO [27], CASTRO [46], CESARI and KANNAN [51], DING [81,82], DRÁBEK [90,91,92,93], FABRY and FONDA [104], FERNANDES, OMARI and ZANOLIN [106], FERNANDES and ZANOLIN [107], de FIGUEIREDO [109], FONDA and HABETS [119], FONDA and MAWHIN [121], GIANNONI and MICHELETTI [133], GUPTA [141], HABETS, RAMOS and SANCHES [145], HARRIS [148], IANNACCI and NKASHAMA [161, 162], IANNACCI, NKASHAMA, OMARI and ZANOLIN [163], IANNACCI, NKASHAMA and WARD [164], KANNAN, LAKSHMIKANTHAM and NIETO [169], NIETO [233], OMARI and ZANOLIN [244-248], RUF [266], SANCHES [270], WARD [294] and WILLEM [295]. Let us mention, for completeness, the following papers concerning weakly nonlinear problems: CAPOZZI, LUPO and SOLIMINI [42], COSTA and OLIVIERA [68], de FIGUEIREDO and GOSSEZ [113], FONDA [116,117], FONDA and GOSSEZ [118], JIAQUAN [167], KENT NAGLE and SINGKOFER [175], MAWHIN and WARD [216], NJOKU and ZANOLIN [235], SCHECHTER [272], SONG-SUN LIN [281].

Let us now consider BVP

$$-\left(|u'(t)|^{p-2}\,u'(t)\right)' = g\big(t,u(t)\big) + f(t)\ ,\quad t\in[0,\pi]\ , \tag{0.6}$$

$$u(0) = u(\pi) = 0\ , \tag{0.7}$$

where $f\in L^1(0,\pi)$, $p\geqq 2$ is a real number and g is a Carathéodory function. In the special case $p=2$ we get a weakly nonlinear problem because the highest order term becomes $-u''(t)$. If $p\neq 2$ then BVP (0.6), (0.7) is called *a strongly nonlinear problem*. The term $|u'(t)|^{p-2}$ can be regarded as *a degeneration* in the equation (0.6). However, this degeneration depends on the unknown solution of BVP (0.6), (0.7) and so it is impossible to apply the theory of weighted Sobolev spaces in a usual way (see e.g. KUFNER and SÄNDIG [182]). The investigation of BVPs of the type (0.6), (0.7) is more complicated than the study of weakly nonlinear problems in spite of the fact that it is possible to prove accurate existence results also for BVP (0.6), (0.7) (see BOCCARDO, DRÁBEK, GIACHETTI and KUČERA [30], DRÁBEK

[84,89]). First we consider *nonresonance problems* where the nonlinearity g does not "interact" with *Fučík's spectrum* of the homogeneous part, i.e. with the set of all couples $(\mu,\nu) \in \mathbb{R}^2$ such that the homogeneous BVP

$$- \left(|u'(t)|^{p-2} u'(t)\right)' - \mu|u(t)|^{p-2} u^+(t) + \nu|u(t)|^{p-2} u^-(t) = 0 ,$$
$$u(0) = u(\pi) = 0$$

has a nontrivial solution. We also consider *a resonance problem*

$$- \operatorname{div} \left(|\nabla u|^{p-2} \nabla u\right) = \lambda_1 |u|^{p-2} u + g(x,u) + f \quad \text{in} \quad \Omega , \qquad (0.8)$$
$$u = 0 \quad \text{on} \quad \partial\Omega \qquad (0.9)$$

for strongly nonlinear problems for partial differential equations with $p > 1$ (cf. BOCCARDO, DRÁBEK and KUČERA [31]). We substantially use the result of ANANE [12] according to which *there exists the first eigenvalue* λ_1 *of* BVP

$$- \operatorname{div} \left(|\nabla u|^{p-2} \nabla u\right) - \lambda |u|^{p-2} u = 0 \quad \text{in} \quad \Omega , \qquad (0.10)$$
$$u = 0 \quad \text{on} \quad \partial\Omega \qquad (0.11)$$

such that $\lambda_1 > 0$, λ_1 *is isolated,* λ_1 *is simple and the corresponding eigenfunction* u *can be chosen positive in* Ω *and such that* $\partial u/\partial\nu < 0$ *on* $\partial\Omega$ ($\partial\Omega$ is supposed to be sufficiently smooth). In fact, for $p \neq 2$ this result is a generalization of a well known Krein-Rutman theorem (see KREIN and RUTMAN [181]). However, we have little information concerning the structure of the spectrum of BVP (0.10), (0.11). By the Ljusternik-Schnirelmann theory it is possible to prove that this spectrum forms an infinite set (see e.g. FUČÍK, NEČAS, SOUČEK and SOUČEK [129]) but we are not sure if all the eigenvalues of BVP (0.10), (0.11) are of Ljusternik-Schnirelmann type. This is the reason why the investigation of BVP (0.8), (0.9) is more difficult than the investigation of analogous problems for ordinary differential equations.

Let us consider the following *bifurcation problem:*

$$- \operatorname{div} \left(|\nabla u|^{p-2} \nabla u\right) = \lambda |u|^{p-2} u + g\left(x,u(x),\lambda\right) \quad \text{in} \quad \Omega , \qquad (0.12)$$
$$u = 0 \quad \text{on} \quad \partial\Omega . \qquad (0.13)$$

We prove that the first eigenvalue $\lambda_1 > 0$ of BVP (0.10), (0.11) is the point of *global bifurcation* (in the sense of RABINOWITZ [260]) of (0.12), (0.13) (cf. DRÁBEK [94]). This result is a generalization of the result from FUČÍK, NEČAS, SOUČEK and SOUČEK [129], according to which λ_1 is the point of *local bifurcation* of (0.12), (0.13) under more restrictive assumptions on g .

In the case of ordinary differential equations and $p > 2$ it is possible to strengthen the bifurcation result for (0.12), (0.13), because according to NEČAS [231] the eigenvalues of the problem

$$- \left(a(t)|u'(t)|^{p-2} u'(t)\right)' - \lambda c(t)|u(t)|^{p-2} u(t) = 0 ,$$
$$u(0) = u(\pi) = 0$$

(with a , c sufficiently smooth) form a countable isolated set of real numbers such that $0 < \lambda_1 < \lambda_2 < \ldots < \lambda_n \to \infty$. Moreover, any eigenvalue λ_n has a *finite multiplicity* in the following sense: there is a finite number of isolated normed eigenfunctions which correspond to λ_n . An analogous result is proved for the fourth order eigenvalue problem

$$\left(a(t)\ |u''(t)|^{p-2} u''(t)\right)'' - \lambda c(t)\ |u(t)|^{p-2} u(t) = 0 ,$$
$$u(0) = u'(0) = u(\pi) = u'(\pi) = 0$$

(see KRATOCHVÍL and NEČAS [180]). Hence we have the global bifurcation result also for BVP

$$\left(a(t)\ |u''(t)|^{p-2} . u''(t)\right)'' - \lambda c(t)\ |u(t)|^{p-2} u(t) =$$
$$= g\left(t,u(t),u'(t),\lambda\right) ,\quad t \in [0,\pi] ,$$
$$u(0) = u'(0) = u(\pi) = u'(\pi) = 0 .$$

In the case of constant coefficients we get a generalization of the result of CRANDALL and RABINOWITZ [69].

Let us remark that the regularity of solutions of differential equations with the main part $\operatorname{div}\left(|\nabla u|^{p-2}\ \nabla u\right)$ is studied in the papers GIAQUINTA and GIUSTI [136], LIEBERMAN [199], LINDQVIST [200-202], TOLKSDORF [285], in the books of LADYZHENSKAYA and URALTSEVA [184] and MORREY [228]. Some applications of these equations are considered in LIBOURTY [198], PÉLLISIER and REYMOND [254]. Numerical methods for BVPs of this type are studied in GLOWINSKI and MAROCCO [138,139]. Let us mention, for completeness, the following papers which study the equations with the main part $\operatorname{div}\left(|\nabla u|^{p-2}\ \nabla u\right)$ from various points of view: ANANE and GOSSEZ [13], AZORERO and ALONSO [20,21], BHATTACHARYA [29], CITTI [60], EGNELL [102], ELOUARDI and de THÉLIN [103], GUEDDA and VERON [140], el HACHIMI and de THÉLIN [146], HEINONEN, KILPELÄINEN and MALÝ [153], HEINONEN, KILPELÄINEN and MARTIO [154], HUANG [160], KILPELÄINEN [178], KILPELÄINEN and MALÝ [179], MANFREDI [206], NABANA and de THÉLIN [229], ÔTANI [252], del PINO, ELGUETA and MANASEVICH [257], del PINO and MANASEVICH [258], de THÉLIN [283,284].

Fučík's spectrum of the weakly nonlinear BVP

$$-\left(a(t)u'\right)' - \mu c(t)u^+ + \nu c(t)u^- = 0 \,, \tag{0.14}$$

$$u(0) = u(\pi) = 0 \,, \tag{0.15}$$

plays an important role in the investigation of the weakly nonlinear BVP (0.1), (0.2). We prove that Fučík's spectrum of the strongly nonlinear BVP

$$-\left(a(t,u)u'\right)' - \mu c(t,u)u^+ + \nu c(t,u)u^- = 0 \,,$$

$$u(0) = u(\pi) = 0 \,,$$

bifurcates in a certain sense from Fučík's spectrum of the weakly nonlinear problem (0.14), (0.15), where $a(t) = a(t,0)$, $c(t) = c(t,0)$ (cf. DRÁBEK and KUČERA [97]).

PART I
Weakly nonlinear problems

CHAPTER 1

Problems of Landesman–Lazer type

1. DIRICHLET PROBLEM FOR ORDINARY DIFFERENTIAL EQUATIONS OF SECOND ORDER

1.1. Let us consider BVP

$$u''(t) + m^2u(t) + g\big(t,u(t)\big) = f(t)\ , \quad t \in [0,\pi]\ , \tag{1.1}$$

$$u(0) = u(\pi) = 0\ , \tag{1.2}$$

where $g : [0,\pi] \times \mathbb{R} \to \mathbb{R}$ is a *Carathéodory function* (i.e. $g(\cdot,s)$ is measurable for all $s \in \mathbb{R}$ and $g(t,\cdot)$ is continuous for a. a. $t \in [0,\pi]$), $f \in L^1(0,\pi)$, $m \in \mathbb{N}$.

A solution of BVP (1.1), (1.2) is a function $u \in C^1([0,\pi])$ such that u' is absolutely continuous in $[0,\pi]$, u satisfies the boundary conditions (1.2) and the equation (1.1) is fulfilled for a. a. $t \in [0,\pi]$.

We will suppose that the function $g = g(t,s)$ satisfies the following *growth condition*. There exist a function $p \in L^1(0,\pi)$ and a constant $q > 0$ such that the inequality

$$|g(t,s)| \leq p(t) + q|s| \tag{1.3}$$

holds for all $s \in \mathbb{R}$ and for a. a. $t \in [0,\pi]$. Moreover, let there exist functions $a, A \in L^1(0,\pi)$ and constants $r, R \in \mathbb{R}$, $r < 0 < R$, such that

$$g(t,s) \geq A(t) \tag{1.4}$$

for a. a. $t \in [0,\pi]$ and for all $s \geq R$;

$$g(t,s) \leq a(t) \tag{1.5}$$

for a. a. $t \in [0,\pi]$ and for all $s \leq r$.

Let us denote

$$g_{+\infty}(t) = \liminf_{s \to +\infty} g(t,s)\ , \quad g^{-\infty}(t) = \limsup_{s \to -\infty} g(t,s)\ .$$

Let us note that $g_{+\infty}(t) = +\infty$ or $g^{-\infty}(t) = -\infty$ can occur for some $t \in [0,\pi]$.

1.2. Remark. It follows from (1.3), (1.4), (1.5) that the function g can be decomposed into the sum

$$g(t,s) = \gamma(t,s)s + h(t,s) \tag{1.6}$$

where $0 \leqq \gamma(t,s) \leqq q_1(t)$, $|h(t,s)| \leqq q_2(t)$ for all $s \in \mathbb{R}$ and for a. a. $t \in [0,\pi]$, with some $q_1, q_2 \in L^1(0,\pi)$.

Indeed, let us define

$$\hat{g}_1(t,s) = \begin{cases} \min\{g(t,s), 1\}, & s \geqq 1, \\ \min\{g(t,s), -1\}, & s \leqq -1, \end{cases}$$

$$\tilde{g}_1(t,s) = g(t,s) - \hat{g}_1(t,s) ,$$

$$\gamma(t,s) = \begin{cases} \dfrac{\tilde{g}_1(t,s)}{s}, & |s| \geqq 1, \\ \tilde{g}_1\left(t, \dfrac{s}{|s|}\right), & 0 < |s| < 1, \\ 0, & s = 0, \end{cases}$$

and

$$h(t,s) = g(t,s) - s\gamma(t,s) .$$

Then $\gamma(t,s) \geqq 0$ and for $|s| \geqq 1$ we have

$$|\gamma(t,s)| \leqq \frac{|\tilde{g}_1(t,s)|}{|s|} \leqq \frac{1}{|s|}\left[|g(t,s)| + |\hat{g}_1(t,s)|\right] \leqq 2[p(t) + q] ,$$

$$|h(t,s)| = |g(t,s) - s\gamma(t,s)| = |\hat{g}_1(t,s)| \leqq \max\{|A(t)|, |a(t)|, 1\} .$$

For $|s| < 1$ we get

$$|\gamma(t,s)| \leqq |\tilde{g}_1(t, \tfrac{s}{|s|})| \leqq |g(t, \tfrac{s}{|s|})| + |\hat{g}_1(t, \tfrac{s}{|s|})| \leqq 2[p(t) + q] ,$$

$$|h(t,s)| = |g(t,s) - s\tilde{g}_1(t, \tfrac{s}{|s|})| \leqq$$

$$\leqq \sup_{|s|<1} |g(t,s)| + \sup_{|s|<1} |\tilde{g}_1(t, \tfrac{s}{|s|})| \leqq 3[p(t) + q] .$$

Hence we can set $q_1(t) = 2[p(t) + q]$ and

$$q_2(t) = |A(t)| + |a(t)| + 1 + 3|p(t)| + 3q .$$

It follows from (1.4), (1.5) that

$$\liminf_{s \to \pm\infty} \frac{g(t,s)}{s} \geqq 0 \tag{1.7}$$

for a. a. $t \in [0,\pi]$.

Let us suppose that there are constants $k_1, k_2 > 0$ such that the inequalities

$$\limsup_{s\to+\infty} \frac{g(t,s)}{s} \leq k_1 , \quad \limsup_{s\to-\infty} \frac{g(t,s)}{s} \leq k_2$$

hold for a. a. $t \in [0,\pi]$. Then (1.6) implies

$$\limsup_{s\to+\infty} \gamma(t,s) \leq k_1 , \quad \limsup_{s\to-\infty} \gamma(t,s) \leq k_2$$

for a. a. $t \in [0,\pi]$.

<u>1.3. Weak formulation.</u> Let us denote by $H = W_0^{1,2}(0,\pi)$ the usual Sobolev space on $(0,\pi)$ with the inner product

$$(u,v) = \int_0^\pi u'(t)\, v'(t)\, dt$$

and the norm

$$\|u\| = (u,u)^{1/2} .$$

Let

$$u(t) = \sum_{k=1}^{\infty} a_k \sin kt$$

be the Fourier series of $u \in H$. Then we will write

$$u(t) = \bar{u}(t) + u^0(t) + \tilde{u}(t) ,$$

where

$$\bar{u}(t) = \sum_{k=1}^{m-1} a_k \sin kt ,$$

$$u^0(t) = a_m \sin mt ,$$

$$\tilde{u}(t) = \sum_{k=m+1}^{\infty} a_k \sin kt$$

(for m see Subsection 1.1). In particular, $\bar{u} = 0$ if $m = 1$. We set

$$u^\perp(t) = u(t) - u^0(t) .$$

Let us define operators $J, S, G : H \to H$ and an element $f^* \in H$ by

$$(Ju,v) = \int_0^\pi u'(t)\, v'(t)\, dt\ ,$$

$$(Su,v) = \int_0^\pi u(t)\, v(t)\, dt\ ,$$

$$\big(G(u),v\big) = \int_0^\pi g\big(t,u(t)\big)\, v(t)\, dt\ ,$$

$$(f^*,v) = \int_0^\pi f(t)\, v(t)\, dt$$

for all $u, v \in H$. The operators S and G are compact by virtue of the compact imbedding of H into $C([0,\pi])$ (see KUFNER, JOHN and FUČÍK [183]). The operator J is the identity on H.

We say that u is a *weak solution* of BVP (1.1), (1.2) if $u \in H$ and

$$Ju = m^2 Su + G(u) + f^* \ . \tag{1.8}$$

The usual *regularity argument* for ordinary differential equations of the second order immediately yields (see FUČÍK [125]) that any weak solution of BVP (1.1), (1.2) is also a solution in the sense mentioned in Subsection 1.1. Moreover, if $f \in C([0,\pi])$ and g is a continuous function (in both variables) then every weak solution u of BVP (1.1), (1.2) satisfies $u \in C^2([0,\pi])$.

1.4. Lemma. *Let us assume that for each* $n \in \mathbb{N}$ *we have* $0 \leqq \chi_n(t)$ *for a. a.* $t \in [0,\pi]$, *and* $\chi_n \rightharpoonup 0$ *in* $L^1(0,\pi)$. *Then there exists a constant* $\rho > 0$ *such that for all* $u \in W^{2,1}(0,\pi) \cap H$,

$$\int_0^\pi \left[u''(t) + m^2 u(t) + \chi_n(t)u(t)\right]\left[\bar{u}(t) + u^0(t) - \tilde{u}(t)\right] dt \geqq$$
$$\geqq \rho \|u^\perp(t)\|^2 \tag{1.9}$$

for all n *large enough.*

Proof. The left hand side of (1.9) is equal to

$$L(u) = \int_0^\pi [-(\bar{u}')^2 + m^2 \bar{u}^2]\, dt + \int_0^\pi \chi_n(t)(\bar{u} + u^0)^2\, dt +$$

$$+ \int_0^\pi [(\tilde{u}')^2 - m^2 \tilde{u}^2 - \chi_n(t)\, \tilde{u}^2]\, dt\ . \tag{1.10}$$

The second integral in (1.10) is nonnegative. By the definition of $\bar{u}$ in Subsection 1.3 we obtain

$$\int_0^\pi [-(\bar{u}')^2 + m^2 \bar{u}^2]\, dt \geqq \rho_1 \|\bar{u}\|^2 \tag{1.11}$$

with $\rho_1 > 0$. Setting $\tilde{v} = \dfrac{\tilde{u}}{\|\tilde{u}\|}$, we conclude that

$$\int_0^\pi [(\tilde{v}')^2 - m^2\tilde{v}^2 - \chi_n(t)\tilde{v}^2]\, dt \geqq 2\rho_2 - \left|\int_0^\pi \chi_n(t)\tilde{v}^2\, dt\right| \geqq \rho_2 \tag{1.12}$$

with $\rho_2 > 0$ for n large enough because $\|\tilde{v}\| = 1$, the imbedding $H \subsetneq\subsetneq C([0,\pi])$ is compact and $\chi_n \rightharpoonup 0$ in $L^1(0,\pi)$. Hence (1.10) - (1.12) yield

$$L(u) \geqq \rho_1\|\bar{u}\|^2 + \rho_2\|\tilde{u}\|^2$$

for all n sufficiently large. Taking $\rho = \min\{\rho_1,\rho_2\}$ we complete the proof. □

We will now formulate our first existence result.

<u>1.5. Theorem</u> *(sublinear growth). Let us suppose that* $g = g(t,s)$ *satisfies the hypotheses formulated in Subsection* 1.1 *and, moreover,*

$$\lim_{s \to \pm\infty} \frac{g(t,s)}{s} = 0 \tag{1.13}$$

uniformly for a. a. $t \in [0,\pi]$. *Then BVP* (1.1), (1.2) *has at least one solution provided*

$$\int_0^\pi g^{-\infty}(t)(\sin mt)^+\, dt - \int_0^\pi g_{+\infty}(t)(\sin mt)^-\, dt < \int_0^\pi f(t) \sin mt\, dt <$$

$$< \int_0^\pi g_{+\infty}(t)(\sin mt)^+\, dt - \int_0^\pi g^{-\infty}(t)(\sin mt)^-\, dt\ . \tag{1.14}$$

Proof. Due to the regularity argument mentioned in Subsection 1.3 it is sufficient to prove the existence of a solution of the operator equation (1.8). Let us fix $\delta \in (0, 2m+1)$ and define $\mathcal{H} : [0,1] \times H \to H$ by

$$\mathcal{H}(\tau,u) = Ju - m^2 Su - (1-\tau)\delta Su - \tau G(u) - \tau f^*$$

for all $u \in H$ and $\tau \in [0,1]$. We will prove that there is $R > 0$ such that

$$\mathcal{H}(\tau,u) \neq 0 \tag{1.15}$$

for all $\tau \in [0,1]$ and $u \in H$, $\|u\| = R$. Assume this is not true. Then there is a sequence $\{\tau_n\} \subset [0,1]$ and a sequence $\{u_n\} \subset H$ such that $\|u_n\| \to \infty$ and

$$\mathcal{H}(\tau_n,u_n) = 0 . \tag{1.16}$$

For $v_n = \dfrac{u_n}{\|u_n\|}$ the equation (1,16) is equivalent to

$$Jv_n - m^2 Sv_n - (1-\tau_n)\delta Sv_n - \tau_n \frac{G(u_n)}{\|u_n\|} - \tau_n \frac{f^*}{\|u_n\|} = 0 . \tag{1.17}$$

By the assumption (1.13) one has

$$\lim_{\|u_n\| \to \infty} \tau_n \frac{G(u_n)}{\|u_n\|} = 0 . \tag{1.18}$$

Compactness of S, (1.17) and (1.18) yield that there is $v \in H$ such that $v_n \to v$ in H, $\tau_n \to \tau \in [0,1]$ (taking a subsequence if necessary) and

$$Jv - m^2 Sv - (1-\tau)\delta Sv = 0 .$$

Hence we should have $\tau = 1$ and either $v(t) = (1/m)(2/\pi)^{1/2} \sin mt$ or $v(t) = -(1/m)(2/\pi)^{1/2} \sin mt$. Let us suppose that $v(t) = (1/m)(2/\pi)^{1/2} \sin mt$. Taking the inner product of (1.16) with $\sin mt$ and noticing that $0 \leqq \tau_n \leqq 1$ we get

$$-\int_0^\pi g\big(t,u_n(t)\big) \sin mt \, dt + \int_0^\pi f(t) \sin mt \, dt \geqq 0 ,$$

i.e.

$$\liminf_{n \to \infty} \int_0^\pi g\big(t,u_n(t)\big) \sin mt \, dt \leqq \int_0^\pi f(t) \sin mt \, dt . \tag{1.19}$$

Suppose for a moment that there is a function $\zeta(t) \in L^1(0,\pi)$ such that

$$g(t,u_n(t)) \sin mt \geq \zeta(t) \tag{1.20}$$

for a. a. $t \in [0,\pi]$ and for all n sufficiently large. Then Fatou's lemma and (1.19) yield

$$\int_0^\pi g_{+\infty}(t)(\sin mt)^+ \, dt - \int_0^\pi g^{-\infty}(t)(\sin mt)^- \, dt \leq \int_0^\pi f(t) \sin mt \, dt ,$$

a contradiction with (1.14). Analogously we proceed in the case $v(t) = - (1/m)(2/\pi)^{1/2} \sin mt$. Hence (1.15) is proved and $\mathcal{H}$ is an *admissible homotopy* of compact perturbations of the identity. The homotopy invariance property of the Leray-Schauder degree implies

$$\deg [J - m^2 S - G - f^*; B_R, 0] = \deg [J - (m^2 + \delta)S; B_R, 0] , \tag{1.21}$$

where $B_R = \{u \in H; \|u\| \leq R\}$. The right hand side of (1.21) is equal to an odd number by the Borsuk theorem (see FUČÍK [125, Chapter 20]). In particular, this means that

$$\deg [J - m^2 S - G - f^*; B_R, 0] \neq 0 ,$$

and consequently, by the existence theorem (FUČÍK [125, Chapter 20]), there exists $u \in B_R$ such that

$$Ju = m^2 Su + G(u) + f^* .$$

To complete the proof it remains to prove (1.20). It follows from

$$\frac{u_n(t)}{\|u_n\|} = \frac{u_n^\perp(t) + u_n^0(t)}{\|u_n\|} \to (1/m)(2/\pi)^{1/2} \sin mt = v(t)$$

that

$$\frac{\|u_n^\perp\|}{\|u_n\|} \to 0 \quad \text{and} \quad \frac{\|u_n^0\|}{\|u_n\|} \to 1 .$$

Then

$$\frac{\|u_n^\perp\|}{\|u_n^0\|} = \frac{\|u_n\|}{\|u_n^0\|} \cdot \frac{\|u_n^\perp\|}{\|u_n\|} \to 0 . \tag{1.22}$$

The regularity argument mentioned in Subsection 1.3 yields that $u_n \in W^{2,1}(0,\pi)$ for any solution u_n of (1.16). We obtain from (1.16) and from Lemma 1.4

(where we put $\chi_n(t) = (1 - \tau_n)\delta + \tau_n\gamma(t,u_n(t))$) that

$$0 = \int_0^\pi [u_n'' + m^2 u_n + (1 - \tau_n)\delta u_n + \tau_n\gamma(t,u_n)u_n +$$

$$+ \tau_n h(t,u_n) - \tau_n f] [\bar{u}_n + u_n^0 - \tilde{u}_n] \, dt \geq$$

$$\geq \rho\|u_n^\perp\|^2 - (\|q_2\|_{L_1} + \|f\|_{L_1})(\|u_n^0\| + \|u_n^\perp\|)$$

for n sufficiently large. Hence there exists a constant $c_1 > 0$, independent of n, such that

$$\|u_n^\perp\|^2 \leq (c_1/2)(\|u_n^0\| + \|u_n^\perp\|) . \tag{1.23}$$

The inequality (1.23) together with (1.22) implies that there is $n_0 \in \mathbb{N}$ such that

$$\frac{\|u_n^\perp\|^2}{\|u_n^0\|} \leq c_1 \tag{1.24}$$

for any $n \geq n_0$.

Using (1.24) we get the estimate

$$\gamma(t,u_n(t)) \; u_n(t) \sin mt = (m/2)(\sqrt{(\pi/2)}) \; \frac{\gamma(t,u_n(t))}{\|u_n^0\|} \cdot$$

$$\cdot \; [(u_n(t))^2 + (u_n^0(t))^2 - (u_n(t) - u_n^0(t))^2] \geq$$

$$\geq - (m/2)(\sqrt{(\pi/2)}) \; \gamma(t,u_n(t)) \; \frac{(u_n^\perp(t))^2}{\|u_n^0\|} \geq$$

$$\geq - c_2\gamma(t,u_n(t)) \; \frac{\|u_n^\perp\|^2}{\|u_n^0\|} \geq - c_2 c_1 \gamma(t,u_n(t)) . \tag{1.25}$$

Now, applying Remark 1.2 and (1.25) one has

$$g(t,u_n(t)) \sin mt = \gamma(t,u_n(t)) \; u_n(t) \sin mt + h(t,u_n(t)) \sin mt \geq$$

$$\geq - c_2 c_1 \gamma(t,u_n(t)) - q_2(t) \geq - c_2 c_1 q_1(t) - q_2(t) \equiv \zeta(t)$$

for $n \geq n_0$, where $\zeta(t) \in L^1(0,\pi)$. Hence (1.20) is proved. This completes the proof. □

1.6. Remarks (i) The assumption (1.13) means that g is a *sublinear function* (in particular, g may be bounded or g may be independent of t).

(ii) The reader should compare the above proof with the methods used in FUČÍK [125, Chapters 13,14], LANDESMAN and LAZER [185], LAZER and LEACH [186]. Our Theorem 1.5 is a generalization of the results presented in these works.

(iii) The method of proof of Theorem 1.5 allows to replace the assumption (1.13) by a more general hypothesis which covers also the case of g with linear growth in the variable s . In this case, however, Landesman-Lazer type conditions (1.14) are sufficient for the existence of a solution of BVP (1.1), (1.2) if the linear growth of $g = g(t,s)$ in s is in a certain sense "controlled" by the spectrum of the linear part of BVP (1.1), (1.2).

In order to formulate a more general existence result we need some preliminaries.

1.7. Fučík's spectrum. Let us consider the *piecewise linear* Dirichlet BVP

$$u''(t) + \mu u^+(t) - \nu u^-(t) = 0 , \quad t \in [0,\pi] , \tag{1.26}$$

$$u(0) = u(\pi) = 0 , \tag{1.27}$$

where μ , ν are real parameters. This BVP has a nontrivial solution $u(t) \not\equiv 0$ if and only if $(\mu,\nu) \in A_{-1}$, where $A_{-1} = \bigcup_{n=1}^{\infty} C_n$,

$$C_1 = \{(\mu,\nu) \in \mathbf{R}^2;\ (\mu - 1)(\nu - 1) = 0\} ,$$

$$C_{2k} = \{(\mu,\nu) \in \mathbf{R}^2;\ \frac{1}{\sqrt{\mu}} + \frac{1}{\sqrt{\nu}} = \frac{1}{k}\} ,$$

$$C_{2k+1} = \{(\mu,\nu) \in \mathbf{R}^2;\ \frac{1}{\sqrt{\mu}} + \frac{1}{\sqrt{\nu}} = \frac{1}{k} - \frac{1}{k\sqrt{\mu}}\} \cup$$
$$\cup \{(\mu,\nu) \in \mathbf{R}^2;\ \frac{1}{\sqrt{\mu}} + \frac{1}{\sqrt{\nu}} = \frac{1}{k} - \frac{1}{k\sqrt{\nu}}\} ,$$

$k = 1,2,\ldots$ (see e.g. FUČÍK [125, Chapter 42]). The set A_{-1} is a generalization of the spectrum of the *linear* BVP

$$u''(t) + \lambda u(t) = 0 , \quad u(0) = u(\pi) = 0 \tag{1.28}$$

and, geometrically, A_{-1} is sketched in Fig. 1 (see Subsection 1.10).

Note that BVP (1.26), (1.27) was studied for the first time in the early seventies by FUČÍK [126] and DANCER [73] in connection with *jumping nonlinearities*. The set A_{-1} is called *Fučík's spectrum*.

The following lemma shows the relation between Fučík's spectrum and the solvability of nonlinear BVPs.

1.8. Lemma. *Let* χ_+ , χ_- *be two functions from* $L^\infty(0,\pi)$. *Let us assume that for* $m \geqq 1$ *there are two points* $(\mu_m,\nu_m) \in C_m$, $(\mu_{m+1},\nu_{m+1}) \in C_{m+1}$ *such that* $(\mu_m,\mu_{m+1}) \times (\nu_m,\nu_{m+1}) \subset \mathbb{R}^2 \setminus A_{-1}$, *and for a. a.* $t \in [0,\pi]$ *we have* $\mu_m \leqq \chi_+(t)$, $\nu_m \leqq \chi_-(t)$ *and* $\chi_+(t) \leqq \mu_{m+1}$, $\chi_-(t) \leqq \nu_{m+1}$. *We suppose that strict inequalities* $\mu_m < \chi_+(t)$, $\nu_m < \chi_-(t)$ *hold on the set* $I \subset [0,\pi]$ *and strict inequalities* $\chi_+(t) < \mu_{m+1}$, $\chi_-(t) < \nu_{m+1}$ *hold on the set* $J \subset [0,\pi]$, *where* meas $I > 0$, meas $J > 0$. *Then the Dirichlet BVP*

$$u''(t) + \chi_+(t)u^+(t) - \chi_-(t)u^-(t) = 0 , \quad t \in [0,\pi], \tag{1.29}$$

$$u(0) = u(\pi) = 0 \tag{1.30}$$

has only the trivial solution.

Proof. Let u be a nontrivial solution of BVP (1.29), (1.30). Then (by uniqueness) u vanishes only at a finite number of points in $[0,\pi]$. Let $I_+^{(i)}$ $(i = 1,\dots,P)$ and $I_-^{(i)}$ $(i = 1,\dots,M)$ be all connected components (open intervals) - if any - of the set where $u > 0$ or $u < 0$, respectively. Then we *claim* that the relations

$$\frac{\pi}{\sqrt{\mu_{m+1}}} \leqq \text{meas } (I_+^{(i)}) \leqq \frac{\pi}{\sqrt{\mu_m}} , \quad i = 1,\dots,P , \tag{1.31}$$

$$\frac{\pi}{\sqrt{\nu_{m+1}}} \leqq \text{meas } (I_-^{(i)}) \leqq \frac{\pi}{\sqrt{\nu_m}} , \quad i = 1,\dots,M , \tag{1.32}$$

hold, and there are strict inequality signs in at least one of the relation (1.31) and (1.32), respectively (more precisely, in any relation corresponding to an interval $I_\pm^{(i)}$ having an intersection of positive measure with the subset I or J). Let us suppose that $m = 2k$. We have either $P = M$, or $P = M + 1$, or $P = M - 1$. Let $P = M$. Then adding (1.31) and (1.32) and taking into account the strict inequality signs we get

$$P\left(\frac{\pi}{\sqrt{\mu_{m+1}}} + \frac{\pi}{\sqrt{\nu_{m+1}}} \right) < \pi < P\left(\frac{\pi}{\sqrt{\mu_m}} + \frac{\pi}{\sqrt{\nu_m}} \right) . \tag{1.33}$$

However, by the definitions of C_{2k}, C_{2k+1}, C_{2k+2} we have

$$\frac{k}{\sqrt{\mu_m}} + \frac{k}{\sqrt{\nu_m}} = 1 \quad \text{and} \quad \frac{k+1}{\sqrt{\mu_{m+1}}} + \frac{k+1}{\sqrt{\nu_{m+1}}} > 1 . \tag{1.34}$$

It follows from (1.33), (1.34) that $P > k$ and simultaneously $P < k + 1$, which is a contradiction. Let $M = P + 1$. Then adding (1.31) and (1.32) we get

$$P\left(\frac{\pi}{\sqrt{\mu_{m+1}}} + \frac{\pi}{\sqrt{\nu_{m+1}}}\right) + \frac{\pi}{\sqrt{\nu_{m+1}}} < \pi < P\left(\frac{\pi}{\sqrt{\mu_m}} + \frac{\pi}{\sqrt{\nu_m}}\right) + \frac{\pi}{\sqrt{\nu_m}} \tag{1.35}$$

and the definitions of C_{2k-1}, C_{2k}, C_{2k+1} imply

$$\frac{k}{\sqrt{\mu_{m+1}}} + \frac{k}{\sqrt{\nu_{m+1}}} + \frac{1}{\sqrt{\nu_{m+1}}} = 1 \quad \text{and} \quad \frac{k-1}{\sqrt{\mu_m}} + \frac{k-1}{\sqrt{\nu_m}} + \frac{1}{\sqrt{\nu_m}} < 1 . \tag{1.36}$$

It follows from (1.35), (1.36) that $P < k$ and simultaneously $P > k - 1$, which is a contradiction. Analogously we get a contradiction if $P = M + 1$. We can proceed in the same way also in the case $m = 2k + 1$.

To prove the *claim* we consider only the inequality $\text{meas}\,(I_+^{(i)}) \leq \frac{\pi}{\sqrt{\mu_m}}$ for some value of i, since the remaining inequalities can be proved in the same way. Suppose that $I_+^{(i)} = [a,b]$ so that $\text{meas}\,(I_+^{(i)}) = b - a$. Let us assume $b - a > \frac{\pi}{\sqrt{\mu_m}}$ i.e. $\mu_m > \left(\frac{\pi}{b-a}\right)^2$. Let us define the sphere

$$\partial B_1 = \{w \in W_0^{1,2}(a,b);\ \int_a^b |w'|^2\, dt = 1\} ,$$

and let $w^* = \sin\left(\frac{\pi}{b-a}t - \frac{\pi a}{b-a}\right)$ be a non-negative eigenfunction for the Picard problem

$$w'' + \left(\frac{\pi}{b-a}\right)^2 w = 0 , \quad w(a) = w(b) = 0 .$$

We can assume that for all t in a set $\tilde{I} \subset I$ with $\text{meas}\,\tilde{I} > 0$ the inequality

$$\chi_+(t) \geq \mu_m + \varepsilon$$

holds with some $\varepsilon > 0$. The variational characterization of the first eigenvalue implies

$$1 = \sup_{w \in \partial B_1} \int_a^b \chi_+(t)\ |w|^2\ dt = \int_a^b \chi_+(t)\ |w^*|^2\ dt =$$

$$= \int_{[a,b]\cap\tilde{I}} \chi_+(t)\ |w^*|^2\ dt + \int_{[a,b]\setminus\tilde{I}} \chi_+(t)\ |w^*|^2\ dt \geq$$

$$\geq \int_{[a,b]\cap\tilde{I}} (\mu_m + \varepsilon)\ |w^*|^2\ dt + \int_{[a,b]\setminus\tilde{I}} \mu_m\ |w^*|^2\ dt =$$

$$= \int_a^b \mu_m\ |w^*|^2\ dt + \varepsilon \int_{[a,b]\cap\tilde{I}} |w^*|^2\ dt >$$

$$> \int_a^b \left(\frac{\pi}{b-a}\right)^2 |w^*|^2\ dt + \varepsilon \int_{[a,b]\cap\tilde{I}} |w^*|^2\ dt = 1 + \varepsilon \int_{[a,b]\cap\tilde{I}} |w^*|^2\ dt\ ,$$

a contradiction even if $\text{meas}\left([a,b] \cap \tilde{I}\right) = 0$. If $\mu_m = \left(\frac{\pi}{b-a}\right)^2$, we get a contradiction provided $\text{meas}\left([a,b] \cap \tilde{I}\right) > 0$. □

1.9. Theorem *(linear growth). Let us suppose that* $g = g(t,s)$ *satisfies the hypotheses formulated in Subsection* 1.1. *Let us assume, moreover, that there is* $(\mu_{m+1}, \nu_{m+1}) \in C_{m+1}$ *such that* $(m^2, \mu_{m+1}) \times (m^2, \nu_{m+1}) \subset \mathbf{R}^2 \setminus A_{-1}$ *if* m *is even, and that for a. a.* $t \in [0,\pi]$ *we have*

$$\limsup_{s \to +\infty} \frac{g(t,s)}{s} \leq \mu_{m+1} - m^2\ , \tag{1.37}$$

$$\limsup_{s \to -\infty} \frac{g(t,s)}{s} \leq \nu_{m+1} - m^2\ . \tag{1.38}$$

We suppose that strict inequalities in (1.37) *and* (1.38) *hold on the set* $J \subset [0,\pi]$, $\text{meas}\ J > 0$. *Then BVP* (1.1), (1.2) *has at least one solution provided* (1.14) *holds.*

Proof. The idea is the same as in the proof of Theorem 1.5. Let us take $0 < \delta < \min\{\mu_{m+1} - m^2,\ \nu_{m+1} - m^2\}$ and define the homotopy $\mathcal{H}$ as in the proof of Theorem 1.5. In order to prove (1.15) we again proceed via contradiction, arriving at (1.17). It follows from (1.3) and (1.17) that there are $v \in H$, $\tau \in [0,1]$ and $g^* \in H$ such that

$$v_n \to v \ , \quad \tau_n \frac{G(u_n)}{\|u_n\|} \to g^* \quad \text{in } H \ , \quad \tau_n \to \tau \in [0,1] \ .$$

Since the sequence $\gamma_n(t) := \gamma(t, u_n(t))$ is both bounded in $L^1(0,\pi)$ and equi-integrable, we can also assume

$$\gamma_n \rightharpoonup \chi \quad \text{in } L^1(0,\pi)$$

(see DUNFORD, SCHWARTZ [101]). It follows from (1.7), (1.37), (1.38) and Remark 1.2 that

$$\chi(t) \geqq 0 \quad \text{a.e. on } [0,\pi] \text{ and}$$

$$\chi(t) \leqq \mu_{m+1} - m^2 \quad \text{a.e. on } \{t \in [0,\pi];\ v(t) > 0\} \ ,$$

$$\chi(t) \leqq \nu_{m+1} - m^2 \quad \text{a.e. on } \{t \in [0,\pi];\ v(t) < 0\} \ ,$$

with strict inequalities on some subset of $[0,\pi]$ of positive measure. By the limiting process in (1.17) and the usual regularity argument mentioned in Subsection 1.3 we obtain that $v \in W^{2,1}(0,\pi) \cap H$ and

$$v''(t) + m^2 v(t) + (1 - \tau)\delta v(t) + \tau\chi(t)v(t) = 0 \ . \tag{1.39}$$

Set

$$\chi_+(t) = m^2 + (1 - \tau)\delta + \tau\chi(t) \quad \text{on } \{t \in [0,\pi];\ v(t) > 0\} \ ,$$

$$\chi_+(t) = (m^2 + \mu_{m+1})/2 \quad \text{elsewhere,}$$

$$\chi_-(t) = m^2 + (1 - \tau)\delta + \tau\chi(t) \quad \text{on } \{t \in [0,\pi];\ v(t) < 0\} \ ,$$

$$\chi_-(t) = (m^2 + \nu_{m+1})/2 \quad \text{elsewhere.}$$

Then $\chi_\pm$ satisfy the assumptions of Lemma 1.8 with $\mu_m = \nu_m = m^2$, i.e. (1.39) has only the trivial solution, if $\tau = 1$ and $\chi(t) \equiv 0$ do not hold simultaneously. Hence we should have $\tau = 1$ (i.e. $\tau_n \to 1$), $\chi(t) \equiv 0$ (i.e. $\gamma_n \rightharpoonup 0$ in $L^1(0,\pi)$) and either $v = (1/m)(2/\pi)^{1/2} \sin mt$ or $v = -(1/m)(2/\pi)^{1/2} \sin mt$. The rest of the proof is the same as that of Theorem 1.5. □

1.10. Remarks. (i) The inequalities (1.7), (1.37), (1.38) have the following *geometrical interpretation:* "for large" $|s|$ and for a.a. $t \in [0,\pi]$ the expression $m^2 + \frac{g(t,s)}{s}$ belongs to $[m^2, \mu_{m+1}] \times [m^2, \nu_{m+1}]$ (see Fig. 1).

(ii) Theorem 1.9 is a generalization of the results published in FUČÍK

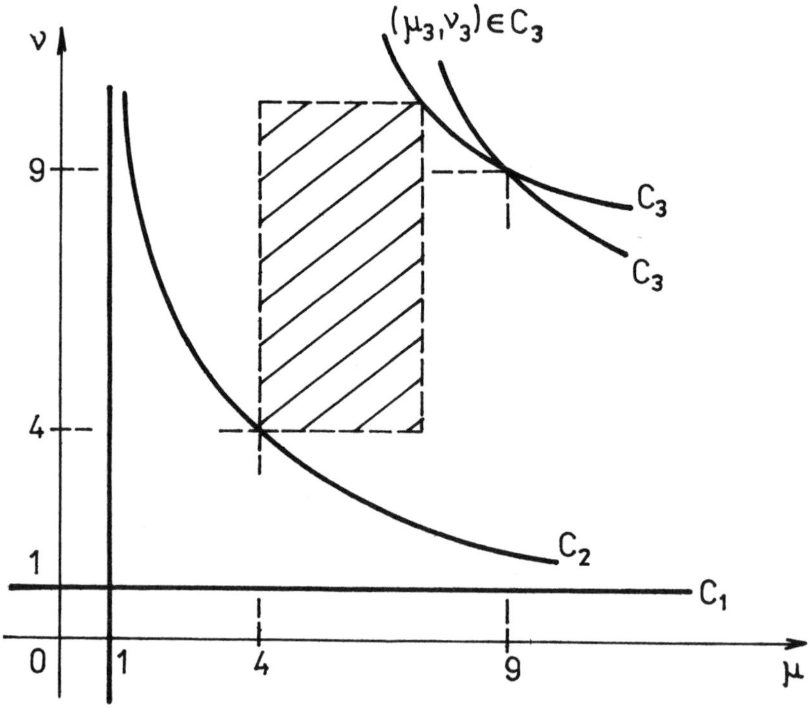

Fig. 1

[125, Chapter 15], SCHECHTER, SHAPIRO and SNOW [273], CESARI and KANNAN [52], AHMAD [3], ARIAS [14], HIRANO [157], IANNACCI and NKASHAMA [161,162], NIETO [232], SANCHES [270].

1.11. Corollary. *Let* g *satisfy all hypotheses from Subsection* 1.1. *Moreover, let*

$$\limsup_{|s|\to\infty} \frac{g(t,s)}{s} \leqq 2m+1 \tag{1.40}$$

with strict inequality on a subset of $[0,\pi]$ *of positive measure. Then BVP* (1.1), (1.2) *has at least one solution provided* (1.14) *holds.*

Proof follows from Theorem 1.9 if we set $\mu_{m+1} = \nu_{m+1} = (m+1)^2$. □

1.12. Examples. (i) Let $g(t,s) = (2m+1)s$ (i.e. the function g does not depend on t). Then the function g satisfies the assumptions from

Subsection 1.1 but we have equality in (1.40) for all $t \in [0,\pi]$. The condition (1.14) is fulfilled with any $f \in L^1(0,\pi)$ (notice that $g_{+\infty}(t) \equiv +\infty$ and $g^{-\infty}(t) \equiv -\infty$) but BVP (1.1), (1.2) has no solution if we take e. g. $f(t) = \sin (m+1)t$.

(ii) Let us define the function g by

$$g(t,s) = \begin{cases} ks & \text{for } s \geqq 0, \quad t \in [0,\pi], \\ 0 & \text{for } s < 0, \quad t \in [0,\pi], \end{cases}$$

where $k > 0$ is a fixed real number. Then BVP (1.1), (1.2) with $m = 1$ and g defined above has a solution for arbitrary $f \in L^1(0,\pi)$, $\int_0^\pi f(t) \sin t \, dt > 0$. Indeed, we have $g_{+\infty}(t) \equiv +\infty$ on $[0,\pi]$, $g^{-\infty}(t) \equiv 0$ on $[0,\pi]$, g satisfies the assumptions of Theorem 1.9 and (1.14) is fulfilled with any $f \in L^1(0,\pi)$, $\int_0^\pi f(t) \sin t \, dt > 0$. Note that we can take $(\mu_2,\nu_2) \in C_2$ such that $\mu_2 > k+1$ because ν_2 may be chosen arbitrarily close to 1 . On the other hand the function g does not satisfy (1.40) if $k \geqq 3$, i.e. this case is not covered by Corollary 1.11.

<u>1.13. Remarks.</u> (i) The following observation follows from the above examples. If the linear growth of g in variable s (at $\pm\infty$) is determined by two consecutive eigenvalues m^2 and $(m+1)^2$ in the sense of (1.40) then BVP (1.1), (1.2) has at least one solution provided (1.14) holds. On the other hand, if we distinguish between the growth of g at $+\infty$ and $-\infty$, more general assumptions (1.37), (1.38) may be considered. However, it follows from the structure of A_{-1} that more general growth conditions at $+\infty$ (at $-\infty$) must be *compensated* by more restrictive growth conditions at $-\infty$ (at $+\infty$, respectively).

(ii) Elementary calculation yields that if $(\mu_{m+1},\nu_{m+1}) \in C_{m+1}$ and ν_{m+1} (or μ_{m+1}) is "close" to m^2 then μ_{m+1} (or ν_{m+1}) is greater than $(m+1)^2$. Hence the difference between the results of Corollary 1.11 and Theorem 1.9 may be understood as follows. While the hypotheses of Corollary 1.11 are satisfied by a nonlinearity g which may asymptotically "touch" the eigenvalue $(m+1)^2$ on the set of positive measure in $[0,\pi]$, the assumptions of Theorem 1.9 are satisfied also by g "jumping" over $(m+1)^2$ (i.e. g is a *jumping nonlinearity*).

(iii) Since the set A_{-1} is expressed analytically it is possible, for fixed m, to describe explicitly the dependence of the growth of g at $+\infty$ on the growth of g at $-\infty$ (and vice versa) in order to fulfil the conditions (1.37), (1.38). Let, for instance, $m = 1$. If

$$\limsup_{s \to +\infty} \frac{g(t,s)}{s} \leqq k$$

holds a.e. in $[0,\pi]$ with some $k > 0$, then the inequality

$$\limsup_{s \to -\infty} \frac{g(t,s)}{s} < \frac{2\sqrt{k+1}+1}{\left(\sqrt{k+1}-1\right)^2}$$

a.e. in $[0,\pi]$ will guarantee that (1.37), (1.38) are satisfied. This, in particular, means that in the case $m = 1$ the linear growth of g at $+\infty$ (or $-\infty$) may be "arbitrarily large" if the linear growth of g at $-\infty$ ($+\infty$, respectively) is "sufficiently small" (cf. DRÁBEK [90]).

(iv) If the growth of g at $+\infty$ (or at $-\infty$) is greater than the distance from the next eigenvalue, we cannot expect uniqueness of the solution of BVP (1.1), (1.2). Let us suppose that there exist finite limits

$$g_+ = \lim_{s \to +\infty} \frac{g(s)}{s}, \quad g_- = \lim_{s \to -\infty} \frac{g(s)}{s}.$$

Then the minimal number of solutions of BVP

$$u''(t) + g\big(u(t)\big) = f(t), \quad t \in [0,\pi], \tag{1.41}$$

$$u(0) = u(\pi) = 0 \tag{1.42}$$

is connected with the number of eigenvalues of BVP (1.28) which belong to the interval (g_+,g_-) or (g_-,g_+). The multiplicity results concerning BVPs of the type (1.41), (1.42) were obtained in several papers published during the last ten years: AHMAD [5], d'AUJOURD'HUI [16,19], BADIALE and LUPO [22], BRÜLL and MAWHIN [35], CARISTI [43], CASTRO and SHIVAJI [49,50], CHABROWSKI [53-55], CHIAPPINELLI, MAWHIN and NUGARI [58], COSTA, de FIGUEIREDO and CONSALVES [67], ČOBANOV [61], DANCER [75-77], FABRY, MAWHIN and NKASHAMA [105], FIEBIG-WITTMAACK [108], de FIGUEIREDO [111], GALLOUËT and KAVIAN [130,131], GIANNONI and MICHELETTI [134,135], HARRIS [149-151], HART, LAZER and McKENNA [152], HIRANO [156,157,158], KENT NAGLE and SINGKOFER [176], LAZER and McKENNA [187-195], MAWHIN and SCHMIDT [214], McKENNA, REDLINGER and WALTER [220], METZEN [222], MICHELETTI [224], NGUYEN P. CÁC [239, 241], RUF [265], RUF and

SRIKANTH [268], SANTANILLA [271], SCHMIDT [274], SOLIMINI [277-279].

(v) If at least one of the numbers g_+ , g_- is not finite (g is *jumping nonlinearity with an infinite jump*), the existence and multiplicity results for BVPs of the type (1.41), (1.42) were obtained in FUČÍK [125, Parts IX, X], BAHRI and BERESTYCKI [23,24], BRÉZIS [32], CAÑADA and ORTEGA [41], CASTRO and KUREPA [47,48], CHANG [56,57], CHIAPPINELLI, MAWHIN and NUGARI [59], COCLITE [62], COCLITE and PALMIERI [63], DRÁBEK [85], FERNANDES and ZANOLIN [107], de FIGUEIREDO [110,112], de FIGUEIREDO and SOLIMINI [115], FORTUNATO and JANNELLI [123], GALLOUËT and MOREL [132], KANNAN and ORTEGA [172], LUPO, SOLIMINI and SRIKANTH [205], MAWHIN [211], MILOJEVIČ [226,227], NKASHAMA and SANTANILLA [238], OMARI, VILLARI and ZANOLIN [243], RAMASWAMY [261], RUF [264], RUF and SOLIMINI [267], RUF and SRIKANTH [269], SOLIMINI [280], TRIEBEL [286], WAN SE KIM [287], WARD [290-292]. Note that in several papers and book mentioned above BVPs for *partial* differential equations and *periodic* problems for *Liénard* equations were studied.

(vi) The generalization of the result of Landesman and Lazer to *systems* of both ordinary and partial differential equations and for nonlinearities g depending also on the *derivatives* of u is dealt with in the papers by CAÑADA [36-38], CAÑADA and MARTINES-AMORES [40], CAÑADA and ORTEGA [41], HETZER [155], KENT NAGLE, POTHOVEN and SINGKOFER [173], KENT NAGLE and SINGKOFER [174], McKENNA and RAUCH [219], SHAW [275] and WARD [288] (see also Section 3 of this book).

(vii) Some partial results concerning Fučík's spectrum for partial differential equations can be found in GALLOUËT and KAVIAN [130,131], MICHELETTI [225], NGUYEN P. CÁC [240,242], RUF [263].

1.14. Reverse growth of the function g . Let us suppose that instead of (1.4), (1.5) the function g satisfies

$$g(t,s) \leqq a(t) \tag{1.4'}$$

for a.a. $t \in [0,\pi]$ and for all $s \geqq R$;

$$g(t,s) \geqq A(t) \tag{1.5'}$$

for a.a. $t \in [0,\pi]$ and for all $s \leqq r$, where the meaning of a , A , r , R is the same as in Subsection 1.1. Note that the hypotheses (1.4'), (1.5') are in a certain sense *dual* to the assumptions (1.4), (1.5).

Let us denote

$$g^{+\infty}(t) = \limsup_{s \to +\infty} g(t,s) , \quad g_{-\infty}(t) = \liminf_{s \to -\infty} g(t,s) .$$

Let us note that (1.4'), (1.5') imply

$$\limsup_{s \to \pm\infty} \frac{g(t,s)}{s} \leqq 0$$

for a.a. $t \in [0,\pi]$.

Now, we will formulate the *dual version* of Theorem 1.9.

1.15. Theorem. *Let* $m \geqq 2$ *and let* g *satisfy* (1.3), (1.4'), (1.5'). *Moreover, let there be* $(\mu_{m-1},\nu_{m-1}) \in C_{m-1}$ *such that* $(\mu_{m-1},m^2) \times (\nu_{m-1},m^2) \subset \subset \mathbb{R}^2 \setminus A_{-1}$ *if* m *is an even number, and for a.a.* $t \in [0,\pi]$ *we have*

$$-\liminf_{s \to +\infty} \frac{g(t,s)}{s} \leqq m^2 - \mu_{m-1} , \tag{1.43}$$

$$-\liminf_{s \to -\infty} \frac{g(t,s)}{s} \leqq m^2 - \nu_{m-1} . \tag{1.44}$$

We suppose that strict inequalities in (1.43) *and* (1.44) *hold on the set* $I \subset [0,\pi]$, meas $I > 0$. *Then BVP* (1.1), (1.2) *has at least one solution provided the following inequalities hold:*

$$\int_0^\pi g^{+\infty}(t)(\sin mt)^+ \, dt - \int_0^\pi g_{-\infty}(t)(\sin mt)^- \, dt <$$

$$< \int_0^\pi f(t) \sin mt \, dt <$$

$$< \int_0^\pi g_{-\infty}(t)(\sin mt)^+ \, dt - \int_0^\pi g^{+\infty}(t)(\sin mt)^- \, dt .$$

1.16. Remark. If $m = 1$, the assertion of Theorem 1.15 holds *without* the assumptions (1.43), (1.44) because there is no point of Fučík's spectrum A_{-1} in the third quadrant of the (μ,ν)-plane (see Fig. 1).

2. PERIODIC PROBLEM FOR ORDINARY DIFFERENTIAL EQUATIONS OF SECOND ORDER

2.1. Let us consider a *periodic* BVP

$$u''(t) + m^2 u(t) + g\big(t,u(t)\big) = f(t) \ , \quad t \in [0,2\pi] \ , \tag{2.1}$$

$$u(0) = u(2\pi) \ , \quad u'(0) = u'(2\pi) \ , \tag{2.2}$$

where $g : [0,2\pi] \times \mathbb{R} \to \mathbb{R}$ is a Carathéodory function, $f \in L^1(0,2\pi)$, $m \geq 0$. We will suppose that g satisfies all hypotheses formulated in Subsection 1.1 with the interval $[0,\pi]$ replaced by $[0,2\pi]$.

2.2. Weak formulation. Denote by H the Sobolev space of absolutely continuous functions $u : [0,2\pi] \to \mathbb{R}$ such that $u' \in L^2(0,2\pi)$ and $u(0) = u(2\pi)$. The symbols $(\cdot,\cdot)$ and $\|\cdot\|$ will denote the inner product and the norm in H, respectively, where

$$\|u\|^2 = (u,u) = \int_0^{2\pi} \big[u'(t)^2 + u(t)^2\big] \, dt \ .$$

Let us define operators $J, S, G : H \to H$ and an element $f^* \in H$ by

$$(Ju,v) = \int_0^{2\pi} u'(t)\, v'(t) \, dt \ ,$$

$$(Su,v) = \int_0^{2\pi} u(t)\, v(t) \, dt \ ,$$

$$\big(G(u),v\big) = \int_0^{2\pi} g\big(t,u(t)\big)\, v(t) \, dt \ ,$$

$$(f^*,v) = \int_0^{2\pi} f(t)\, v(t) \, dt$$

for all $u, v \in H$. The operators S and G are compact by virtue of the compact imbedding of H into $C([0,2\pi])$. The operator $u \mapsto Ju + Su$ is the identity on H.

Using the standard regularity argument for ordinary differential equations it can be shown that, if $u \in H$ is a solution of the abstract equation

$$Ju = m^2 Su + G(u) + f^*$$

then $u \in W^{2,1}(0,2\pi)$ is the *solution* of (2.1), (2.2), i.e. $u \in C^1([0,2\pi])$, u' is absolutely continuous in $[0,2\pi]$, the equality (2.1) holds a.e. in $[0,2\pi]$ and u satisfies the boundary conditions (2.2).

For given $m \geq 0$ we will write for any $u \in H$

$$u(t) = \bar{u}(t) + u^0(t) + \tilde{u}(t) ,$$

where

$$\bar{u}(t) = a_0 + \sum_{k=1}^{m-1} (a_k \cos kt + b_k \sin kt) ,$$

$$u^0(t) = a_m \cos mt + b_m \sin mt ,$$

$$\tilde{u}(t) = \sum_{k=m+1}^{\infty} (a_k \cos kt + b_k \sin kt)$$

provided

$$u(t) = a_0 + \sum_{k=1}^{\infty} (a_k \cos kt + b_k \sin kt)$$

is the Fourier series of u.

Note that $\bar{u} = 0$ and $u^0(t) \equiv a_0$ (= const.) if $m = 0$. Put $u^{\perp}(t) = u(t) - u^0(t)$.

The following assertion can be proved in the same way as Lemma 1.4 (see DRÁBEK [93]).

2.3. Lemma. *Let us assume that for* $n \in \mathbb{N}$ *one has* $0 \leq \chi_n(t)$ *for a. a.* $t \in [0,2\pi]$, *and* $\chi_n \rightharpoonup 0$ *in* $L^1(0,2\pi)$. *Then there is a constant* $\rho > 0$ *such that for all* $u \in W^{2,1}(0,2\pi)$, *one has*

$$\int_0^{2\pi} [u''(t) + m^2 u(t) + \chi_n(t)\, u(t)]\,[\bar{u}(t) + u^0(t) - \tilde{u}(t)]\, dt \geq \rho \|u^{\perp}\|^2$$

for n *sufficiently large.*

2.4. Fučík's spectrum for the periodic problem. Let us consider a piecewise linear periodic BVP

$$u''(t) + \mu u^+(t) - \nu u^-(t) = 0 , \quad t \in [0,2\pi] , \tag{2.3}$$

$$u(0) = u(2\pi) , \quad u'(0) = u'(2\pi) \tag{2.4}$$

with real parameters μ and ν. This BVP has a nontrivial solution $u(t) \not\equiv 0$

if and only if $(\mu,\nu) \in \hat{A}_{-1}$, where

$$\hat{A}_{-1} = \bigcup_{n=0}^{\infty} \hat{C}_n ,$$

$$\hat{C}_0 = \{(\mu,\nu) \in \mathbb{R}^2;\ \mu\cdot\nu = 0\} ,$$

$$\hat{C}_n = \{(\mu,\nu) \in \mathbb{R}^2;\ \mu > \frac{n^2}{4},\quad \nu > \frac{n^2}{4},\quad \frac{1}{\sqrt{\mu}} + \frac{1}{\sqrt{\nu}} = \frac{2}{n}\} ,$$

$n = 1,2,\ldots$ (see FUČÍK [125, Chapter 42] and Fig. 2 in Subsection 2.7).

<u>2.5. Lemma.</u> *Let* χ_+ , χ_- *be two functions from* $L^\infty(0,2\pi)$. *Let us assume that either*

(i) *there is a point* $(\mu_1,\nu_1) \in \hat{C}_1$ *such that for a.a.* $t \in [0,2\pi]$ *we have*

$$\chi_+(t) \leqq \mu_1 ,\quad \chi_-(t) \leqq \nu_1 ;$$

let strict inequalities $\chi_+(t) < \mu_1$, $\chi_-(t) < \nu$ *hold on the set of positive measure in* $[0,2\pi]$, *or*

(ii) *there is an integer* $m \geqq 0$ *and two points* $(\mu_m,\nu_m) \in \hat{C}_m$, $(\mu_{m+1},\nu_{m+1}) \in \hat{C}_{m+1}$ *such that for a.a.* $t \in [0,2\pi]$ *we have*

$$\mu_m \leqq \chi_+(t) ,\quad \nu_m \leqq \chi_-(t) \quad \text{and} \quad \chi_+(t) \leqq \mu_{m+1} ,\quad \chi_-(t) \leqq \nu_{m+1} ;$$

let strict inequalities $\mu_m < \chi_+(t)$, $\nu_m < \chi_-(t)$ *hold on the set* $I \subset [0,2\pi]$ *and strict inequalities* $\chi_+(t) < \mu_{m+1}$, $\chi_-(t) < \nu_{m+1}$ *hold on the set* $J \subset [0,2\pi]$, *where* $\text{meas } I > 0$, $\text{meas } J > 0$.

Then the Dirichlet BVP

$$u''(t) + \chi_+(t)\, u^+(t) - \chi_-(t)\, u^-(t) = 0 \quad \text{in} \quad [0,2\pi] ,$$
$$u(0) = u(2\pi) = 0$$

has no nontrivial solutions satisfying

$$\text{sign } u'(0) = \text{sign } u'(2\pi) .$$

<u>*Proof*</u> is essentially the same as that of Lemma 1.8 (cf. INVERNIZZI [165]).

<u>2.6. Theorem.</u> *Let us suppose that* $g = g(t,s)$ *satisfies the hypotheses formulated in Subsection* 1.1 *with* $[0,\pi]$ *replaced by* $[0,2\pi]$. *Assume, moreover, that there is a point* $(\mu_{m+1},\nu_{m+1}) \in \hat{C}_{m+1}$ *such that for a.a.* $t \in [0,2\pi]$ *we have*

$$\limsup_{s\to+\infty} \frac{g(t,s)}{s} \leqq \mu_{m+1} - m^2 , \tag{2.5}$$

$$\limsup_{s\to-\infty} \frac{g(t,s)}{s} \leqq \nu_{m+1} - m^2 . \tag{2.6}$$

We suppose that strict inequalities in (2.5), (2.6) *hold on the set* $J \subset [0,2\pi]$, meas $J > 0$. *Then the periodic BVP* (2.1), (2.2) *has at least one solution provided*

$$\int_0^{2\pi} f(t)\, v(t)\, dt < \int_{v>0} g_{+\infty}(t)\, v(t)\, dt + \int_{v<0} g^{-\infty}(t)\, v(t)\, dt$$

holds for any $v \in \text{Span}\,\{\cos mt, \sin mt\} \setminus \{0\}$.

Proof. The main idea of the proof is the same as the idea of the proof of Theorem 1.9. Using the same homotopy we obtain that $v \in W^{2,1}(0,2\pi) \cap H$, $\|v\| = 1$ is a solution of

$$v''(t) + m^2 v(t) + (1-\tau)\delta v(t) + \tau\chi(t)v(t) = 0 , \quad t \in [0,2\pi] , \tag{2.7}$$

with $\chi(t) \geqq 0$ satisfying

$$\chi(t) \leqq \mu_{m+1} - m^2 \quad \text{a.e. on} \quad \{t \in [0,2\pi];\ v(t) > 0\} ,$$

$$\chi(t) \leqq \nu_{m+1} - m^2 \quad \text{a.e. on} \quad \{t \in [0,2\pi];\ v(t) < 0\} ,$$

with strict inequalities on a subset of positive measure in $[0,2\pi]$. Set

$$\chi_+(t) = m^2 + (1-\tau)\delta + \tau\chi(t) \quad \text{on} \quad \{t \in [0,2\pi];\ v(t) > 0\} ,$$

$$\chi_+(t) = (m^2 + \mu_{m+1})/2 \quad \text{elsewhere;}$$

$$\chi_-(t) = m^2 + (1-\tau)\delta + \tau\chi(t) \quad \text{on} \quad \{t \in [0,2\pi];\ v(t) < 0\} ,$$

$$\chi_-(t) = (m^2 + \nu_{m+1})/2 \quad \text{elsewhere.}$$

We obtain that, provided $\tau = 1$ and $\chi(t) = 0$ a.e. on $[0,2\pi]$ do not hold simultaneously, χ_+ and χ_- satisfy the assumptions of Lemma 2.5 with $\mu_m = \nu_m = m$. Indeed, integrating the equation (2.7) on $[0,2\pi]$ and taking into account the periodic boundary data, we conclude in this case that v has at least one node in $[0,2\pi]$. If we denote the smallest nodal point of v by $t_1 \geqq 0$ then, extending f and v by 2π-periodicity onto the whole real line, the substitution $\tilde{f}(t) := f(t - t_1)$, $\tilde{v}(t) := v(t - t_1)$ yields, by Lemma 2.5, that $\tilde{v} = 0$ on $[0,2\pi]$, a contradiction with $\|v\| = 1$. In particular, this means that $v \in \text{Span}\{\sin mt, \cos mt\} \setminus \{0\}$. The remaining part of the proof follows the same lines as that of Theorem 1.5 using Lemma 2.3 instead of Lemma 1.4 (cf. DRÁBEK [93]). □

<u>2.7. Remarks.</u> (i) Analogously as in Subsection 1.10 the growth conditions (2.5), (2.6) can be geometrically interpreted in such a way that for large s and for a.a. $t \in [0,2\pi]$ the expression $m^2 + \frac{g(t,s)}{s}$ belongs to $[m^2, \mu_{m+1}] \times [m^2, \nu_{m+1}]$ (see Fig. 2).

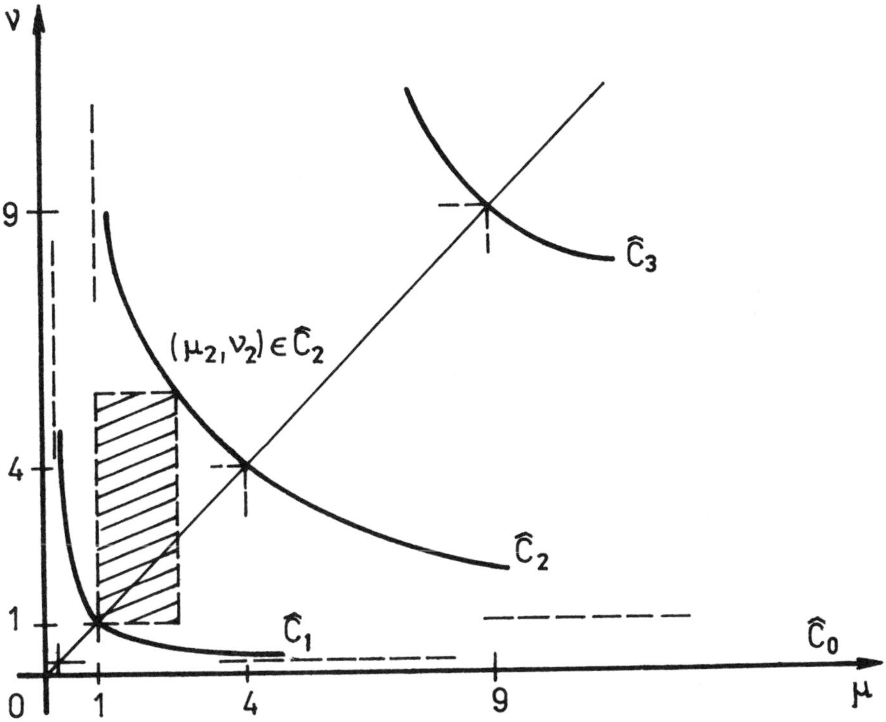

Fig. 2

(ii) Setting $\mu_{m+1} = \nu_{m+1} = (m+1)^2$ in Theorem 2.6 we obtain the result of IANNACCI, NKASHAMA [162] as a special case. The assumptions (2.5), (2.6) reduce to

$$\lim_{|s| \to \infty} \frac{g(t,s)}{s} \leqq 2m + 1 \tag{2.8}$$

with strict inequality on a subset of $[0,2\pi]$ of positive measure.

(iii) Analogously as Theorem 1.10, also Theorem 2.6 covers the case of a jumping nonlinearity g. By virtue of the analytic representation of $\hat{A}_{-1}$ e.g. in the case $m = 0$, we are able to deal with nonlinearities g with an arbitrarily large rate of linear growth with respect to s at $+\infty$. We must, however, assume $\limsup_{s \to -\infty} \frac{g(t,s)}{s} \leq \frac{1}{4}$ with strict inequality on set of positive measure in $[0,2\pi]$ (and vice versa).

(iv) Let us consider a function $g : [0,2\pi] \times \mathbb{R} \to \mathbb{R}$ defined by

$$g(t,s) = \begin{cases} 0 & \text{for } s < 0, \quad t \in [0,2\pi], \\ ks & \text{for } s \geq 0, \quad t \in [0, \frac{3}{2}\pi], \\ 0 & \text{for } s \geq 0, \quad t \in (\frac{3}{2}\pi, 2\pi], \end{cases}$$

where $k > 0$ is a fixed real number. Then according to our Theorem 2.6 the periodic problem

$$u''(t) + u(t) + g\big(t,u(t)\big) = f(t), \quad t \in [0,2\pi],$$
$$u(0) = u(2\pi), \quad u'(0) = u'(2\pi)$$

has a solution for an arbitrary $f \in L^1(0,2\pi)$. Indeed, we have $g_{+\infty}(t) \equiv +\infty$ on $[0, \frac{3}{2}\pi]$, $g_{+\infty}(t) \equiv 0$ on $(\frac{3}{2}\pi, 2\pi]$, $g^{-\infty}(t) \equiv 0$ on $[0,2\pi]$, and any $v \in \mathrm{Span}\{\sin x, \cos x\} \setminus \{0\}$ is positive on a set of positive measure in $[0, \frac{3}{2}\pi]$. At the same time, $(\mu_2,\nu_2) \in \hat{C}_2$ such that $\mu_2 > k+1$ may be always chosen. On the other hand, if $k \geq 3$, then the function g defined above does not satisfy the assumption (2.8) which is less general than (2.5), (2.6).

(v) Similarly as in Theorem 1.5 we can formulate and prove the existence result for the periodic BVP (2.1), (2.2) with a *sublinear* nonlinearity g.

Now, we will formulate the dual version of Theorem 2.6.

2.8. Theorem. *Let* $m \geq 1$ *and let a nonlinear function* g *satisfy all hypotheses formulated in Subsection* 1.14 *with the interval* $[0,\pi]$ *replaced by* $[0,2\pi]$. *Assume, moreover, that there exists a point* $(\mu_{m-1},\nu_{m-1}) \in \hat{C}_{m-1}$ *such that for a.a.* $t \in [0,2\pi]$ *we have*

$$-\liminf_{s \to +\infty} \frac{g(t,s)}{s} \leq m^2 - \mu_{m-1}, \tag{2.9}$$

$$-\liminf_{s\to-\infty}\frac{g(t,s)}{s} \leqq m^2 - \nu_{m-1} . \tag{2.10}$$

We suppose that strict inequalities in (2.9), (2.10) *hold on the set* $I \subset [0,2\pi]$, meas $I > 0$. *Then there exists at least one solution of the periodic BVP* (2.1), (2.2) *provided*

$$\int_0^{2\pi} f(t)\, v(t)\, dt < \int_{v>0} g_{-\infty}(t)\, v(t)\, dt + \int_{v<0} g^{+\infty}(t)\, v(t)\, dt$$

holds for any $v \in \mathrm{Span}\,\{\cos mt, \sin mt\} \setminus \{0\}$.

2.9. Remarks. (i) The proof of Theorem 2.8 is similar to that of Theorem 2.6. If $m = 0$ the assertion of Theorem 2.8 holds without the assumptions (2.9), (2.10).

(ii) If $m \geqq 2$ then an elementary calculation yields that the assumptions (2.9), (2.10) are also satisfied when the nonlinearity g "is jumping over" the eigenvalue $(m-1)^2$. More precisely, it means that when $\liminf_{s\to-\infty}\frac{g(t,s)}{s}$ is close to zero then the value of $-\liminf_{s\to+\infty}\frac{g(t,s)}{s}$ may be larger than $2m-1 = m^2-(m-1)^2$, and vice versa.

2.10. Duffing's equation. Let us consider the periodic BVP

$$u''(t) + cu'(t) + g\big(t,u(t)\big) = f(t) , \quad t \in [0,2\pi] , \tag{2.11}$$

$$u(0) = u(2\pi) , \quad u'(0) = u'(2\pi) , \tag{2.12}$$

where $c \neq 0$ is a real number and f , g satisfy the assumptions from Subsection 2.1. The *solution* of the periodic BVP (2.11), (2.12) is a continuously differentiable function u in $[0,2\pi]$ such that u' is absolutely continuous, the equality (2.11) holds a.e. in $[0,2\pi]$, and u satisfies (2.12). In order to study the solvability of periodic BVP we use the properties of Fučík's spectrum introduced in Subsection 2.4. In the case of *nonzero damping term* $(c \neq 0)$ we will need also the following assertion.

2.11. Lemma. *Let* $(\mu,\nu) \in \mathbb{R}^2$, $c \in \mathbb{R}$, $c \neq 0$. *The periodic BVP*

$$u'' + cu' + \mu u^+ - \nu u^- = 0 \quad \textit{on} \quad [0,2\pi] , \tag{2.13}$$

$$u(0) = u(2\pi) , \quad u'(0) = u'(2\pi) \tag{2.14}$$

has a nontrivial solution if and only if $(\mu,\nu) \in \hat{C}_0$.

Proof. Multiplying (2.13) by u' and then integrating over $[0,2\pi]$ we get (taking (2.4) into account) that $u \equiv$ const. Let us suppose that $(\mu,\nu) \notin \hat{C}_0$. Then the continuous function from $\mathbb{R}$ to $\mathbb{R}$ defined by $s \mapsto \mu s^+ - \nu s^-$ vanishes only at $s = 0$. In this case $u \equiv 0$ on $[0,2\pi]$. On the other hand, $u \equiv 1$ and $u \equiv -1$ are nontrivial solutions of (2.13), (2.14) if $\mu = 0$ and $\nu = 0$, respectively. □

2.12. Theorem. *Assume that there exists a point* $(\tilde{\mu}_1,\tilde{\nu}_1) \in \mathbb{R}^2$ *such that* $(\tilde{\mu}_1 - \frac{c^2}{4}, \tilde{\nu}_1 - \frac{c^2}{4}) \in \hat{C}_1$ *and the inequalities*

$$\limsup_{s \to +\infty} \frac{g(t,s)}{s} \leqq \tilde{\mu}_1 \quad \text{a.e. in } [0,2\pi] , \tag{2.15}$$

$$\limsup_{s \to -\infty} \frac{g(t,s)}{s} \leqq \tilde{\nu}_1 \quad \text{a.e. in } [0,2\pi] \tag{2.16}$$

are strict in a subset of positive measure. Then the periodic BVP (2.11), (2.12) *has at least one solution provided*

$$\int_0^{2\pi} g^{-\infty}(t)\, dt < \int_0^{2\pi} f(t)\, dt < \int_0^{2\pi} g_{+\infty}(t)\, dt . \tag{2.17}$$

Proof. We will work in the Banach space $X = L^1(0,2\pi)$ with the usual norm $\| u \| = \int_0^{2\pi} |u(t)|\, dt$. Fix $\lambda \in (0,1)$ and define the linear operator $K : X \to X$ in the following way: Kw is the unique solution u of the linear periodic BVP : $u'' + cu' + \lambda u = w$, $u(0) = u(2\pi)$, $u'(0) = u'(2\pi)$. A straightforward argument shows that K is compact. Moreover, the standard regularity argument for ordinary differential equations proves that K maps bounded sets in $L^1(0,2\pi)$ into relatively compact sets in $C([0,2\pi])$. The Nemytskiĭ's operators induced by g and by the mappings $u \mapsto u^+$, $u \mapsto u^-$ are all continuous from X into X and map bounded sets into bounded sets. Let us denote by Δ_d the d-th closed quadrant of $\mathbb{R}^2$. The proof of Theorem 2.12 will be performed in several steps.

Step 1. *Let* $f \in X$ *be given. Consider the continuous path*

$$\sigma \in [0,1] \mapsto (\mu_\sigma,\nu_\sigma) \in (\Delta_1 \cup \Delta_3) \setminus \hat{C}_0 \tag{2.18}$$

with endpoints (μ_0,ν_0) *and* (μ_1,ν_1) *with* $\mu_1 = \nu_1$. *Then there is* $R > 0$ *sufficiently large such that the Leray-Schauder degree at* 0 *with respect to the ball* $B_R = \{x \in X;\ \|x\| < R\}$ *of the mapping* $X \to X$ *defined by*

$$u \mapsto u - K\big(-\mu_\sigma u^+ + \nu_\sigma u^- + \lambda u + (1-\sigma)f\big) \tag{2.19}$$

is constant in $[0,1]$. *This constant is equal to an odd integer.*

The mapping (2.19) is odd for $\sigma = 1$ and hence by the homotopy invariance property of the Leray-Schauder degree it is sufficient to show that there exists $R > 0$ such that

$$\tilde{\mathcal{H}}(\sigma,u) = u - K\big(-\mu_\sigma u^+ + \nu_\sigma u^- + \lambda u + (1-\sigma)f\big) \neq 0$$

for any $\sigma \in [0,1]$ and $u \in X$, $\|u\| = R$. Let us supppose the contrary. Then there are $\sigma_n \in [0,1]$ and $u_n \in X$, $\|u_n\| \to \infty$,

$$\tilde{\mathcal{H}}(\sigma_n,u_n) = 0 \tag{2.20}$$

for all $n \in \mathbb{N}$. The equation (2.20) is equivalent to the periodic BVP

$$u_n'' + cu_n' + \mu_{\sigma_n} u_n^+ - \nu_{\sigma_n} u_n^- = (1-\sigma_n)f , \tag{2.21}$$

$$u_n(0) = u_n(2\pi) , \quad u_n'(0) = u_n'(2\pi) . \tag{2.22}$$

Put $v_n = \dfrac{u_n}{\|u_n\|}$. Then passing to a subsequence, if necessary, we obtain from (2.21), (2.22) that

$$v_n \to v \ \text{ in } X , \quad \sigma_n \to \sigma_0 \in [0,1] ,$$

$$v'' + cv' + \mu_{\sigma_0} v^+ - \nu_{\sigma_0} v^- = 0 ,$$

$$v(0) = v(2\pi) , \quad v'(0) = v'(2\pi) .$$

By the assumption (2.18), this contradicts the assertion of Lemma 2.11.

<u>*Step 2.*</u> *Let us suppose that*

$$(\mu_0,\nu_0) \in [0,\tilde{\mu}_1] \times [0,\tilde{\nu}_1] \setminus \hat{C}_0 .$$

Consider the homotopy $\mathcal{H}: [0,1] \times X \to X$ *defined by*

$$\mathcal{H}(\tau,u) = u - K\big(-\tau g(\cdot,u) - (1-\tau)[\mu_0 u^+ - \nu_0 u^-] + \lambda u + f\big) .$$

Then there exists $R > 0$ *such that* $\mathcal{H}(\tau,u) \neq 0$ *for any* $\tau \in [0,1]$ *and* $u \in X$, $\|u\| = R$.

Let us suppose the contrary. Then there is a sequence $(\tau_n, u_n) \in [0,1] \times X$ such that

$$u_n = K\big(-\tau_n g(\cdot, u_n) + (1-\tau_n)[\mu_0 u_n^+ - \nu_0 u_n^-] + \lambda u_n + f\big) , \tag{2.23}$$

and $\|u_n\| \to \infty$. The normalized sequence $v_n = \dfrac{u_n}{\|u_n\|}$ satisfies

$$v_n = K\Big(-\tau_n \frac{g(\cdot, u_n)}{\|u_n\|} - (1-\tau_n)[\mu_0 v_n^+ + \nu_0 v_n^-] + \lambda v_n + \frac{f}{\|u_n\|}\Big) . \tag{2.24}$$

Due to the growth restrictions on g the sequence $g_n = \dfrac{g(\cdot, u_n)}{\|u_n\|}$ is bounded in X . Therefore, passing to a subsequence if necessary, we can assume that $v_n \to v$ uniformly on $[0,2\pi]$. We have

$$|g_n(t)| \leqq \frac{p(t)}{\|u_n\|} + q|v_n(t)| \leqq r(t)$$

for all $n \in \mathbb{N}$, with some $r \in X$. Hence

$$\int_{t_1}^{t_2} |g_n(t)| \, dt \to 0 \quad \text{for} \quad |t_1 - t_2| \to 0$$

uniformly with respect to $n \in \mathbb{N}$. Therefore the sequence $\{g_n\}_{n=1}^{\infty} \subset X$ is weakly sequentially compact (see DUNFORD, SCHWARTZ [101]), i.e. there is $h \in X$ such that a subsequence of $\{g_n\}_{n=1}^{\infty}$ converges weakly to h in X . We can suppose that also $\tau_n \to \tau \in [0,1]$. Since any bounded linear mapping $X \to X$ is both continuous and weakly continuous, we can pass to the weak limit in (2.24) obtaining

$$v = K\big(-\tau h + (1-\tau)[\mu_0 v^+ - \nu_0 v^-] + \lambda v\big) . \tag{2.25}$$

It is a direct consequence of Lebesgue's theorem, Fatou's lemma, the growth restrictions on g , (2.15) and (2.16) that

$$h(t) = \tilde{\chi}_+(t) v^+(t) - \tilde{\chi}_-(t) v^-(t) \quad \text{a.e. on} \quad [0,2\pi] ,$$

where

$$0 \leq \tilde{\chi}_+(t) \leq \tilde{\mu}_1 , \quad 0 \leq \tilde{\chi}_-(t) \leq \tilde{\nu}_1 \quad \text{a.e. on} \quad [0,2\pi] .$$

The mappings $\tilde{\chi}_\pm : [0,2\pi] \to \mathbb{R}$ are defined as follows:

$$\tilde{\chi}_\pm(t) = h(t)/v(t) \quad \text{on} \quad \{t \in [0,2\pi];\ v(t) \gtrless 0\} ,$$

$$\tilde{\chi}_+(t) = \mu_0 , \quad \tilde{\chi}_-(t) = \nu_0 \quad \text{on} \quad \{t \in [0,2\pi];\ v(t) = 0\}$$

(see DRÁBEK, INVERNIZZI [95]). Set

$$\hat{\chi}_+(t) = \tau\tilde{\chi}_+(t) + (1-\tau)\mu_0 \ , \quad \hat{\chi}_-(t) = \tau\tilde{\chi}_-(t) + (1-\tau)\nu_0 \ .$$

Then $v \in X$, $\|v\| = 1$ is a solution of the periodic BVP

$$v'' + cv' + \hat{\chi}_+(t)v^+ - \hat{\chi}_-(t)v^- = 0 \quad \text{a.e. on} \quad [0,2\pi] \ , \tag{2.26}$$

$$v(0) = v(2\pi) \ , \quad v'(0) = v'(2\pi) \ , \tag{2.27}$$

and

$$0 \leqq \hat{\chi}_+(t) \leqq \tilde{\mu}_1 \ , \quad 0 \leqq \hat{\chi}_-(t) \leqq \tilde{\nu}_1 \quad \text{a.e. on} \quad [0,2\pi] \ .$$

Let us suppose that $\hat{\chi}_\pm(t) \geqq 0$ holds with strict inequality on a set of positive measure in $[0,2\pi]$. Then integrating (2.26) on $[0,2\pi]$, we obtain (by virtue of (2.27)) that neither $v > 0$ nor $v < 0$ holds on the whole $[0,2\pi]$. Hence v has at least two nodes in $[0,2\pi]$, i.e. we can find $t^* \in [0,2\pi]$ such that $v(t^*) = 0$ and $C = 1/v'(t^*) > 0$ (by uniqueness). Let us extend v and $\hat{\chi}_\pm$ by 2π-periodicity onto the whole real line and define $w, \gamma_\pm : [0,2\pi] \to \mathbb{R}$ by the relations $w(t) = Cv(t - t^*)$, $\gamma_\pm(t) = \hat{\chi}_\pm(t - t^*)$. We obtain

$$w'' + cw' + \gamma_+(t)w^+ - \gamma_-(t)w^- = 0 \quad \text{a.e. on} \quad [0,2\pi] \ ,$$

$$w(0) = w(2\pi) = 0 \ , \quad w'(0) = w'(2\pi) = 1 \ .$$

Introducing $z : [0,2\pi] \to \mathbb{R}$, $z(t) = \exp\big((c/2)t\big)\, w(t)$, a simple computation shows that z is a solution of the nonlinear Dirichlet BVP

$$z'' + \left(\gamma_+(t) - \frac{c^2}{4}\right)z^+ - \left(\gamma_-(t) - \frac{c^2}{4}\right)z^- = 0 \ ,$$

$$z(0) = z(2\pi) = 0$$

verifying

$$\operatorname{sign} z'(0) = \operatorname{sign} z'(2\pi) \ .$$

Simultaneously $\chi_\pm(t) = \gamma_\pm(t) - c^2/4$ verify

$$\chi_+(t) \leqq \mu_1 = \tilde{\mu}_1 - \frac{c^2}{4} \ ,$$

$$\chi_-(t) \leqq \nu_1 = \tilde{\nu}_1 - \frac{c^2}{4} \ ,$$

with strict inequality signs on a set of positive measure in $[0,2\pi]$. Then Lemma 2.5 (i) implies $z(t) \equiv 0$ on $[0,2\pi]$ which contradicts $\|v\| = 1$. Hence either $\hat{\chi}_+(t) = 0$ a.e. on $[0,2\pi]$ or $\hat{\chi}_-(t) = 0$ a.e. on $[0,2\pi]$. It follows directly from (2.26), (2.27) (integrating (2.26) on $[0,2\pi]$) that either $v \equiv \frac{1}{2\pi}$ or $v \equiv -\frac{1}{2\pi}$ on $[0,2\pi]$. Let us suppose that $v \equiv \frac{1}{2\pi}$ on $[0,2\pi]$ (the other case $v \equiv -\frac{1}{2\pi}$ on $[0,2\pi]$ can be treated similarly). Then the uniform convergence $v_n \to \frac{1}{2\pi}$ on $[0,2\pi]$ implies $u_n(t) \to +\infty$ uniformly on $[0,2\pi]$. Hence the operator equation (2.23) is, for large n , equivalent to the periodic BVP

$$u_n'' + cu_n' + \tau_n g(t,u_n) + (1-\tau_n)\mu_0 u_n^+ = f , \tag{2.28}$$

$$u_n(0) = u_n(2\pi) , \quad u_n'(0) = u_n'(2\pi) . \tag{2.29}$$

Integrating (2.28) on $[0,2\pi]$, we obtain by using Fatou's lemma and (2.29):

$$\int_0^{2\pi} \liminf_{n\to\infty} \left[\tau_n g(t,u_n) + (1-\tau_n)\mu_0 u_n^+\right] dt \leqq$$

$$\leqq \liminf_{n\to\infty} \int_0^{2\pi} \left[\tau_n g(t,u_n) + (1-\tau_n)\mu_0 u_n^+\right] dt = \int_0^{2\pi} f(t)\, dt . \tag{2.30}$$

On the other hand, the assumption (2.17) yields

$$\int_0^{2\pi} f(t)\, dt < \int_0^{2\pi} \liminf_{n\to\infty} \left[\tau_n g(t,u_n) + (1-\tau_n)\mu_0 u_n^+\right] dt ,$$

which contradicts (2.30).

<u>*Step 3.*</u> *The periodic BVP* (2.11), (2.12) *has at least one solution.*

The periodic BVP (2.11), (2.12) is equivalent to the operator equation

$$u - K\left(-g(\cdot,u) + \lambda u + f\right) = 0 \tag{2.31}$$

(this follows by the standard regularity argument). By *Step 2* the Leray-Schauder degree of the operator on the left hand side of (2.31) with respect to B_R is equal to the degree of the operator

$$u \mapsto u - K(-\mu_0 u^+ + \nu_0 u^- + \lambda u + f) \tag{2.32}$$

provided $R > 0$ is large enough. According to *Step 1* the degree of (2.32) is different from zero. Hence the operator equation (2.31) has at least one solution. □

<u>2.13. Theorem.</u> *Suppose that a function* g *satisfies all hypotheses*

formulated in Subsection 1.14 *with the interval* $[0,\pi]$ *replaced by* $[0,2\pi]$. *Then the periodic BVP* (2.11), (2.12) *has at least one solution provided*

$$\int_0^{2\pi} g^{+\infty}(t)\, dt < \int_0^{2\pi} f(t)\, dt < \int_0^{2\pi} g_{-\infty}(t)\, dt .$$

Proof. We can proceed in the same way as in the previous case. We do not need the assumptions of the type (2.15), (2.16) because there is no point of Fučík's spectrum in Δ_3 (cf. DRÁBEK [91]).

2.14. Remarks. (i) The assertions of Theorems 2.12 and 2.13 generalize in a certain sense the results of AHMAD [4], METZEN [221] and WARD [290].

(ii) Let us also mention the recently published paper by METZEN [223] where fourth order problems related to (2.11), (2.12) are studied.

3. DIRICHLET PROBLEM FOR PARTIAL DIFFERENTIAL EQUATIONS OF HIGHER ORDER WITH NONLINEARITY DEPENDENT ON DERIVATIVES

3.1. Let Ω be a bounded open set in $\mathbb{R}^N$ with boundary $\partial\Omega$. Let us denote by $L^2(\Omega)$ the usual function space with the inner product $(\cdot,\cdot)_2$ and the norm $\|\cdot\|_2$. Let $W^{2m,2}(\Omega)$ $(m \geqq 1)$ be the usual Sobolev space with the norm

$$\|u\| = \Big(\sum_{|\alpha|\leqq 2m} \int_\Omega |D^\alpha u(x)|^2\, dx\Big)^{1/2} .$$

We will consider *the formal differential operator*

$$A = - \sum_{|\alpha|\leqq 2m} a_\alpha(x)\, D^\alpha ,$$

where

$$D^\alpha = \frac{\partial^{|\alpha|}}{\partial x_1^{\alpha_1} \partial x_2^{\alpha_2} \dots \partial x_N^{\alpha_N}} , \qquad |\alpha| = \sum_{j=1}^N \alpha_j .$$

Let B be a system of *linear boundary operators* of orders less than $2m$ defined on $\partial\Omega$. We denote by H the closed vector subspace of $W^{2m,2}(\Omega)$ of functions u satisfying $Bu = 0$ on $\partial\Omega$. Let us note that H with the norm $\|\cdot\|$ is a Hilbert space and due to the compact imbedding $H \subsetneq\subsetneq L^2(\Omega)$ the operator $S : H \to L^2(\Omega)$ defined by $Su = u$, $u \in H$, is compact.

We will suppose that the following conditions are satisfied. Let us denote by $L : H \to L^2(\Omega)$ the linear operator generated by the differential operator A and boundary operators B. We suppose that L is *symmetric*, i.e. $(Lu,v)_2 = (Lv,u)_2$ for any $u, v \in H$, L is *one-to-one* and *continuous* with a *continuous inverse*

$$L^{-1} : L^2(\Omega) \to H .$$

Moreover, let us suppose that λ is an *isolated eigenvalue* of L and the operator $L_\lambda u = Lu - \lambda Su$ has a *finite-dimensional kernel* $\operatorname{Ker} L_\lambda$. We denote by $v \in \operatorname{Ker} L_\lambda$ an arbitrary eigenfunction corresponding to λ such that $\|v\| = 1$.

Let us suppose that the following version of *the unique continuation property holds:*

(U) If $w \in \operatorname{Ker} L_\lambda$, $w \neq 0$, then for each α_i, $1 \leq i \leq k$, the equality $D^{\alpha_i} w(x) = 0$ holds only on a set of measure zero in Ω.

For a fixed $v \in \operatorname{Ker} L_\lambda$ we will use the following notation:

$$\Omega(+,+,\dots,+) = \{x \in \Omega;\ D^{\alpha_1} v(x) > 0,\ D^{\alpha_2} v(x) > 0, \dots, D^{\alpha_k} v(x) > 0\} ,$$

$$\Omega(-,+,\dots,+) = \{x \in \Omega;\ D^{\alpha_1} v(x) < 0,\ D^{\alpha_2} v(x) > 0, \dots, D^{\alpha_k} v(x) > 0\} ,$$

$$\vdots$$

$$\Omega(-,-,\dots,-) = \{x \in \Omega;\ D^{\alpha_1} v(x) < 0,\ D^{\alpha_2} v(x) < 0, \dots, D^{\alpha_k} v(x) < 0\} .$$

Thus, Ω is divided into 2^k parts and according to (U) we have

$$\operatorname{meas} \Omega = \operatorname{meas} \big(\Omega(+,+,\dots,+) \cup \Omega(-,+,\dots,+) \cup \dots \cup \Omega(-,-,\dots,-)\big) .$$

We suppose that $g : \Omega \times \mathbb{R} \times \mathbb{R}^k \to \mathbb{R}^k$ is a *Carathéodory function.* Let there exist a function $h \in L^2(\Omega)$ such that

$$|g(x,s,r_1,\dots,r_k)| \leq h(x)$$

for a.a. $x \in \Omega$ and for all $s \in \mathbb{R}$, $r_i \in \mathbb{R}$, $1 \leq i \leq k$. Let us denote

$$\underline{g}(x,+;\pm,\pm,\dots,\pm) = \liminf_{\substack{s\to+\infty\\ r_i\to\pm\infty}} g(x,s,r_1,r_2,\dots,r_k)\ ,$$

$$\overline{g}(x,-;\pm,\pm,\dots,\pm) = \limsup_{\substack{s\to-\infty\\ r_i\to\pm\infty}} g(x,s,r_1,r_2,\dots,r_k)\ .$$

Note that the operator $G : H \longrightarrow L^2(\Omega)$ defined by

$$G(u)(x) = g\left(x,u(x),D^{\alpha_1}u(x),D^{\alpha_2}u(x),\dots,D^{\alpha_k}u(x)\right)$$

is *bounded* and *compact* (because of the boundedness of the function g by a function $h(x) \in L^2(\Omega)$ and the fact that $|\alpha_i| \leqq 2m - 1$ for all multiindices α_i, $1 \leqq i \leqq k$).

In the next subsection we will prove solvability of the semilinear BVP

$$-\sum_{|\alpha|\leqq 2m} a_\alpha(x)D^\alpha u(x) - \lambda u(x) + g\left(x,u(x),D^{\alpha_1}u(x),\dots,D^{\alpha_k}u(x)\right) =$$

$$= f(x)\ ,\quad x \in \Omega\ , \tag{3.1}$$

$$Bu(x) = 0\ ,\quad x \in \partial\Omega\ , \tag{3.2}$$

where $f \in L^2(\Omega)$.

<u>3.2. Theorem.</u> *Let us suppose that all hypotheses formulated above are satisfied. Moreover, let us suppose that* $f \in L^2(\Omega)$ *satisfies the following Landesman-Lazer type condition for any* $v \in \operatorname{Ker} L_\lambda$:

$$\int_\Omega f(x)\,v(x)\,dx < \Big[\int_{\Omega(+,\dots,+)} \underline{g}(x,+;+,\dots,+)\,v^+(x)\,dx +$$

$$+ \int_{\Omega(-,\dots,+)} \underline{g}(x,+;-,\dots,+)\,v^+(x)\,dx + \dots +$$

$$+ \int_{\Omega(-,\dots,-)} \underline{g}(x,+;-,\dots,-)\,v^+(x)\,dx\Big] - \Big[\int_{\Omega(+,\dots,+)} \overline{g}(x,-;+,\dots,+)\,v^-(x)\,dx +$$

$$+ \int_{\Omega(-,\dots,+)} \overline{g}(x,-;-,\dots,+)\,v^-(x)\,dx + \dots +$$

$$+ \int_{\Omega(-,\dots,-)} \overline{g}(x,-;-,\dots,-)\,v^-(x)\,dx\Big]\ . \tag{3.3}$$

Then BVP (3.1), (3.2) *has at least one solution* $u \in H$.

Proof. We will use the Leray-Schauder degree theory. To this end, we write BVP (3.1), (3.2) in an *equivalent operator form*

$$Lu - \lambda Su + G(u) = f . \tag{3.4}$$

Linearity of L^{-1} implies that the equation (3.4) is equivalent to

$$u - \lambda L^{-1}Su + L^{-1}G(u) - L^{-1}f = 0 . \tag{3.5}$$

By our assumptions the operators $L^{-1}G, L^{-1}S : H \to H$ are *compact* and hence it is possible to apply the Leray-Schauder degree theory to the operator

$$F = I - \lambda L^{-1}S + L^{-1}G(\cdot) - L^{-1}f ,$$

where I is the identity on H .

The *main idea* of the proof is the following. We will find a suitable homotopy $\mathcal{H}(\tau,\cdot)$ which joins the operator F with some odd operator $\tilde{F}$. The degree of the odd operator $\tilde{F}$ is different from zero and hence by the homotopy invariance property the degree of F is also different from zero. The basic property of the Leray-Schauder degree then implies the existence of $u \in H$ such that $F(u) = 0$. Hence, $u \in H$ is a solution of (3.4), i.e. u is a solution of BVP (3.1), (3.2).

Take $\delta > 0$ sufficiently small and define the homotopy $\mathcal{H}(\tau,u)$: $[0,1] \times H \to H$ in the following way:

$$\mathcal{H}(\tau,u) = u - \lambda L^{-1}Su + (1 - \tau)\delta L^{-1}Su + \tau L^{-1}G(u) - \tau L^{-1}f .$$

We will prove that this homotopy is *admissible*.

There exists $R > 0$ *such that*

$$\mathcal{H}(\tau,u) \neq 0 \tag{3.6}$$

for any $\tau \in [0,1]$ *and for any* $u \in H$, $\|u\| = R$.

Let us suppose to the contrary that there are sequences $\{\tau_n\}_{n=1}^{\infty} \subset [0,1]$ and $\{u_n\}_{n=1}^{\infty} \subset H$ such that $\lim_{n\to\infty} \|u_n\| = \infty$ and

$$\mathcal{H}(\tau_n,u) = 0 . \tag{3.7}$$

The equality (3.7) is equivalent to

$$Lu_n - \lambda Su_n + (1 - \tau_n)\delta Su_n + \tau_n G(u_n) - \tau_n f = 0 . \tag{3.8}$$

We will divide (3.8) by $\|u_n\|$. Setting $v_n = \frac{u_n}{\|u_n\|}$, we get

$$Lv_n - \lambda Sv_n + (1 - \tau_n)\delta Sv_n + \tau_n \frac{G(u_n)}{\|u_n\|} - \tau_n \frac{f}{\|u_n\|} = 0 \ . \tag{3.9}$$

Since H is a Hilbert space, we can suppose (after passing to suitable subsequences) that there exist $\tau \in [0,1]$ and $v \in H$ such that

$$v_n \rightharpoonup v \ \text{ in } H \ \text{ and } \ \tau_n \to \tau \ . \tag{3.10}$$

The boundedness of G implies

$$\frac{G(u_n)}{\|u_n\|} \to 0 \ \text{ in } L^2(\Omega) \ \text{ and } \ \frac{f}{\|u_n\|} \to 0 \ \text{ in } L^2(\Omega) \ . \tag{3.11}$$

Furthermore,

$$Sv_n \to Sv \ \text{ in } L^2(\Omega) \tag{3.12}$$

because S is a compact operator.

Taking into account (3.10), (3.11) and (3.12) we can pass to the limit (for $n \to +\infty$) in the equation (3.9). Then the continuity of L^{-1} implies that

$$v_n \to v \ \text{ in } H \ , \ \|v\| = 1 \ , \tag{3.13}$$

and from (3.9) we obtain the limit equation

$$Lv - \big(\lambda - (1 - \tau)\delta\big) Sv = 0 \ . \tag{3.14}$$

If $\tau \in [0,1)$ and $\delta > 0$ is small enough then $\lambda - (1 - \tau)\delta$ is not an eigenvalue of L (note that λ is an isolated eigenvalue of L). Hence (3.14) contradicts (3.13).

Let us suppose $\tau = 1$. Then (3.14) reduces to

$$Lv - \lambda Sv = 0 \ ,$$

and, consequently, $v \in \operatorname{Ker} L_\lambda$. It follows from (3.8) that

$$\begin{aligned} &(Lu_n,v)_2 - \lambda(Su_n,v)_2 + (1 - \tau_n)\delta(Su_n,v)_2 + \\ &+ \tau_n\big(G(u_n),v\big)_2 - \tau_n(f,v)_2 = 0 \ . \end{aligned} \tag{3.15}$$

By the symmetry of L and S we obtain

$$(Lu_n,v)_2 - \lambda(Su_n,v)_2 = (Lv,u_n)_2 - \lambda(Sv,u_n)_2 = 0 \ .$$

It means that (3.15) is equivalent to

$$(1-\tau_n)\delta(Su_n,v)_2 + \tau_n\big(G(u_n),v\big)_2 - \tau_n(f,v)_2 = 0 \,. \tag{3.16}$$

In particular, (3.13) implies that $v_n \to v$ in $L^2(\Omega)$ and hence

$$(Su_n,v)_2 = \int_\Omega u_n(x)\ v(x)\ dx = \|u_n\| \int_\Omega v_n(x)\ v(x)\ dx > 0$$

for $n \geqq n_0$. Then, by virtue of (3.16), we have

$$\big(G(u_n),v\big)_2 < (f,v)_2 \tag{3.17}$$

for $n \geqq n_0$. The inequality (3.17) can be written as

$$\int_\Omega g\big(x,u_n(x),D^{\alpha_1}u_n(x),\dots,D^{\alpha_k}u_n(x)\big)\ v(x)\ dx < \int_\Omega f(x)\ v(x)\ dx \tag{3.18}$$

for $n \geqq n_0$. Consequently (3.18) implies

$$\liminf_{n\to+\infty} \int_\Omega g\big(x,u_n(x),D^{\alpha_1}u_n(x),\dots,D^{\alpha_k}u_n(x)\big)\ v(x)\ dx \leqq$$

$$\leqq \int_\Omega f(x)\ v(x)\ dx \,. \tag{3.19}$$

It follows from (3.13) that

$$D^{\alpha_i}v_n(x) \to D^{\alpha_i}v(x) \quad \text{in} \quad L^2(\Omega) \tag{3.20}$$

for any $i = 1,2,\dots,k$. The convergence $v_n \to v$ in $L^2(\Omega)$ together with (3.20) implies that $u_n(x) \to +\infty$, $D^{\alpha_1}u_n(x) \to \pm\infty,\dots, D^{\alpha_k}u_n(x) \to \pm\infty$ for a.a. $x \in \{x \in \Omega;\ v(x) > 0\} \cap \Omega(\pm,\pm,\dots,\pm)$ and $u_n(x) \to -\infty$, $D^{\alpha_1}u_n(x) \to \pm\infty,\dots, D^{\alpha_k}u_n(x) \to \pm\infty$ for a.a. $x \in \{x \in \Omega;\ v(x) < 0\} \cap \Omega(\pm,\pm,\dots,\pm)$.

To prove this, let us suppose for instance that $u_n(x) \to +\infty$ is not true on a set $\mathcal{A} \subset \{x \in \Omega;\ v(x) > 0\}$, meas $\mathcal{A} > 0$. Then there exist a constant $a > 0$ and a subsequence $\{u_{n_k}\}_{k=1}^{\infty} \subset \{u_n\}_{n=1}^{\infty}$ such that

$$u_{n_k}(x) \leqq a$$

for $x \in \mathcal{A}$. Consequently,

$$v_{n_k}(x) = \frac{u_{n_k}(x)}{\|u_{n_k}(x)\|} \leqq \frac{a}{\|u_{n_k}\|}$$

for $x \in \mathcal{A}$. Thus for all n_k large enough we have

$$\|v - v_{n_k}\|_2^2 \geq \int_{\mathcal{A}} |v(x) - v_{n_k}(x)|^2 \, dx \geq \frac{1}{2} \int_{\mathcal{A}} |v(x)|^2 \, dx > 0$$

a contradiction with $v_{n_k} \longrightarrow v$ in $L^2(\Omega)$. The other cases can be treated in the same way.

Since g is bounded by $h \in L^2(\Omega)$, we can apply Fatou's lemma in (3.19):

$$\int_\Omega f(x)\, v(x)\, dx \geq \liminf_{n \to +\infty} \int_\Omega g\big(x, u_n(x), D^{\alpha_1} u_n(x), \ldots, D^{\alpha_k} u_n(x)\big)\, v(x)\, dx \geq$$

$$\geq \int_\Omega \liminf_{n \to +\infty} g\big(x, u_n(x), D^{\alpha_1} u_n(x), \ldots, D^{\alpha_k} u_n(x)\big)\, v(x)\, dx =$$

$$= \int_\Omega \liminf_{n \to +\infty} g\big(x, u_n(x), D^{\alpha_1} u_n(x), \ldots, D^{\alpha_k} u_n(x)\big)\, v^+(x)\, dx -$$

$$- \int_\Omega \limsup_{n \to +\infty} g\big(x, u_n(x), D^{\alpha_1} u_n(x), \ldots, D^{\alpha_k} u_n(x)\big)\, v^-(x)\, dx =$$

$$= \Big[\int_{\Omega(+,\ldots,+)} \underline{g}(x,+;+,\ldots,+)\, v^+(x)\, dx + \int_{\Omega(-,\ldots,+)} \underline{g}(x,+;-,\ldots,+) v^+(x) dx + \ldots \Big] -$$

$$- \Big[\int_{\Omega(+,\ldots,+)} \overline{g}(x,-;+,\ldots,+) v^-(x) dx + \int_{\Omega(-,\ldots,+)} \overline{g}(x,-;-,\ldots,+) v^-(x) dx \ldots \Big] .$$

This is a contradiction with the assumption (3.3). Hence $\mathcal{H}$ is an admissible homotopy.

Since $\tilde{F} = I - (\lambda - \delta)L^{-1}S$ is an odd operator and $\lambda - \delta$ is not an eigenvalue of L, the Leray-Schauder degree of $\tilde{F}$ is well defined and we have

$$\deg\, [I - (\lambda - \delta)L^{-1}S;\ B_R,\ 0] \neq 0 . \tag{3.21}$$

By the homotopy invariance property of the degree we have

$$\deg\, [I - \lambda L^{-1}S + L^{-1}G - L^{-1}f;\ B_R,\ 0] =$$

$$= \deg\, [\mathcal{H}(1,\cdot);\ B_R,\ 0] = \deg\, [\mathcal{H}(0,\cdot);\ B_R,\ 0] =$$

$$= \deg\, [I - (\lambda - \delta)L^{-1}S;\ B_R,\ 0] . \tag{3.22}$$

It follows from (3.21) and (3.22) that

$$\deg\left[I - \lambda L^{-1}S + L^{-1}G - L^{-1}f;\ B_R,\ 0\right] \neq 0\ .$$

The basic property of the degree implies the existence of $u \in B_R \subset H$ such that (3.5) is satisfied. Hence $u \in H$ is the solution of BVP (3.1), (3.2). This completes the proof of Theorem 3.2. □

3.3. The case of a positive eigenfunction. In this and the following subsections we will suppose that

$$\dim \operatorname{Ker} L_\lambda = 1\ , \tag{3.23}$$

that *the eigenfunctions* $v \in \operatorname{Ker} L_\lambda$ *do not change sign* in Ω and that

$$(L_\lambda u, u)_2 \geqq 0 \tag{3.24}$$

for any $u \in H$.

Instead of the condition

$$|g(x,s,r_1,\dots,r_k)| \leqq h(x)$$

for a.a. $x \in \Omega$ and for all $s \in \mathbb{R}$, $r_i \in \mathbb{R}$, $1 \leqq i \leqq k$ we will suppose that *more general hypotheses.* are satisfied:

(i) there are functions $A, a \in L^2(\Omega)$, $A(x) < 0$, $a(x) > 0$ for a.a. $x \in \Omega$ and a real number $\gamma > 0$ such that

$$g(x,s,r_1,\dots,r_k) \geqq A(x) \tag{3.25}$$

for a.a. $x \in \Omega$, for all $s \geqq \gamma$, $r_i \in \mathbb{R}$, $i = 1,\dots,k$,

$$g(x,s,r_1,\dots,r_k) \leqq a(x) \tag{3.26}$$

for a.a. $x \in \Omega$, for all $s \leqq -\gamma$, $r_i \in \mathbb{R}$, $i = 1,\dots,k$;

(ii) there exist a function $h(x) \in L^2(\Omega)$ and a constant $c > 0$ such that

$$|g(x,s,r_1,\dots,r_k)| \leqq h(x) + c|s| \tag{3.27}$$

for a.a. $x \in \Omega$ and for all $s \in \mathbb{R}$, $r_i \in \mathbb{R}$, $i = 1,2,\dots,k$;

(iii) g has a *sublinear growth* in s , i.e.

$$\lim_{s \to \pm\infty} \frac{g(x,s,r_1,\dots,r_k)}{s} = 0 \tag{3.28}$$

uniformly for a.a. $x \in \Omega$ and for all $r_i \in \mathbb{R}$, $i = 1,2,\dots,k$.

3.4. Theorem. *Let the assumptions of Theorem* 3.2 *be fulfilled. Moreover, let us suppose* (3.23), (3.24) *and replace the boundedness of* g *by* $h \in L^2(\Omega)$ *by* (3.25) - (3.28). *Then BVP* (3.1), (3.2) *has at least one solution* $u \in H$ *for any* $f \in L^2(\Omega)$ *satisfying*

$$\int_{\Omega(+,\dots,+)} \overline{g}(x,-;+,\dots,+)\, v(x)\, dx + $$

$$+ \int_{\Omega(-,\dots,+)} \overline{g}(x,-;-,\dots,+)\, v(x)\, dx + \dots < \int_{\Omega} f(x)\, v(x)\, dx <$$

$$< \int_{\Omega(+,\dots,+)} \underline{g}(x,+;+,\dots,+)\, v(x)\, dx +$$

$$+ \int_{\Omega(-,\dots,+)} \underline{g}(x,+;-,\dots,+)\, v(x)\, dx + \dots , \tag{3.29}$$

where $v \in \operatorname{Ker} L_\lambda$, $\|v\| = 1$, $v > 0$ *in* Ω .

Proof. The idea of the proof of Theorem 3.4 is the same as that of the proof of Theorem 3.2. By the assumption (3.28) we obtain (as in (3.11))

$$\frac{G(u_n)}{\|u_n\|} \longrightarrow 0 \quad \text{in} \quad L^2(\Omega)$$

and we can follow the proof of Theorem 3.2 until we obtain $\tau = 1$, $v \in \operatorname{Ker} L_\lambda$, $Lv - \lambda Sv = 0$. Without loss of generality we may assume that $v > 0$ in Ω . It follows from (3.8) that

$$(Lu_n,v_n)_2 - \lambda(Su_n,v_n)_2 + (1 - \tau_n)\delta(Su_n,v_n)_2 +$$
$$+ \tau_n\big(G(u_n),v_n\big)_2 - \tau_n(f,v_n)_2 = 0 . \tag{3.30}$$

By virtue of (3.24) we have

$$(Lu_n,v_n)_2 - \lambda(Su_n,v_n)_2 \geqq 0 , \tag{3.31}$$

and by the same reasoning as in Subsection 3.2 we obtain

$$(Su_n,v_n)_2 > 0 \tag{3.32}$$

for n sufficiently large. The inequalities (3.31) and (3.32) imply

$$\big(G(u_n),v_n\big)_2 < (f,v_n)_2$$

or equivalently

$$\int_\Omega g\big(x,u_n(x),D^{\alpha_1}u_n(x),\dots,D^{\alpha_k}u_n(x)\big)\, v_n(x)\, dx < \int_\Omega f(x)\, v_n(x)\, dx . \qquad (3.33)$$

We take lim inf in (3.33) with respect to $n \to +\infty$. On the right hand side we immediately obtain

$$\liminf_{n\to+\infty} \int_\Omega f(x)\; v_n(x)\; dx = \int_\Omega f(x)\; v(x)\; dx , \qquad (3.34)$$

taking into account the convergence $v_n \to v$ in H .

In order to pass to lim inf on the left hand side of (3.33), we need the following assertion.

Let $\{u_n\}_{n=1}^\infty$, $\{v_n\}_{n=1}^\infty$ *be as above and let the function* g *satisfy* (3.25) - (3.27). *Then*

$$\liminf_{n\to\infty} \int_\Omega g\big(x,u_n(x),D^{\alpha_1}u_n(x),\dots,D^{\alpha_k}u_n(x)\big)\; v_n(x)\; dx \geq$$

$$\geq \int_{\Omega(+,\dots,+)} \underline{g}(x,+;+,\dots,+)\; v(x)\; dx +$$

$$+ \int_{\Omega(-,\dots,+)} \underline{g}(x,+;-,\dots,+)\; v(x)\; dx + \dots . \qquad (3.35)$$

Let us introduce a function $\tilde v_n$ by

$$\tilde v_n(x) = v(x) \quad \text{for } x \in \Omega ,\quad v_n(x) \in [-v(x),\, v(x)] ,$$

$$\tilde v_n(x) = v(x) \quad \text{for } x \in \Omega ,\quad v_n(x) > v(x) ,$$

$$\tilde v_n(x) = -v(x) \quad \text{for } x \in \Omega ,\quad v_n(x) < -v(x) .$$

Clearly, $\lim\limits_{n\to\infty} \|\tilde v_n - v\|_2 = 0$ and $\lim\limits_{n\to\infty} \|\tilde v_n - v_n\|_2 = 0$.

Hence by using (3.25) - (3.27) we get

$$\int_\Omega g\big(x,u_n(x),D^{\alpha_1}u_n(x),\dots,D^{\alpha_k}u_n(x)\big)\big(v_n(x) - \tilde v_n(x)\big)\; dx \geq$$

$$\geq \int_{\Omega_n^+} A(x)\; |v_n(x) - \tilde v_n(x)|\; dx - \int_{\Omega_n^-} a(x)\; |v_n(x) - \tilde v_n(x)|\; dx -$$

$$- \int_{\Omega_n} \left(h(x) + c|\gamma|\right) |v_n(x) - \tilde{v}_n(x)| \, dx \to 0 \; , \tag{3.36}$$

where $\Omega_n^+ = \{x \in \Omega;\ u_n(x) \geqq \gamma\}$, $\Omega_n^- = \{x \in \Omega;\ u_n(x) \leqq -\gamma\}$ and $\Omega_n =$
$= \{x \in \Omega;\ |u_n(x)| < \gamma\}$.

By the definition of $\tilde{v}_n$ and by (3.25) - (3.27) we have

$$\begin{cases} g\left(x,u_n(x),D^{\alpha_1}u_n(x),\dots,D^{\alpha_k}u_n(x)\right)\tilde{v}_n(x) \geqq A(x)v(x) \; , & x \in \Omega_n^+ \; , \\ g\left(x,u_n(x),D^{\alpha_1}u_n(x),\dots,D^{\alpha_k}u_n(x)\right)\tilde{v}_n(x) \geqq -\, a(x)v(x) \; , & x \in \Omega_n^- \; , \\ g\left(x,u_n(x),D^{\alpha_1}u_n(x),\dots,D^{\alpha_k}u_n(x)\right)\tilde{v}_n(x) \geqq -\left(h(x) + c|\gamma|\right)v(x) \; , & x \in \Omega_n \; . \end{cases} \tag{3.37}$$

We apply Fatou's lemma and by (3.36), (3.37) we get

$$\liminf_{n\to\infty} \int_\Omega g\left(x,u_n(x),D^{\alpha_1}u_n(x),\dots,D^{\alpha_k}u_n(x)\right) v_n(x)\, dx =$$

$$= \liminf_{n\to\infty} \left[\int_\Omega g\left(x,u_n(x),D^{\alpha_1}u_n(x),\dots,D^{\alpha_k}u_n(x)\right) \tilde{v}_n(x)\, dx + \right.$$

$$\left. + \int_\Omega g\left(x,u_n(x),D^{\alpha_1}u_n(x),\dots,D^{\alpha_k}u_n(x)\right)\left(v_n(x) - \tilde{v}_n(x)\right) dx \right] \geqq$$

$$\geqq \liminf_{n\to\infty} \int_\Omega g\left(x,u_n(x),D^{\alpha_1}u_n(x),\dots,D^{\alpha_k}u_n(x)\right) \tilde{v}_n(x)\, dx \geqq$$

$$\geqq \int_\Omega \liminf_{n\to\infty} g\left(x,u_n(x),D^{\alpha_1}u_n(x),\dots,D^{\alpha_k}u_n(x)\right) \tilde{v}_n(x)\, dx =$$

$$= \int_{\Omega(+,\dots,+)} \underline{g}(x,+;+,\dots,+)\, v(x)\, dx +$$

$$+ \int_{\Omega(-,\dots,+)} \underline{g}(x,+;-,\dots,+)\, v(x)\, dx + \dots \; , \tag{3.38}$$

which completes the proof of the assertion.

Now, it follows from (3.33), (3.34) and (3.35) that

$$\int_{\Omega(+,\dots,+)} \underline{g}(x,+;+,\dots,+)\, v(x)\, dx + \int_{\Omega(-,\dots,+)} \underline{g}(x,+;-,\dots,+)\, v(x)\, dx + \dots$$

$$\leq \int_{\Omega} f(x)\, v(x)\, dx ,$$

which contradicts (3.29).

If the limit function $v \in \operatorname{Ker} L_\lambda$, $\|v\| = 1$ is negative in Ω , we can proceed in a similar way in order to get a contradiction with the second part of (3.29). This completes the proof of Theorem 3.4. □

3.5. Remark. Let us denote

$$\bar{g}(x,+;\pm,\dots,\pm) = \limsup_{\substack{s \to +\infty \\ r_i \to \pm\infty}} g(x,s,r_1,\dots,r_k) ,$$

$$\underline{g}(x,-;\pm,\dots,\pm) = \liminf_{\substack{s \to -\infty \\ r_i \to \pm\infty}} g(x,s,r_1,\dots,r_k) .$$

Then the assertion of Theorem 3.2 remains true if we *replace* (3.3) by the *condition*

$$\int_{\Omega} f(x)\, v(x)\, dx > \Big[\int_{\Omega(+,\dots,+)} \bar{g}(x,+;+,\dots,+)\, v^+(x)\, dx +$$

$$+ \int_{\Omega(-,\dots,+)} \bar{g}(x,+;-,\dots,+)\, v^+(x)\, dx +$$

$$+ \dots + \int_{\Omega(-,\dots,-)} \bar{g}(x,+;-,\dots,-)\, v^+(x)\, dx \Big] -$$

$$- \Big[\int_{\Omega(+,\dots,+)} \underline{g}(x,-;+,\dots,+)\, v^-(x)\, dx +$$

$$+ \int_{\Omega(-,\dots,+)} \underline{g}(x,-;-,\dots,+)\, v^-(x)\, dx +$$

$$+ \dots + \int_{\Omega(-,\dots,-)} \underline{g}(x,-;-,\dots,-)\, v^-(x)\, dx \Big] .$$

The proof of this modification of Theorem 3.2 is the same but we must take $\delta < 0$ with sufficiently small modulus $|\delta|$.

3.6. Example. Let us consider the equation

$$- \Delta u - 2u + b(x,y) \operatorname{arc\,tan} u_x + c(x,y) \sin u_x + \frac{d(x,y)}{1 + u^2} = f(x,y) , \quad (x,y) \in \Omega \qquad (3.39)$$

with the boundary conditions

$$\begin{cases} u(0,y) = u_x\left(\frac{\pi}{2}, y\right) = 0 & 0 < y < \frac{\pi}{2} , \\ u_y(x,0) = u\left(x, \frac{\pi}{2}\right) = 0 & 0 < x < \frac{\pi}{2} . \end{cases} \qquad (3.40)$$

where $\Omega = \left(0, \frac{\pi}{2}\right) \times \left(0, \frac{\pi}{2}\right)$, $b, c, d \in L^2(\Omega)$, b , c are positive in Ω . The linear operator A is $-\Delta$. The operator L generated by A and by the boundary conditions B given by (3.40) satisfies the assumptions from Subsection 3.1, $\lambda = 2$ is the principal eigenvalue of L , and the kernel $\operatorname{Ker} L_\lambda$ is spanned by the function $v(x,y) = \sin x \cos y$. The both functions v and v_x are positive in Ω . In this case $H = \{u \in W^{2,2}(\Omega);\ u$ satisfies (3.40)$\}$. The nonlinear function g has the form $g(x,y,u,u_x) =$ $= b(x,y) \operatorname{arc\,tan} u_x + c(x,y) \sin u_x + \dfrac{d(x,y)}{1 + u^2}$ and satisfies the assumptions from Subsection 3.1 and we have

$$\underline{g}(x,y,+;+) = \liminf_{\substack{s \to +\infty \\ r \to +\infty}} g(x,y,s,r) = b(x,y) \frac{\pi}{2} - c(x,y) ,$$

$$\underline{g}(x,y,+;-) = \liminf_{\substack{s \to +\infty \\ r \to -\infty}} g(x,y,s,r) = - b(x,y) \frac{\pi}{2} - c(x,y) ,$$

$$\overline{g}(x,y,-;+) = \limsup_{\substack{s \to -\infty \\ r \to +\infty}} g(x,y,s,r) = b(x,y) \frac{\pi}{2} + c(x,y) ,$$

$$\overline{g}(x,y,-;-) = \limsup_{\substack{s \to -\infty \\ r \to -\infty}} g(x,y,s,r) = - b(x,y) \frac{\pi}{2} + c(x,y) .$$

Then the *inequality* (3.3) in Theorem 3.2 has the *form*

$$\int_\Omega \left[- b(x,y) \frac{\pi}{2} + c(x,y)\right] v(x,y)\, dx\, dy < \int_\Omega f(x,y)\, v(x,y)\, dx\, dy <$$

$$< \int_{\Omega} \left[b(x,y) \frac{\pi}{2} - c(x,y) \right] v(x,y)\, dx\, dy \, . \tag{3.41}$$

If we put $b(x,y) = c(x,y) \equiv 1$ on Ω then by virtue of

$$\int_{\Omega} v(x,y)\, dx\, dy = \int_0^{\pi/2} \int_0^{\pi/2} \sin x \cos y\, dx\, dy = 1$$

the inequalities (3.41) are reduced to

$$1 - \frac{\pi}{2} < \int_0^{\pi/2} \int_0^{\pi/2} f(x,y) \sin x \cos y\, dx\, dy < \frac{\pi}{2} - 1 \, .$$

<u>3.7. Example.</u> Consider BVP

$$- \Delta u - 2u + \operatorname{arc\,cotan} u + \cos u + \arctan u_x = f(x,y) \, , \quad (x,y) \in \Omega \, , \tag{3.42}$$

$$u(x,y) = 0 \, , \quad (x,y) \in \partial\Omega \, , \tag{3.43}$$

where $\Omega = (0,\pi) \times (0,\pi)$. The linear operator L generated by $- \Delta$ and by the boundary conditions (3.43) satisfies the assumptions from Subsection 3.1, and the kernel of $L_\lambda u = - \Delta u - 2\lambda u$ is spanned by the function $v(x,y) = \sin x \sin y$. We have $H = W^{2,2}(\Omega) \cap W_0^{1,2}(\Omega)$ and the nonlinear function g is given by

$$g(x,y,u,u_x) = \operatorname{arc\,cotan} u + \cos u + \arctan u_x \, .$$

It satisfies the assumptions from Subsection 3.1 and we have

$$\bar{g}(x,y,+;+) = 1 + \frac{\pi}{2} \, , \quad \bar{g}(x,y,+;-) = 1 - \frac{\pi}{2} \, ,$$

$$\underline{g}(x,y,-;+) = \frac{3\pi}{2} - 1 \, , \quad \underline{g}(x,y,-;-) = \frac{\pi}{2} - 1 \, .$$

Then it follows from Theorem 3.2 and Remark 3.5 that BVP (3.42), (3.43) has at least one solution $u \in H$ for any $f \in L^2(\Omega)$, satisfying

$$\left(1 + \frac{\pi}{2}\right) \int_{\Omega} v(x,y)\, dx\, dy + \left(1 - \frac{\pi}{2}\right) \int_{\Omega} v(x,y)\, dx\, dy <$$

$$< \int_{\Omega} f(x,y)\, v(x,y)\, dx\, dy <$$

$$< \left(\frac{3\pi}{2} - 1\right) \int_{\Omega} v(x,y)\, dx\, dy + \left(\frac{\pi}{2} - 1\right) \int_{\Omega} v(x,y)\, dx\, dy \, . \tag{3.44}$$

Since $\int_0^\pi \int_0^\pi \sin x \sin y \, dx \, dy = 4$, the inequalities (3.44) reduce to

$$8 < \int_0^\pi \int_0^\pi f(x,y) \sin x \sin y \, dx \, dy < 8(\pi - 1) .$$

3.8.Example. Let us consider BVP

$$- \Delta u - 2u + (u)^{\frac{1}{3}} + b \arctan u_y = f(x,y) , \quad (x,y) \in \Omega , \qquad (3.45)$$

$$u(x,y) = 0 , \quad (x,y) \in \partial\Omega , \qquad (3.46)$$

where $\Omega = (0,\pi) \times (0,\pi)$ and $b \in \mathbb{R}$ is an arbitrary constant. The linear part of this BVP is the same as in the previous example and satisfies the assumptions (3.23), (3.24). The nonlinearity g is of the form

$$g(x,y,u,u_y) = (u)^{\frac{1}{3}} + b \arctan u_y .$$

This function satisfies the assumptions (3.25) - (3.28) and we have

$$\underline{g}(x,y,+;+) = +\infty, \ \underline{g}(x,y,+;-) = +\infty, \ \overline{g}(x,y,-;+) = -\infty, \ \overline{g}(x,y,-;-) = -\infty .$$

The inequality (3.29) in Theorem 3.4 has the form

$$- \infty < \int_\Omega f(x,y) \, v(x,y) \, dx \, dy < + \infty .$$

Thus BVP (3.45), (3.46) has at least one solution $u \in W^{2,2}(\Omega) \cap W_0^{1,2}(\Omega)$ for an arbitrary right hand side $f \in L^2(\Omega)$.

3.9. Example. Let us consider BVP

$$- \Delta u - 2u + \arctan u + \sin u + b \min \{0, \arctan u_x\} = f(x,y) ,$$
$$(x,y) \in \Omega , \qquad (3.47)$$

$$\frac{\partial u(x,y)}{\partial \nu} = 0 , \quad (x,y) \in \partial\Omega , \qquad (3.48)$$

where $\Omega = (0,\pi) \times (0,\pi)$ and $b \in \mathbb{R}$ is an arbitrary positive number. The operator $Au = -\Delta u + \varepsilon u$ (for some $\varepsilon > 0$) together with the Neumann boundary condition (3.48) generates a linear operator L satisfying the assumptions from Subsection 3.1 for which $\lambda = 2 + \varepsilon$ is the second eigenvalue. The kernel of $L_\lambda u = -\Delta u - 2u$ is spanned by the function $v(x,y) = \cos x \cos y$. In this case $H = \{u \in W^{2,2}(\Omega);\ \frac{\partial u}{\partial \nu} = 0 \text{ on } \partial\Omega\}$. The nonlinear function g has the form

$$g(x,y,u,u_x) = \operatorname{arc\,tan} u + \sin u + b \min\{0, \operatorname{arc\,tan} u_x\}.$$

It satisfies all the assumptions from Subsection 3.1 and

$$\underline{g}(x,y,+;+) = \frac{\pi}{2} - 1, \quad \underline{g}(x,y,+;-) = \frac{\pi}{2} - 1 - \frac{b\pi}{2},$$

$$\overline{g}(x,y,-;+) = 1 - \frac{\pi}{2}, \quad \overline{g}(x,y,-;-) = 1 - \frac{\pi}{2} - \frac{b\pi}{2}.$$

The inequalities (3.3) in Theorem 3.2 have the form

$$\left(1 - \frac{\pi}{2}\right) \int_{\Omega(+)} v^+(x,y)\,dx\,dy + \left(1 - \frac{\pi}{2} - \frac{b\pi}{2}\right) \int_{\Omega(-)} v^+(x,y)\,dx\,dy -$$

$$- \left(\frac{\pi}{2} - 1\right) \int_{\Omega(+)} v^-(x,y)\,dx\,dy - \left(\frac{\pi}{2} - 1 - \frac{b\pi}{2}\right) \int_{\Omega(-)} v^-(x,y)\,dx\,dy <$$

$$< \int_{\Omega} f(x,y)\, v(x,y)\,dx\,dy <$$

$$< \left(\frac{\pi}{2} - 1\right) \int_{\Omega(+)} v^+(x,y)\,dx\,dy + \left(\frac{\pi}{2} - 1 - \frac{b\pi}{2}\right) \int_{\Omega(-)} v^+(x,y)\,dx\,dy -$$

$$- \left(1 - \frac{\pi}{2}\right) \int_{\Omega(+)} v^-(x,y)\,dx\,dy - \left(1 - \frac{\pi}{2} - \frac{b\pi}{2}\right) \int_{\Omega(-)} v^-(x,y)\,dx\,dy.$$

Since we have

$$\int_{\Omega(+)} v^+\,dx\,dy = \int_{\Omega(-)} v^+\,dx\,dy = \int_{\Omega(+)} v^-\,dx\,dy = \int_{\Omega(-)} v^-\,dx\,dy = 1,$$

we get

$$4 - 2\pi < \int_0^\pi \int_0^\pi f(x,y) \cos x \cos y\,dx\,dy < 2\pi - 4.$$

<u>3.10. Example.</u> Set $\Omega = (0,\pi) \times (0,\pi)$ and consider BVP

$$\Delta^2 u - 4u - \operatorname{arc\,tan} u_{yy} + \cos u_{xxx} = f(x,y), \quad (x,y) \in \Omega, \tag{3.49}$$

$$\begin{cases} u(x,y) = 0 , & (x,y) \in \partial\Omega , \\ u_{xx}(0,y) = u_{xx}(\pi,y) = 0 , & y \in (0,\pi) , \\ u_{yy}(x,0) = u_{yy}(x,\pi) = 0 , & x \in (0,\pi) , \end{cases} \tag{3.50}$$

where $\Delta^2 u = \dfrac{\partial^4 u}{\partial x^4} + 2\dfrac{\partial^4 u}{\partial x^2 \partial y^2} + \dfrac{\partial^4 u}{\partial y^4}$ is the *biharmonic operator*. In this case A is given by $\Delta^2 u$. The operator L generated by A and the boundary conditions (3.50) satisfy the assumptions from Subsection 3.1, $\lambda = 4$ is the principal eigenvalue of L, and the kernel $\operatorname{Ker} L_\lambda$ is spanned by the function $v(x,y) = \sin x \sin y$. In this case $H = \{u \in W^{4,2}(\Omega);\ u \text{ satisfies } (3.50)\}$, and the nonlinearity g has the form

$$g(x,y,u,u_{yy},u_{xxx}) = -\arctan u_{yy} + \cos u_{xxx} .$$

It satisfies the assumptions from Subsection 3.1 and

$$\underline{g}(x,y,+;+,+) = -\frac{\pi}{2} - 1 , \quad \underline{g}(x,y,+;-,+) = \frac{\pi}{2} - 1 ,$$

$$\underline{g}(x,y,+;+,-) = -\frac{\pi}{2} - 1 , \quad \underline{g}(x,y,+;-,-) = \frac{\pi}{2} - 1 ,$$

$$\overline{g}(x,y,-;+,+) = -\frac{\pi}{2} + 1 , \quad \overline{g}(x,y,-;-,+) = \frac{\pi}{2} + 1 ,$$

$$\overline{g}(x,y,-;+,-) = -\frac{\pi}{2} + 1 , \quad \overline{g}(x,y,-;-,-) = \frac{\pi}{2} + 1 .$$

Further, we have $v(x,y) > 0$, $v_{yy}(x,y) < 0$, $(x,y) \in \Omega$ (i.e. $\Omega(+,\pm) = \emptyset$), $v_{xxx}(x,y) < 0$ for $(x,y) \in \Omega(-,-) = \left(0, \frac{\pi}{2}\right) \times (0,\pi)$ and $v_{xxx}(x,y) > 0$ for $(x,y) \in \Omega(-,+) = \left(\frac{\pi}{2}, \pi\right) \times (0,\pi)$. Hence, the inequality (3.3) in Theorem 3.2 has the form

$$\left(-\frac{\pi}{2} + 1\right) \int_0^{\pi/2}\int_0^{\pi} \sin x \sin y \, dx \, dy + \left(-\frac{\pi}{2} + 1\right) \int_{\pi/2}^{\pi}\int_0^{\pi} \sin x \sin y \, dx \, dy <$$

$$< \int_0^{\pi}\int_0^{\pi} f(x,y) \sin x \sin y \, dx \, dy <$$

$$< \left(\frac{\pi}{2} - 1\right) \int_0^{\pi/2}\int_0^{\pi} \sin x \sin y \, dx \, dy + \left(\frac{\pi}{2} - 1\right) \int_{\pi/2}^{\pi}\int_0^{\pi} \sin x \sin y \, dx \, dy ,$$

i.e. BVP (3.49), (3.50) has at least one solution $u \in H$ for any right hand side $f \in L^2(\Omega)$ satisfying

$$4 - 2\pi < \int_0^\pi \int_0^\pi f(x,y) \sin x \sin y \, dx \, dy < 2\pi - 4 .$$

<u>3.11. Example.</u> Let Ω be as in Example 3.10 and consider the equation

$$\Delta^2 u - 4u + g(x,y,u,u_{yy},u_{xxx}) = f(x,y) , \quad (x,y) \in \Omega \tag{3.51}$$

with the boundary conditions (3.50), where g is defined by

$$g(x,y,u,u_{yy},u_{xxx}) = b(x,y) \max \left(0,(u)^{3/5}\right) +$$

$$+ c(x,y) \operatorname{arc\,tan} u - \operatorname{arc\,tan} u_{yy} + \cos u_{xxx} ,$$

$$b(x,y) = 1 , \quad c(x,y) = 0 , \quad (x,y) \in \left(0, \tfrac{\pi}{2}\right) \times (0,\pi) ,$$

$$b(x,y) = 0 , \quad c(x,y) = -1 , \quad (x,y) \in \left(\tfrac{\pi}{2} , \pi\right) \times (0,\pi) .$$

The linear operator L satisfies the assumptions (3.23), (3.24) and the nonlinear function g satisfies the assumptions (3.25) - (3.28). In this case we have

$$\underline{g}(x,y,+;\pm,\pm) = +\infty \quad \text{on} \quad \left(0, \tfrac{\pi}{2}\right) \times (0,\pi) ,$$

$$\underline{g}(x,y,+;+,\pm) = -\pi - 1 , \quad \underline{g}(x,y,+;-,\pm) = -1 \quad \text{on} \quad \left(\tfrac{\pi}{2} , \pi\right) \times (0,\pi) ,$$

$$\overline{g}(x,y,-;+,\pm) = -\tfrac{\pi}{2} + 1 , \quad \overline{g}(x,y,-;-,\pm) = \tfrac{\pi}{2} + 1$$
$$\text{on} \quad \left(0, \tfrac{\pi}{2}\right) \times (0,\pi) ,$$

$$\overline{g}(x,y,-;+,\pm) = 1 , \quad \overline{g}(x,y,-;-,\pm) = \pi + 1 \quad \text{on} \quad \left(\tfrac{\pi}{2} , \pi\right) \times (0,\pi) .$$

Note that g is *not an ultimately increasing* function in the sense of McKENNA, RAUCH [219]. The inequality (3.29) in Theorem 3.4 has the form

$$\left(-\tfrac{\pi}{2} + 1\right) \int_0^{\pi/2} \int_0^\pi \sin x \sin y \, dx \, dy + \int_{\pi/2}^\pi \int_0^\pi \sin x \sin y \, dx \, dy <$$

$$< \int_0^\pi \int_0^\pi f(x,y) \sin x \sin y \, dx \, dy < + \infty ,$$

i.e. BVP (3.51), (3.50) has at least one solution for any $f \in L^2(\Omega)$ satisfying

$$4 - \pi < \int_0^\pi \int_0^\pi f(x,y) \sin x \sin y \, dx \, dy .$$

3.12. Remarks. (i) The generalizations of the results of LANDESMAN and LAZER [185] and WILLIAMS [296] to nonlinear terms g which may depend upon the partial derivatives of u of order less than or equal to $2m - 1$ were considered by several authors. In FUČÍK, KUČERA and NEČAS [127] the authors deal with nonlinearities in the very special form $\sum_{i=1}^{k} D^{\alpha_i} g_i(D^{\alpha_i} u)$. The papers by SHAW [275] and HETZER [155] generalize the results of LANDESMAN and LAZER [185] to nonlinearities of the form $g(u) + h(x,u,D^{\alpha_1} u,\dots,D^{\alpha_k} u)$, where h may depend on the partial derivatives of u up to the order $2m - 1$. However, in papers [275] and [155] the behaviour of the term h is not so important as the properties of g . More general nonlinearities are considered in the papers KENT NAGLE, POTHOVEN and SINGKOFER [173] and KENT NAGLE and SINGKOFER [174]. The authors of these papers need an additional hypothesis of monotonicity type for g . This condition is eliminated in the paper CAÑADA [38] the results of which seem to be the most general. In McKENNA and RAUCH [219] the assumption of nonnegativity of A is essential and g is supposed to be an ultimately increasing function. The papers CAÑADA [37] and WARD [288] are devoted to the study of ordinary differential equations. Systems of ordinary differential equations are considered also in CAÑADA [36], and the nonlinear term g is supposed to be contractive. In WARD [288] a version of nonnegativity condition is essential.

(ii) Let us point out that the solvability of BVPs from Examples 3.6 – 3.11 is not covered by any paper mentioned above (cf. DRÁBEK and NICOLOSI [98]).

CHAPTER 2

Weakly nonlinear problems with vanishing nonlinearity

4. DIRICHLET PROBLEM FOR HIGHER ORDER PARTIAL DIFFERENTIAL EQUATIONS

4.1. Let Ω be a bounded open set in $\mathbb{R}^N$ with lipschitzian boundary $\partial\Omega$, and let $H = W_0^{m,2}(\Omega)$. Let us denote by $\|\cdot\|$ the norm in H, by $\|\cdot\|_2$ the norm in $L^2(\Omega)$ and by $(\cdot,\cdot)$ and $(\cdot,\cdot)_2$ the inner product in H and in $L^2(\Omega)$, respectively. Let us consider the formal differential operator

$$A = - \sum_{|\alpha|=|\beta|=m} (-1)^{|\alpha|} D^{\alpha}(a_{\alpha\beta}D^{\beta}) .$$

We assume that $a_{\alpha\beta} = a_{\beta\alpha} \in L^{\infty}(\Omega)$ and there exists a constant $\gamma > 0$ such that

$$\sum_{|\alpha|=|\beta|=m} a_{\alpha\beta}(x)\ \xi^{\alpha}\ \xi^{\beta} \geqq \gamma|\xi|^{2m}$$

for a.a. $x \in \Omega$ and for each $\xi \in \mathbb{R}^N$. In this section we will study the *nonlinear Dirichlet problem*

$$Au + \lambda_k u + g(x,u) = f(x)\ , \quad x \in \Omega\ , \tag{4.1}$$

$$Du = 0 \quad \text{on} \quad \partial\Omega\ , \tag{4.2}$$

where λ_k is the eigenvalue of A, $g = g(x,s) : \Omega \times \mathbb{R} \to \mathbb{R}$ is a nonlinear bounded function, $f \in L^2(\Omega)$ and D is the Dirichlet boundary operator.

For $u, v \in H$ set

$$((u,v)) = \int_{\Omega} \sum_{|\alpha|=|\beta|=m} a_{\alpha\beta}\ D^{\alpha}u\ D^{\beta}v\ dx .$$

Let us consider the linear operator $L : H \to H$ defined by $(Lu,v) = - ((u,v))$. L is a selfadjoint operator with infinitely many eigenvalues $0 < \lambda_1 \leqq \lambda_2 \leqq \dots$ and a corresponding complete orthonormal system of eigenfunctions $\phi_1,\phi_2,\dots$. It is known that each λ_k has the variational characterization

$$\lambda_k = \min\left\{\frac{((v,v))}{\|v\|_2^2}\ ;\quad v \in H\ ,\quad (v,\phi_i)_2 = 0\ ,\quad i = 1,2,\ldots,k-1\right\}.$$

Let us denote by L_k the linear operator defined by

$$(L_k u,v) = (Lu,v) + \lambda_k (u,v)_2\ .$$

Then L_k is a Fredholm mapping of index zero.

We suppose that λ_k is an eigenvalue of multiplicity $m \geqq 1$, i.e.

$$\lambda_{k-1} < \lambda_k = \lambda_{k+1} = \ldots = \lambda_{k+m-1} < \lambda_{k+m}\ .$$

We set $V = \mathrm{Ker}\ L_k$ and denote by $V^\perp$ its orthogonal complement so that $H = V \oplus V^\perp$ and $u \in H$ can be written in the form $u = v + w$, where $v \in V$ and $w \in V^\perp$.

We assume that V has the following *unique continuation property* : for every $v \in V$, $v \neq 0$ the set $\{x \in \Omega;\ v(x) = 0\}$ has zero Lebesgue measure.

Let $g = g(x,s) : \Omega \times \mathbf{R} \to \mathbf{R}$ be a function which is measurable in $x \in \Omega$ for all $s \in \mathbf{R}$ and continuously differentiable in s for a.a. $x \in \Omega$. Moreover, we assume:

(g1) there exists $M > 0$ such that

$$|g(x,s)| \leqq M$$

for all $(x,s) \in \Omega \times \mathbf{R}$;

(g2) $\int_0^{-\infty} g(x,s)\,ds = \int_0^{+\infty} g(x,s)\,ds$ for a.a. $x \in \Omega$ and the integral

$$\int_\Omega \int_0^{+\infty} g(x,s)\,ds\,dx \in \mathbf{R} \cup \{\pm\infty\}$$ exists (we take the Lebesgue integrals);

(g3) $\lambda_{k-1} < \mathrm{const} \leqq \lambda_k + g_s'(x,s) \leqq \mathrm{const} < \lambda_{k+m}$ if $k > 1$;

$\mathrm{const} \leqq g_s'(x,s) + \lambda_1 \leqq \mathrm{const} < \lambda_{m+1}$ if $k = 1$

for all $(x,s) \in \Omega \times \mathbf{R}$.

If g satisfies (g1), we can define a mapping $G : H \to H$ by

$$\big(G(u),v\big) = \big(g(x,u),v\big)_2$$

for all $v \in H$. Moreover, the operator G is continuously Fréchet differentiable.

A function $u \in H$ is called a *weak solution* of BVP (4.1), (4.2) if

$$L_k u + G(u) = f^* , \tag{4.3}$$

where $f^* \in H$ is the representation of $f \in L^2(\Omega)$ defined by

$$(f^*, v) = (f, v)_2$$

for all $v \in H$.

4.2. Lyapunov-Schmidt method. Let us denote by P the L^2-orthogonal projection of H onto V and set $Q = I - P$, where I is the identity on H . Applying P and Q to (4.3) we obtain the system

$$L_k w + QG(v + w) = Qf^*, \tag{4.4}$$

$$PG(v + w) = Pf^*. \tag{4.5}$$

It is evident that this system is equivalent to (4.3).

In the following lemmas we assume that hypotheses formulated in Subsection 4.1 are fulfilled.

4.3. Lemma. *For any fixed* $f \in H$ *the equation* (4.4) *has for each* $v \in V$ *precisely one solution* $w(v) \in V^{\perp}$. *The function* $v \mapsto w(v)$ *is a* C^1 *function of* v *and there exists* $k > 0$ *such that* $\|w(v)\| \leq k$ *for all* $v \in V$.

Proof. Consider the mapping

$$w \mapsto L_k w + QG(v + w) .$$

Using (g3) and the variational characterization of the eigenvalues λ_{k-1} , λ_{k+p} it is possible to show that the mapping is locally invertible on $V^{\perp}$. Moreover, since g is bounded, the above mapping is proper, and therefore it is a global homeomorphism on $V^{\perp}$. The other statements of Lemma 4.3 are consequences of the fact that g is a C^1 function in s and bounded (cf. AMBROSETTI and MANCINI [9,10]). □

4.4. Lemma. *We have*

$$\lim_{\ell \to +\infty} \operatorname{meas} \{ x \in \Omega ; |w(v)(x)| \geq \ell \} = 0$$

uniformly with respect to $v \in V$.

Proof of this lemma is an immediate consequence of the inequality $\|w(v)\| \leqq k$ for all $v \in V$ (see Lemma 4.3). □

4.5. Lemma. *For each* $\ell \in \mathbb{N}$ *we have*

$$\lim_{\|v\|\to\infty,\ v\in V} \text{meas } \{x \in \Omega;\ |v(x)| \leqq \ell\} = 0 .$$

Proof. Suppose the contrary. Let there exist $\ell_0 \in \mathbb{N}$, $v_n \in V$, $\|v_n\| \to \infty$ such that

$$\text{meas } \{x \in \Omega;\ |v_n(x)| \leqq \ell_0\} \geqq \varepsilon_0 > 0 .$$

Put $\hat{v}_n = \dfrac{v_n}{\|v_n\|}$. Then

$$\text{meas } \{x \in \Omega;\ |\hat{v}_n(x)| \leqq \frac{\ell_0}{\|v_n\|}\} \geqq \varepsilon_0 . \tag{4.6}$$

Since $\dim V < +\infty$ we can suppose that $\hat{v}_n \to v_0 \in V$ in $L^2(\Omega)$. By Jegorov's theorem for each $\eta > 0$ there exists $\Omega' \subset \Omega$, meas $\Omega' < \eta$ and $\hat{v}_n \to v_0$ uniformly on $\Omega \setminus \Omega'$. If we put $\eta = \varepsilon_0/2$ and take the limit for $n \to \infty$ in (4.6), we obtain

$$\text{meas } \{x \in \Omega;\ |v_0(x)| \leqq 0\} \geqq \frac{\varepsilon_0}{2} > 0 ,$$

which contradicts the unique continuation property of V (see Subsection 4.1). □

It is well known that the restriction $L_k|V^\perp : V^\perp \to V^\perp$ is an algebraic isomorphism. Its inverse $(L_k|V^\perp)^{-1}$ will be denoted by K. Let us suppose that $f^* \in V^\perp$ is fixed. Then applying K on both sides of (4.4) we obtain

$$w + KQG(v + w) = Kf^*.$$

4.6. Lemma. *If* $\displaystyle\int_\Omega \int_0^{+\infty} g(x,s)\, ds\, dx \in \mathbb{R}$ *then*

$$\lim_{\|v\|\to\infty} \|w(v) - Kf^*\| = 0 \quad \textit{and} \quad \lim_{\|v\|\to\infty} \|L_k w(v) - f^*\| = 0 .$$

Proof. Using the Hölder inequality we obtain

$$\| w(v) - Kf^*\|^2 \leq \|K\|^2 \int_\Omega |g(x, v + w(v))|^2 \, dx$$

and

$$\|L_k w(v) - f^*\|^2 \leq \int_\Omega |g(x, v + w(v))|^2 \, dx .$$

Choose $\varepsilon > 0$. By the assumptions of the lemma, (g1) and the properties of the Lebesgue integral we have

$$\int_0^{+\infty} \int_\Omega |g(x,s)|^2 \, dx \, ds < \infty .$$

Hence (recall the boundedness of $g_s'(x,s)$ in (g3)) there exists $k > 0$ such that

$$\sup_{|s| \geq k} \int_\Omega |g(x,s)|^2 \, dx < \frac{\varepsilon}{2} . \tag{4.7}$$

According to Lemmas 4.4 and 4.5 there exists $\kappa > 0$ such that for $\|v\| \geq \kappa$, $v \in V$ we have

$$\text{meas } \Omega_k = \text{meas } \{x \in \Omega ;\ |v(x) + w(v)(x)| \leq k\} < \frac{\varepsilon}{2M^2} . \tag{4.8}$$

Using (4.7) and (4.8) we obtain for all $v \in V$, $\|v\| \geq \kappa$:

$$\int_\Omega |g(x, v + w(v))|^2 \, dx \leq \int_{\Omega_k} |g(x, v + w(v))|^2 \, dx + \int_{\Omega \setminus \Omega_k} |g(x, v + w(v))|^2 \, dx \leq$$

$$\leq \int_{\Omega_k} M^2 \, dx + \sup_{|s| \geq k} \int_\Omega |g(x,s)|^2 \, dx < \varepsilon .$$

□

Let us introduce a function $F : V \to \mathbb{R}$ defined by

$$F(v) = \frac{1}{2} \left(L_k w(v), w(v)\right) + \int_\Omega \int_0^{v+w(v)} g(x,s) \, ds \, dx - \left(f^*, w(v)\right) . \tag{4.9}$$

4.7. Lemma. *We have*

(i) $$\lim_{\|v\| \to \infty} F(v) = -\frac{1}{2} (f^*, Kf^*) + \int_\Omega \int_0^{+\infty} g(x,s) \, ds \, dx$$

provided $\int_\Omega \int_0^{+\infty} g(x,s)\,ds\,dx \in \mathbb{R}$;

(ii) $\lim_{\|v\| \to \infty} F(v) = \pm \infty$ *if* $\int_\Omega \int_0^{+\infty} g(x,s)\,ds\,dx = \pm \infty$.

Proof. (i) Let $\int_\Omega \int_0^{+\infty} g(x,s)\,ds\,dx \in \mathbb{R}$. According to Lemma 4.6 we have

$$\lim_{\|v\| \to \infty} \left[\tfrac{1}{2}\left(L_k w(v), w(v)\right) - \left(f^*, w(v)\right)\right] = -\tfrac{1}{2}(f^*, Kf^*) \ .$$

Let $\varepsilon > 0$ be arbitrary but fixed. We have $x \mapsto \int_0^{+\infty} |g(x,s)|\,ds \in L^1(\Omega)$. Hence the functions $g_n(x) = \int_0^n g(x,s)\,ds$ are uniformly integrable over Ω , $g_n(\cdot) \to \int_0^{\pm\infty} g(\cdot,s)\,ds$ a.e. in Ω if $n \to \pm\infty$. Using Vitali's theorem we obtain the existence of such a $k \in \mathbb{N}$ that

$$\int_\Omega \left| \int_0^{\pm n} g(x,s)\,ds - \int_0^{\pm\infty} g(x,s)\,ds \right| dx < \frac{\varepsilon}{3} \tag{4.10}$$

for all $n \geqq k$. Applying Lemma 4.5 we can choose such a $\kappa > 0$ that

$$\int_{\Omega_k} \int_0^{+\infty} |g(x,s)|\,ds\,dx < \frac{\varepsilon}{3} \quad \text{and} \quad \int_{\Omega_k} \int_{-\infty}^{0} |g(x,s)|\,ds\,dx < \frac{\varepsilon}{3} \tag{4.11}$$

for all $v \in V$, $\|v\| \geqq \kappa$ (for the definition of Ω_k see the proof of Lemma 4.6) Using (g2), (4.10) and (4.11) we obtain

$$\left| \int_\Omega \int_0^{v+w(v)} g(x,s)\,ds\,dx - \int_\Omega \int_0^{+\infty} g(x,s)\,ds\,dx \right| \leqq$$

$$\leqq \int_{\Omega \setminus \Omega_k} \left| \int_0^{v+w(v)} g(x,s)\,ds - \int_0^{+\infty} g(x,s)\,ds \right| dx +$$

$$+ \left| \int_{\Omega_k} \int_0^{v+w(v)} g(x,s)\,ds\,dx \right| + \int_{\Omega_k} \left| \int_0^{+\infty} g(x,s)\,ds\,dx \right| < \varepsilon$$

for all $\|v\| \geq \kappa$, which implies

$$\lim_{\|v\| \to \infty} \int_{\Omega} \int_0^{v+w(v)} g(x,s)\, ds\, dx = \int_{\Omega} \int_0^{+\infty} g(x,s)\, ds\, dx .$$

(ii) Let $\int_{\Omega} \int_0^{+\infty} g(x,s)\, ds\, dx = +\infty$. Then for an arbitrary $\ell > 0$ there exist $k > 0$ and $\eta > 0$ such that

$$\int_{\Omega \setminus \Omega'} \int_0^{\pm n} g(x,s)\, ds\, dx > \ell \tag{4.12}$$

for all $n \geq k$ and $\Omega' \subset \Omega$, meas $\Omega' < \eta$.

According to Lemmas 4.4 and 4.5 we may choose a $\kappa > 0$ such that for $v \in V$, $\|v\| \geq \kappa$ we have meas $\Omega_k < \eta$ and

$$\int_{\Omega_k} \int_0^{\pm k} |g(x,s)|\, ds\, dx < \frac{1}{\ell} . \tag{4.13}$$

Using (4.12) and (4.13) we obtain

$$\int_{\Omega} \int_0^{v+w(v)} g(x,s)\, ds\, dx \geq \int_{\Omega \setminus \Omega_k} \int_0^{v+w(v)} g(x,s)\, ds\, dx - \int_{\Omega_k} \int_0^{\pm k} | g(x,s) |\, ds\, dx \geq \ell - \frac{1}{\ell}$$

for all $v \in V$, $\|v\| \geq \kappa$. This implies that $\lim_{\|v\| \to \infty} \int_{\Omega} \int_0^{v+w(v)} g(x,s)\, ds\, dx = +\infty$ and taking into account the boundedness of $\|w(v)\|$, we conclude $\lim_{\|v\| \to \infty} F(v) = +\infty$. The remaining case $(-\infty)$ is quite analogous. □

<u>4.8. Theorem</u> *(existence result). Assume* (g1) - (g3) *and let* $f^* \in V^{\perp}$ *be given. Then there exists at least one* $u \in H$ *such that* (4.3) *holds.*

<u>*Proof.*</u> It follows from Lemma 4.7 that the function $F(\cdot)$ has at least one critical point $v_0 \in V$. By the assertion of Lemma 4.3 the function $F(\cdot)$ is of class C^1 , i.e.

$$\left(F'(v_0), h\right) = 0$$

for all $h \in V$. By an elementary calculation we obtain from (4.9) that

$$\frac{1}{2}\left(L_k w'(v_0)h, w(v_0)\right) + \frac{1}{2}\left(L_k w(v_0), w'(v_0)h\right) +$$

$$+ \int_\Omega g\left(x, w(v_0) + v_0\right) h \, dx + \int_\Omega g\left(x, w(v_0) + v_0\right) w'(v_0) h \, dx -$$

$$- \left(f^*, w'(v_0)h\right) = 0$$

holds for each $h \in V$ (the symbol $w'(v_0)h$ denotes the value of the linear functional $w'(v_0)$ at h). Using the symmetry of L_k and the equation (4.4) we obtain

$$\int_\Omega g\left(x, v_0 + w(v_0)\right) h \, dx = 0$$

for all $h \in V$, which is nothing else than (4.5). The equivalence of (4.3) with (4.4), (4.5) implies that $u_0 = v_0 + w(v_0)$ is a solution of (4.3) and the theorem is proved. □

In the forthcoming subsections we will assume that the nonlinear function $g : \Omega \times \mathbf{R} \to \mathbf{R}$ satisfies

$$\lim_{s \to \pm\infty} g(x,s) = 0 \tag{4.14}$$

uniformly for a.a. $x \in \Omega$.

4.9. Theorem. *The range of the operator*

$$u \mapsto L_k u + G(u) \tag{4.15}$$

is closed.

Proof. Let $\{f_n^*\}_{n=1}^\infty$ be any sequence of elements from the range of (4.15) such that $f_n^* \to f^*$ in H. We will prove that there exists $u \in H$ such that $L_k u + G(u) = f^*$. By Lemma 4.3 there exists a sequence $\{v_n\}_{n=1}^\infty \subset V$ such that $PG\left(v_n + w(v_n)\right) = Pf_n^*$, where $w(v_n) \in V^\perp$ are uniformly bounded solutions of the equation (4.4) with the right hand side Qf_n^*. If $Pf_n^* \to 0$ in V then $Pf^* = 0$, i.e. $f^* \in V^\perp$ and the assertion follows from Theorem 4.8. If $\|Pf_n^*\| \geq \text{const} > 0$ then by virtue of (4.14) and Lemmas 4.4, 4.5 the sequence $\{v_n\}_{n=1}^\infty \subset V$ is bounded in the norm $\|\cdot\|$. Hence $u_n = v_n + w(v_n)$ is a bounded sequence in H and, possibly after passing to a suitable subsequence, we can suppose that $u_n \rightharpoonup u_0$ in H. In virtue of the compact imbedding of H into $L^2(\Omega)$ we have $G(u_n) \to G(u_0)$ in H and hence $L_k u_n \to L_k u_0$ in H. Passing to the limit in $L_k u_n + G(u_n) = f_n^*$ we conclude that u_0 is the solution of (4.3) with the right hand side f^*. □

In order to prove multiplicity result we need the following lemma.

4.10. Lemma. *Let* $\Phi : \mathbb{R}^m \to \mathbb{R}$ *have a continuous second Fréchet derivative which attains its local maximum at an isolated critical point* $x_0 \in \mathbb{R}^m$. *Then there exists an open ball* $B_\rho(x_0)$ *centred at* x_0 *with radius* $\rho > 0$ *such that*

$$\deg_B [\Phi'; B_\rho(x_0), 0] = (-1)^m .$$

Let Φ *attain its local minimum at an isolated critical point* $x_0 \in \mathbb{R}^m$. *Then*

$$\deg_B [\Phi'; B_\rho(x_0), 0] = 1 .$$

Proof of this assertion can be found in AMANN [7]. □

4.11. Theorem *(multiplicity result). Let* $f_2^* \in V^\perp$ *be given. Then either* (i) *or* (ii) *holds, where*

(i) *the equation* (4.3) *with the right hand side* $f^* = f_1^* + f_2^*$, $f_1^* \in V$, *has no solution provided* $f_1^* \neq 0$ *and possesses infinitely many solutions provided* $f_1^* = 0$; *these solutions may be expressed as* $u = v + w(v)$, *where* $w(v)$ *is the solution of* (4.4) *with the right hand side* f_2^* , *and they form a* m-*dimensional* C^1-*manifold in* H ;

(ii) *there exists* $\varepsilon(f_2^*) > 0$ *such that* (4.3) *has at least one solution provided* $\|f_1^*\| \leq \varepsilon(f_2^*)$; *if* $0 < \|f_1^*\| < \varepsilon(f_2^*)$ *then* (4.3) *has at least two distinct solutions.*

Proof. Let us introduce the function

$$\Phi(v) = F(v) - (f_1^*, v) , \quad v \in V$$

(for definition of $F(\cdot)$ see (4.9)). By an elementary calculation it is easy to see that the solutions of (4.3) with the right hand side $f^* = f_1^* + f_2^*$ are in a one-to-one correspondence with the critical points of $\Phi(\cdot)$. Hence if $F(\cdot) : V \to \mathbb{R}$ is a constant function on V, we immediately obtain the first conclusion of the theorem. In the sequel let us assume that $F(\cdot)$ is not a constant. Then without loss of generality we may suppose that F attains its minimum at a point $v_0 \in V$ (cf. Lemma 4.7). Hence there exists a ball B_r with sufficiently large radius $r > 0$ such that $F(v) > F(v_0)$ for all $v \in \partial B_r$. It is now obvious that there exists $\varepsilon(f_2^*) > 0$ such that $\Phi(v) > \Phi(v_1)$ for all $v \in \partial B_r$, where f_1^* is taken as follows : $\|f_1^*\| < \varepsilon(f_2^*)$. This fact implies that $\Phi(\cdot)$ attains its minimum on B_r at a point $v_1 \in B_r$, and so the corresponding function $u_1 = v_1 + w(v_1)$ is a solution of (4.3) with the right hand side $f^* = f_1^* + f_2^*$. According to Theorem 4.9 the solution of (4.3) exists also if $\|f_1^*\| = \varepsilon(f_2^*)$. Take $0 < \|f_1^*\| < \varepsilon(f_2^*)$. Let us consider the ball $B_\rho(v_1)$ with a sufficiently small radius $\rho > 0$. If there is another $\tilde{v}_1 \in \overline{B_\rho(v_1)}$, $\tilde{v}_1 \neq v_1$, and $\tilde{v}_1$ is also a critical point of $\Phi(\cdot)$, then $\tilde{u}_1 = \tilde{v}_1 + w(\tilde{v}_1)$ is another solution of (4.3) with the right hand side $f^* = f_1^* + f_2^*$ and $\tilde{u}_1 \neq u_1$. If no such $\tilde{v}_1 \in \overline{B_\rho(v_1)}$ exists we may define the Brouwer degree $\deg_B [\Phi'; B_\rho(v_1), 0]$, where

$$\Phi'(v) = PG\big(v + w(v)\big) - f_1^* .$$

According to Lemma 4.10 we have

$$\deg_B [\Phi'; B_\rho(v_1), 0] \neq 0 . \tag{4.16}$$

Let us take $r > 0$ sufficiently large so that

$$\|PG\big(v + w(v)\big)\| < \frac{1}{2} \|f_1^*\| \tag{4.17}$$

for all $v \in \partial B_r$. This is possible due to the assumption (4.14) and to the unique continuation property of V (see the proof of Lemma 4.6 for quite similar estimates). By virtue of (4.17) and the homotopy invariance property of the Brouwer degree it follows that

$$\deg_B [\tau PG\big(\cdot + w(\cdot)\big) - f_1^*; B_r, 0] = c$$

for all $\tau \in [0,1]$. Since for $\tau = 0$ we obtain the Brouwer degree of a constant mapping, we have $c = 0$, and hence

$$\deg_B [\Phi'; B_r, 0] = 0 . \tag{4.18}$$

Therefore, using (4.16) and (4.18) we obtain

$$\deg_B [\Phi'; B_r \setminus \overline{B_\rho(v_1)}, 0] \neq 0$$

and the equation $\Phi'(v) = 0$ has at least one other solution $\tilde{v}_1$ in $B_r \setminus \overline{B_\rho(v_1)}$. Then $\tilde{u}_1 = \tilde{v}_1 + w(\tilde{v}_1) \neq u_1$ is another solution of (4.3). This completes the proof. $\square$

The next theorem gives a more precise information about the range of $L_k + G$ on the assumption that the *kernel* of the linear part L_k is *one-dimensional*.

<u>4.12. Theorem</u> *(multiplicity result - the case of simple eigenvalue). Let* $f_2^* \in V$ *be given and let us suppose, moreover, that the eigenvalue* λ_k *has multiplicity one. Denote the corresponding eigenfunction by* ϕ_k , $\|\phi_k\| = 1$. *Then either* (i) *or* (ii) *holds, where* (i) *is the same as in Theorem 4.11 and*

(ii) *there exist* $\varepsilon_1(f_2^*) < 0 < \varepsilon_2(f_2^*)$ *such that* (4.3) *with the right hand side* $f^* = f_1^* + f_2^*$ *has at least one solution if and only if* $f_1^* = t\phi_k$ *is such that* $t \in [\varepsilon_1(f_2^*), \varepsilon_2(f_2^*)]$; *moreover, if* $t \in (\varepsilon_1(f_2^*), 0) \cup (0, \varepsilon_2(f_2^*))$ *then* (4.3) *has at least two distinct solutions.*

<u>Proof.</u> If $F(\cdot)$ is a constant function on V we again obtain the first conclusion of the theorem. In the opposite case $F(\cdot)$ attains either its maximum or minimum on V . Without loss of generality we may suppose that for $v_0 \in V$ we have

$$F(v_0) = \min_{v \in V} F(v) < \lim_{\|v\| \to \infty} F(v) . \tag{4.19}$$

Then the function $\psi : \mathbb{R} \to \mathbb{R}$ defined by

$$\psi(t) = \left(G\left(t\phi_k + w(t\phi_k)\right), \phi_k\right)$$

for all $t \in \mathbb{R}$ is such that $\psi(t_0) = 0$ if $t_0\phi_k = v_0$. By virtue of (4.14) we have

$$\lim_{t \to \pm\infty} \psi(t) = 0 ,$$

and using (4.19) we conclude that $\psi(t_1) > 0$ for some $t_1 > t_0$ and $\psi(t_2) < 0$ for some $t_2 < t_0$. Moreover, $\psi(\cdot)$ is a continuous function and hence using its properties stated above we have such σ_1 , σ_2 that

$$\psi(\sigma_2) = \max_{t \in \mathbb{R}} \psi(t) > 0 > \min_{t \in \mathbb{R}} \psi(t) = \psi(\sigma_1) .$$

Set $\psi_t(\tau) = \psi(\tau) - (t\phi_k, \phi_k) = \psi(\tau) - t$. Then if $t \in [\psi(\sigma_1), \psi(\sigma_2)]$, we obtain the existence of at least one $\tau_0 \in \mathbb{R}$ such that $\psi_t(\tau_0) = 0$, and $u_0 = \tau_0\phi_k + w(\tau_0\phi_k)$ is the corresponding solution of (4.3). If

$t \notin [\psi(\sigma_1), \psi(\sigma_2)]$ then no such $\tau_0 \in \mathbb{R}$ exist. Moreover, it is easy to see that if $t \in (\psi(\sigma_1), 0) \cup (0, \psi(\sigma_2))$, we obtain at least two distinct points $\tau_1 \neq \tau_2 \in \mathbb{R}$ such that $\psi_t(\tau_i) = 0$, $i = 1,2$. Hence $u_i = \tau_i\phi_k + w(\tau_i\phi_k)$, $i = 1,2$ are two distinct solutions of (4.3). These considerations imply that if we take $\varepsilon_1(f_2^*) = \psi(\sigma_1)$, $\varepsilon_2(f_2^*) = \psi(\sigma_2)$, the second conclusion of the theorem is proved. □

4.13. Examples. The above results may be applied, for instance, to the following types of semilinear elliptic boundary value problems :

$$\Delta u(x) + \lambda_k u(x) + \beta(x)\, u(x)\, e^{-u^2(x)} = f(x) \ , \quad x \in \Omega \ , \tag{4.20}$$

$$u(x) = 0 \ , \quad x \in \partial\Omega \ ; \tag{4.21}$$

$$\Delta u(x) + \lambda_k u(x) + \beta(x)\, e^{-u^2(x)} \sin u(x) = f(x) \ , \quad x \in \Omega \ , \tag{4.22}$$

$$u(x) = 0 \ , \quad x \in \partial\Omega \ ; \tag{4.23}$$

$$- \Delta^2 u(x) + \lambda_k u(x) + \frac{\beta(x)\ u(x)}{1 + u^8(x)} = f(x) \ , \quad x \in \Omega \ , \tag{4.24}$$

$$u(x) = \frac{\partial u(x)}{\partial \nu} = 0 \ , \quad x \in \partial\Omega \ ; \tag{4.25}$$

$$- \Delta^2 u(x) + \lambda_k u(x) + g(u(x)) = f(x) \ , \quad x \in \Omega \ , \tag{4.26}$$

$$u(x) = \frac{\partial u(x)}{\partial \nu} = 0 \ , \quad x \in \partial\Omega \ , \tag{4.27}$$

where g is a bounded, odd, continuously differentiable function with compact support in $\mathbb{R}$ satisfying (g3), ν denotes the outer normal with respect to $\partial\Omega$.

We set $H = W_0^{1,2}(\Omega)$ or $H = W_0^{2,2}(\Omega)$ for the equations (4.20) - (4.23) or (4.24) - (4.27), respectively. The operator L_k is defined by

$$(L_k u, v) = \int_\Omega \nabla u\, \nabla v\, dx - \lambda_k \int_\Omega u\, v\, dx$$

for (4.20) - (4.23);

$$(L_k u, v) = \int_\Omega \Delta u\, \Delta v\, dx - \lambda_k \int_\Omega u\, v\, dx$$

for (4.24) - (4.27). We suppose that λ_k is any eigenvalue of the Laplace operator Δ or of the biharmonic operator Δ^2, respectively, with the Dirichlet boundary conditions. Then the operator L_k satisfies all the assumptions from Subsection 4.1. The function $\beta = \beta(x)$ is supposed to be measurable in x, bounded a.e. on Ω and such that (g3) is fulfilled.

4.14. Remarks. (i) Let us note that the distance of λ_k from the preceding and the following eigenvalue depends also on the shape of the domain Ω.

(ii) The results of the preceding subsections generalize some results from FUČÍK [125] and from some papers mentioned there in the bibliography.

(iii) Let us mention here also the works published after 1980 which deal with related topics : CONCALVES [65], DRÁBEK [88], LUPO and SOLIMINI [204], SOLIMINI [280].

(iv) The assumption (g2) can be replaced by the stronger assumption

(g2') $g(x,s)$ is odd in s for a.a. $x \in \Omega$ and

$$\int_\Omega \int_0^{+\infty} g(x,s)\, ds\, dx \in \mathbb{R} \cup \{\pm \infty\} .$$

All nonlinear perturbations from (4.20) - (4.27) satisfy this assumption.

5. NEUMANN PROBLEM FOR SECOND ORDER PARTIAL DIFFERENTIAL EQUATIONS

5.1. In this section we will study *nonlinear Neumann BVP* for partial differential equations

$$- \sum_{i,j=1}^{N} \frac{\partial}{\partial x_j} \left(a_{ij}(x) \frac{\partial u(x)}{\partial x_i}\right) + g\left(u(x)\right) = f(x) , \quad x \in \Omega , \tag{5.1}$$

$$Bu \equiv \sum_{i,j=1}^{N} a_{ij}(x) \frac{\partial u(x)}{\partial x_i} \cos (\nu, x_j) = 0 , \quad x \in \partial\Omega , \tag{5.2}$$

where ν is the outer normal with respect to $\partial\Omega$, $a_{ij}(x) \in C^1(\bar{\Omega})$ and g is a bounded and continuous function. The operator

$$A : u \mapsto - \sum_{i,j=1}^{N} \frac{\partial}{\partial x_j} \left(a_{ij}(x) \frac{\partial u}{\partial x_i}\right)$$

is *strictly elliptic* on $\Omega \subset \mathbb{R}^N$, i.e. there exists a constant $\gamma > 0$ such that

$$\sum_{i,j=1}^{N} a_{ij}(x)\ \xi_i\ \xi_j \geqq \gamma|\xi|^2$$

for all $x \in \Omega$ and for each $\xi = (\xi_1,\ldots,\xi_N) \in \mathbf{R}^N$.

The function $u \in C^2(\Omega) \cap C^1(\bar{\Omega})$ is called a *classical solution of the Neumann problem* (5.1), (5.2) if (5.1) and (5.2) hold for every $x \in \Omega$ and $x \in \partial\Omega$, respectively.

It is well known that BVP (5.1), (5.2) with $g \equiv 0$ is solvable if and only if f satisfies the relation

$$\int_\Omega f(x)\ dx = 0\ .$$

Let us define the projection $P : L^1(\Omega) \to L^1(\Omega)$ by

$$Pu = \frac{1}{\text{meas}\ \Omega} \int_\Omega u(x)\ dx\ ,$$

$u \in L^1(\Omega)$. Set

$$\tilde{L}^p(\Omega) = L^p(\Omega) \cap \text{Ker}\ P$$

for any $p \geqq 1$. Then every element $f \in L^1(\Omega)$ can be written as

$$f = \bar{f} + \tilde{f}\ ,$$

where $\bar{f} = Pf$, $\tilde{f} \in \tilde{L}^1(\Omega)$.

Let us suppose that p and q satisfy

$$1 < q < \frac{N}{N-1}\ , \qquad 1 < p < \frac{Nq}{N-q}\ .$$

Then $W^{1,q}(\Omega)$ is compactly imbedded into $L^p(\Omega)$ (see e.g. KUFNER, JOHN and FUČÍK [183]).

A function $u \in W^{1,q}(\Omega)$ is called a *weak solution of the Neumann problem* (5.1), (5.2) if

$$\int_\Omega \sum_{i,j=1}^{N} a_{ij}(x) \frac{\partial u}{\partial x_i} \frac{\partial v}{\partial x_j}\ dx + \int_\Omega g(u)\ v\ dx = \int_\Omega f\ v\ dx \tag{5.3}$$

holds for every $v \in W^{1,\infty}(\Omega)$.

5.2. The linear problem. It is well known that the problem (5.1), (5.2) with

$g \equiv 0$ has for each $f \in \tilde{L}^1(\Omega)$ a unique weak solution $u \in W^{1,q}(\Omega)$ and that there exists a constant $c_q > 0$ (independent of $f \in \tilde{L}^1(\Omega)$) such that

$$\|u\|_{1,q} \leqq c_q \|f\|_1 \, . \tag{5.4}$$

Let $Kf = u$ for $f \in \tilde{L}^1(\Omega)$ be the unique weak solution of the problem (5.1), (5.2) with $g \equiv 0$. Then (5.4) can be written as

$$\|Kf\|_{1,q} \leqq c_q \|f\|_1 \, ,$$

$f \in \tilde{L}^1(\Omega)$. Set $X = W^{1,q}(\Omega) \cap \tilde{L}^1(\Omega)$. Then $W^{1,q}(\Omega) = \mathbb{R} \oplus X$ and the operator K maps $\tilde{L}^1(\Omega)$ into $W^{1,q}(\Omega)$ continuously. Let $\xi : W^{1,q}(\Omega) \subsetneq\subsetneq L^p(\Omega)$ be the compact imbedding operator. Then

$$T = \xi \circ K : \tilde{L}^1(\Omega) \to L^p(\Omega) \quad \text{and} \quad T(I - P) : L^1(\Omega) \to L^p(\Omega)$$

are compact operators. We define an operator $L : L^p(\Omega) \to L^1(\Omega)$ by

$$\mathrm{dom}(L) = \mathbb{R} \oplus \mathrm{Im}(T) \, ,$$
$$L(\alpha + \tilde{u}) = f \, ,$$

where $f \in \tilde{L}^1(\Omega)$, $Tf = \tilde{u} \in \mathrm{Im}(T)$, $\alpha \in \mathbb{R}$. L is an abstract formulation of the problem (5.1), (5.2) with $g \equiv 0$ in the space $L^p(\Omega)$. L is a Fredholm operator, $\mathrm{Im}(L) = \tilde{L}^1(\Omega)$, $\mathrm{Ker}\, L = \mathbb{R}$, and since $L^1(\Omega)/\tilde{L}^1(\Omega) = \mathbb{R}$ ($L^1(\Omega)/\tilde{L}^1(\Omega)$ is the *factor space*), the index of L is 0 (see WARD [291]).

5.3. Nonlinearity. Lyapunov-Schmidt method. Let $g : \mathbb{R} \to \mathbb{R}$ be a continuous and bounded function and let $b > 0$ be such that

$$|g(s)| \leqq b$$

for all $s \in \mathbb{R}$. Then the Nemytskiĭ operator

$$G(u)(x) = g\big(u(x)\big)$$

is bounded and continuous in every $L^p(\Omega)$, $1 \leqq p < \infty$, and

$$\|G(u)\|_p \leqq b(\mathrm{meas}\ \Omega)^{\frac{1}{p}} \, ,$$

$u \in L^p(\Omega)$.

Then (5.3) has an equivalent formulation as the operator equation

$$Lu + G(u) = f \, , \tag{5.5}$$

$f \in L^1(\Omega)$.

Let $f \in L^1(\Omega)$ be decomposed to $f = \bar{f} + \tilde{f}$, where $\bar{f} = Pf$, $\tilde{f} \in \tilde{L}^1(\Omega)$, and $u = \bar{u} + \tilde{u}$, with $\bar{u} \in \operatorname{Ker} L = \mathbb{R}$. The equation (5.5) is equivalent to the system

$$L\tilde{u} + G(\bar{u} + \tilde{u}) - PG(\bar{u} + \tilde{u}) = \tilde{f} , \tag{5.6}$$

$$PG(\bar{u} + \tilde{u}) = \bar{f} . \tag{5.7}$$

<u>5.4. Lemma.</u> *For each fixed* $\bar{u} \in \mathbb{R}$ *and* $\tilde{f} \in \tilde{L}^1(\Omega)$ *the equation* (5.6) *has a solution* $\tilde{u} \in L^p(\Omega)$ *with* p *satisfying*

$$1 < p < \frac{Nq}{N - q} , \text{ where } 1 < q < \frac{N}{N - 1} .$$

Moreover, if $\tilde{f} \in L^\infty(\Omega)$ *then* $\tilde{u} \in C^1(\bar{\Omega})$. *If* g *and* $\tilde{f}$ *are Hölder continuous then* $\tilde{u}$ *is a classical solution, that is* $\tilde{u} \in C^2(\Omega)$.

Proof of the lemma consists in a standard application of the Schauder fixed point theorem (see Lemma 5.5 below) and the regularity results (see, for example AGMON, DOUGLIS and NIRENBERG [2]). □

Let us denote by Σ the "solution set" of the equation (5.6), that is

$$\Sigma = \{(\bar{u},\tilde{u}) \in \mathbb{R} \times \tilde{L}^p(\Omega) : L\tilde{u} + G(\bar{u} + \tilde{u}) - PG(\bar{u} + \tilde{u}) = \tilde{f}\} .$$

We have $\Sigma \neq \emptyset$ by Lemma 5.4.

<u>5.5. Lemma.</u> *For every* $\alpha > 0$ *there exists a connected subset* Σ_α *of* Σ *such that*

$$[-\alpha,\alpha] \subset \operatorname{proj}_{\mathbb{R}} \Sigma_\alpha .$$

Proof. The equation (5.6) is equivalent to

$$\tilde{u} + TG(\bar{u} + \tilde{u}) - TPG(\bar{u} + \tilde{u}) - T\tilde{f} = 0 .$$

Set

$$C(\bar{u},\tilde{u}) = TG(\bar{u} + \tilde{u}) - TPG(\bar{u} + \tilde{u}) - T\tilde{f} .$$

Then $C(\bar{u},\cdot) : \tilde{L}^p(\Omega) \to \tilde{L}^p(\Omega)$ is a bounded and compact operator. Moreover, there exists $r > 0$ such that $\|C(\bar{u},\tilde{u})\|_p < r$ for all $(u,\tilde{u}) \in \mathbb{R} \times \tilde{L}^p(\Omega)$. Then the Leray-Schauder degree $\deg [I - C(\bar{u},\cdot); B_r, 0]$ is well defined and it is obvious that

$$\deg [I - C(\bar{u},\cdot); B_r, 0] = \deg [I; B_r, 0] = 1$$

for every $\bar{u} \in \mathbb{R}$, where I is the identity on $\tilde{L}^p(\Omega)$ and B_r is the ball in $\tilde{L}^p(\Omega)$. This implies that $\mathrm{proj}_{\mathbb{R}} \Sigma = \mathbb{R}$.

Let $\alpha > 0$ be fixed and let $\mathcal{A} = [-\alpha,\alpha] \times \overline{B}_r$. Furthermore, let $\mathcal{K} = \Sigma \cap \mathcal{A}$ and $\mathcal{K}_\pm = \Sigma \cap (\{\pm\alpha\} \times \overline{B}_r)$. Then $\mathcal{K}$ is a compact metric space and $\mathcal{K}_\pm$ are nonempty disjoint closed subsets of $\mathcal{K}$. Suppose that there exists no connected subset of $\mathcal{K}$ joining $\mathcal{K}_+$ and $\mathcal{K}_-$. Then there are disjoint compact sets $\mathcal{C}_\pm \supset \mathcal{K}_\pm$ with $\mathcal{K} = \mathcal{C}_+ \cup \mathcal{C}_-$ (cf. WHYBURN [297]). Observe that

$$\mathcal{C}_- \cap \left(\mathcal{C}_+ \cup ([-\alpha,\alpha] \times \partial B_r) \cup (\{\alpha\} \times \overline{B}_r)\right) = \emptyset .$$

Consequently, there exists an open subset $\mathcal{U}$ of $\mathcal{A}$ such that $\mathcal{C}_- \subset \mathcal{U}$ and

$$\overline{\mathcal{U}} \cap \left(\mathcal{C}_+ \cup ([-\alpha,\alpha] \times \partial B_r) \cup (\{\alpha\} \times \overline{B}_r)\right) = \emptyset .$$

Hence

$$\tilde{u} - C(\overline{u},\tilde{u}) \neq 0$$

for all $(\overline{u},\tilde{u})$ on the boundary of $\mathcal{U}$ (relative to $\mathcal{A}$), and $\mathcal{U}_\alpha = \{\tilde{u} \in \tilde{L}^p(\Omega);\ (\alpha,\tilde{u}) \in \mathcal{U}\} = \emptyset$. Therefore, by the excision property and the general homotopy invariance property of the Leray-Schauder degree, it follows that

$$1 = \deg\left[I - C(-\alpha,\cdot);\ B_r,\ 0\right] = \deg\left[I - C(-\alpha,\cdot);\ \mathcal{U}_{-\alpha},\ 0\right] =$$
$$= \deg\left[I - C(\alpha,\cdot);\ \mathcal{U}_\alpha,\ 0\right] = 0 .$$

This contradiction implies the existence of a connected subset $\Sigma_\alpha \subset \Sigma$ joining $\mathcal{K}_-$ and $\mathcal{K}_+$, i.e.

$$[-\alpha,\alpha] \subset \mathrm{proj}_{\mathbb{R}} \Sigma_\alpha . \qquad \square$$

Let us note that a more general version of Lemma 5.5 is proved in AMANN, AMBROSETTI and MANCINI [8].

We will assume that for any given $R > 0$ there is $\alpha > 0$ such that

$$\frac{1}{\mathrm{meas}\ \Omega} \int_\Omega g(-\alpha + \tilde{u})\, dx < \overline{f} < \frac{1}{\mathrm{meas}\ \Omega} \int_\Omega g(\alpha + \tilde{v})\, dx \tag{5.8}$$

for all $\tilde{u}, \tilde{v} \in \tilde{L}^p(\Omega)$ with $\|\tilde{u}\|_p \leq R$, $\|\tilde{v}\|_p \leq R$.

5.6. Theorem *(existence result). Let us suppose that the hypotheses stated above are fulfilled,* $f \in L^1(\Omega)$. *Then BVP* (5.1), (5.2) *has a weak solution*

$u \in W^{1,q}(\Omega)$. *Moreover, if* $f \in L^\infty(\Omega)$ *and* (5.8) *is fulfilled with* $\tilde{u}, \tilde{v} \in \tilde{L}^p(\Omega) \cap C^1(\bar{\Omega})$, $\|\tilde{u}\|_{C^1} \leq R$, $\|\tilde{v}\|_{C^1} \leq R$, *then the solution of BVP* (5.1), (5.2) *satisfies* $u \in C^1(\bar{\Omega})$. *If* f *and* g *are Hölder continuous then* u *is a classical solution of BVP* (5.1), (5.2).

Proof. The weak solution of BVP (5.1), (5.2) is a function $u = \bar{u} + \tilde{u}$ such that $(\bar{u},\tilde{u}) \in \Sigma$ and

$$\frac{1}{\text{meas }\Omega} \int_\Omega g(\bar{u} + \tilde{u})\, dx = \bar{f} . \tag{5.9}$$

It follows from the boundedness of g that for fixed $\tilde{f} \in \tilde{L}^1(\Omega)$ the solution $\tilde{u}$ of (5.6) the existence of which is guaranteed by Lemma 5.4 satisfies

$$\|\tilde{u}\|_p \leq R ,$$

where $R > 0$ is independent of $\bar{u} \in \mathbb{R}$. Let $\alpha > 0$ be a constant associated with $R > 0$ by our assumption (5.8). It follows from Lemma 5.5 that there is a connected set $\Sigma_\alpha \subset \Sigma$ such that $[-\alpha,\alpha] \subset \text{proj}_{\mathbb{R}} \Sigma_\alpha$. Then the assumption (5.8) together with the connectedness of Σ_α implies the existence of $(\bar{u},\tilde{u}) \in \Sigma_\alpha$ such that (5.9) holds. The other parts of the assertion follow from the regularity result similarly as in Lemma 5.4. □

Let us suppose in the sequel that there exist limits

$$\lim_{s \to \pm\infty} g(s) = g_\pm . \tag{5.10}$$

Set

$$\underline{W} = \inf_{\alpha \in \mathbb{R}} \ \sup_{v_\alpha : (\alpha, v_\alpha) \in \Sigma} \frac{1}{\text{meas }\Omega} \int_\Omega g(\alpha + v_\alpha)\, dx ,$$

$$\overline{W} = \sup_{\alpha \in \mathbb{R}} \ \inf_{v_\alpha : (\alpha, v_\alpha) \in \Sigma} \frac{1}{\text{meas }\Omega} \int_\Omega g(\alpha + v_\alpha)\, dx ,$$

and assume that

$$\underline{W} < \overline{W} . \tag{5.11}$$

5.7. Theorem *(multiplicity result). Let us suppose that the assumptions of Theorem* 5.6 *and* (5.10), (5.11) *are satisfied. Then for the right hand side* $f = \bar{f} + \tilde{f}$, *BVP* (5.1), (5.2) *has*

(a) *at least one solution if* $\bar{f} \in (\underline{W}, \overline{W})$.

Moreover, BVP (5.1), (5.2) *has*

(b) *at least two distinct solutions if*

$$\underline{W} < g_- \leqq g_+ < \overline{W} , \quad \bar{f} \in (\underline{W}, g_-) \cup (g_+, \overline{W}) .$$

Proof. Let $\tilde{f} \in \tilde{L}^1(\Omega)$ be fixed. If $\bar{f} \in (\underline{W}, \overline{W})$ then there exist $\alpha_1, \alpha_2 \in \mathbb{R}$ such that for all $(\alpha_1, v) \in \sum$, $(\alpha_2, w) \in \sum$ we have

$$\frac{1}{\text{meas } \Omega} \int_\Omega g(\alpha_1 + v)\, dx < \bar{f} \tag{5.12}$$

and

$$\frac{1}{\text{meas } \Omega} \int_\Omega g(\alpha_2 + w)\, dx > \bar{f} . \tag{5.13}$$

The assertion of Lemma 5.5 implies the existence of a connected set $\sum_\alpha \subset \sum$ with $\alpha = \max\{|\alpha_1|, |\alpha_2|\}$ such that $[\alpha_1, \alpha_2] \subset \text{proj}_{\mathbb{R}} \sum_\alpha$. Then part (a) follows from (5.12), (5.13) and the connectedness of $\sum_\alpha$ similarly as the assertion of Theorem 5.6. If $\bar{f} \in (\underline{W}, g_-)$ then by the definition of $\underline{W}$ there exists $\alpha_1 \in \mathbb{R}$ such that (5.12) holds for all $(\alpha_1, v) \in \sum$. It is sufficient to prove the existence of $\alpha_2, \alpha_3 \in \mathbb{R}$ such that

$$\frac{1}{\text{meas } \Omega} \int_\Omega g(\alpha_i + w)\, dx > \bar{f} \tag{5.14}$$

for all $(\alpha_i, w) \in \sum$, $i = 2,3$. Let us denote

$$\Omega_{n,\alpha} = \{x \in \Omega;\ \alpha + v(x) \leqq n \ \text{ for all } \ (\alpha, v) \in \textstyle\sum\} ,$$

$$\Omega_{-n,\alpha} = \{x \in \Omega;\ \alpha + v(x) \geqq -n \ \text{ for all } \ (\alpha, v) \in \textstyle\sum\} .$$

It is easy to see that

$$\lim_{\alpha \to \pm\infty} \text{meas } \Omega_{\pm n,\alpha} = 0$$

for each $n \in \mathbb{N}$. By virtue of (5.10), for sufficiently small $\varepsilon > 0$ we can choose such an $\alpha_0 \in \mathbb{R}$ that for $\alpha_2 = -\alpha_0$ we have

$$\left| \int_{\Omega \setminus \Omega_{-n,\alpha_2}} g(\alpha_2 + v)\, dx - g_- \right| < \frac{\varepsilon}{2} , \tag{5.15}$$

$$\left| \int_{\Omega_{-n,\alpha_2}} g(\alpha_2 + v)\, dx \right| < \frac{\varepsilon}{2} , \tag{5.16}$$

and for $\alpha_3 = \alpha_0$ we have

$$\left| \int_{\Omega \setminus \Omega_{n,\alpha_3}} g(\alpha_3 + v)\, dx - g_+ \right| < \frac{\varepsilon}{2} , \tag{5.17}$$

$$\left| \int_{\Omega_{n,\alpha_3}} g(\alpha_3 + v)\, dx \right| < \frac{\varepsilon}{2} \tag{5.18}$$

for all $(\alpha_i, v) \in \sum$, $i = 2,3$. From (5.15) - (5.18) we obtain

$$\left| \int_{\Omega} g(\alpha_2 + v)\, dx - g_- \right| < \varepsilon , \tag{5.19}$$

$$\left| \int_{\Omega} g(\alpha_3 + v)\, dx - g_+ \right| < \varepsilon \tag{5.20}$$

for all $(\alpha_i, v) \in \sum$, $i = 2,3$. The last inequalities (5.19) and (5.20) imply that (5.14) is true. The existence of at least two distinct solutions follows by applying Lemma 5.5. If $\bar{f} \in (g_+, \overline{W})$ the proof is analogous. □

5.8. Examples. (i) Let us consider the Neumann BVP

$$- \Delta u + ue^{-u^2} = f \quad \text{in} \quad \Omega , \tag{5.21}$$

$$\frac{\partial u}{\partial \nu} = 0 \quad \text{on} \quad \partial\Omega . \tag{5.22}$$

Suppose $f \in L^\infty(\Omega)$ and $\int_\Omega f(x)\, dx = 0$. By Theorem 5.6 this problem has a solution $u \in C^1(\bar{\Omega})$. We will now write the right hand side of (5.21) in the form $f = \bar{f} + \tilde{f}$. Then Theorem 5.7 implies that BVP (5.21), (5.22) has at least two distinct solutions if $\bar{f} \in (\underline{W}, 0) \cup (0, \overline{W})$, where

$$\overline{W} = \overline{W}(\tilde{f}) > 0 \quad \text{and} \quad \underline{W} = \underline{W}(\tilde{f}) < 0 .$$

(ii) The Neumann BVP

$$- \Delta u + e^{-u^2} = f \quad \text{in} \quad \Omega ,$$

$$\frac{\partial u}{\partial \nu} = 0 \quad \text{on} \quad \partial\Omega$$

has at least two distinct solutions if

$$\bar{f} \in (0,\overline{W}) ,$$

because in this case $\underline{W}(\tilde{f}) = g_{\pm} \equiv 0$ and $\overline{W}(\tilde{f}) > 0$.

6. DIRICHLET PROBLEM FOR SECOND ORDER PARTIAL DIFFERENTIAL EQUATIONS

6.1. Let $\Omega \subset \mathbb{R}^N$ be a bounded domain with a smooth boundary $\partial\Omega$; we suppose $\partial\Omega$ is at least of a class $C^{1,\mu}$, $0 < \mu < 1$, and let

$$Au = - \sum_{i,j=1}^{N} \frac{\partial}{\partial x_i} \left(a_{ij}(x) \frac{\partial u}{\partial x_j}\right) - a_0(x)u$$

be a second order symmetric uniformly elliptic operator with smooth coefficients. More precisely, we suppose

$$a_{ij}(x) = a_{ji}(x) , \quad 1 \leqq i,j \leqq N , \quad a_0(x) \geqq 0 \quad \text{in} \quad \Omega ,$$

$$\sum_{i,j=1}^{N} a_{ij}(x)\, \xi_i\, \xi_j \geqq \gamma|\xi|^2$$

for all $x \in \bar{\Omega}$, $\xi \in \mathbb{R}^N \setminus \{0\}$, $a_{ij} \in C^1(\bar{\Omega})$, $1 \leqq i,j \leqq N$, $a_0 \in L^\infty(\Omega)$, with some constant $\gamma > 0$.

In this section we will discuss the solvability of the selfadjoint BVP

$$Au - \lambda_1 u + g(x,u) = f \quad \text{in} \quad \Omega , \tag{6.1}$$

$$u = 0 \quad \text{on} \quad \partial\Omega , \tag{6.2}$$

where $\lambda_1 > 0$ is the first eigenvalue of $- A$, $f \in L^p(\Omega)$ with $p > N$ and $g : \Omega \times \mathbb{R} \to \mathbb{R}$ is a Carathéodory function which grows at most linearly, i.e. we will suppose that there exist a constant $c_1 > 0$ and a function $c_2 \in L^p(\Omega)$, $p > N$ such that

$$|g(x,s)| \leqq c_2(x) + c_1|s| \tag{6.3}$$

for a.e. $x \in \Omega$ and for all $s \in \mathbb{R}$.

Let us note that the first eigenvalue $\lambda_1 > 0$ of A is simple and the corresponding eigenspace is generated by a smooth function ϕ. We have $\phi > 0$ in Ω and $\frac{\partial\phi}{\partial\nu} < 0$ on $\partial\Omega$ (where $\frac{\partial}{\partial\nu}$ is the outer normal derivative). These facts follow from *Bony's maximum principle* and the abstract *Krein-Rutman theorem* (see e.g. BERS, JOHN and SCHECHTER [28]).

In what follows we will denote by P the orthogonal $L^2(\Omega)$ projection onto the eigenspace generated by ϕ, $\|\phi\|_2 = 1$, and by $Q = I - P$ the complementary projection.

Let us consider the operator $L : W^{2,p}(\Omega) \cap W_0^{1,2}(\Omega) \to L^2(\Omega)$ defined by

$$L : u \mapsto Au - \lambda_1 u .$$

Any function $f \in L^p(\Omega)$, $p > N$, can be written in the form

$$f = \tau\phi + h = Pf + Qf ,$$

where $\tau \in \mathbb{R}$, $h \in L^p(\Omega) \cap \mathrm{Im}(L)$. Moreover, the right inverse $K = L^{-1}$ is a well-defined operator from $\mathrm{Im}(L)$ onto $\mathrm{dom}(L) \cap \mathrm{Im}(L)$,

$$K\big(\mathrm{Im}(L) \cap L^p(\Omega)\big) \subset W^{2,p}(\Omega) \cap W_0^{1,2}(\Omega) , \quad p > N ,$$

and for any $f \in \mathrm{Im}(L) \cap L^p(\Omega)$ we have

$$\|Kf\|_{2,p} \leq c_p \|f\|_p .$$

In what follows G will be the Nemytskiĭ operator generated by $g = g(x,u)$, i.e.

$$G(u)(x) = g\big(x,u(x)\big) .$$

Due to (6.3) the operator G is continuous from $L^p(\Omega)$ into itself, $p > N$.

Using our notation, BVP (6.1), (6.2) can be written in the equivalent operator form

$$Lu + G(u) = f . \tag{6.4}$$

Any function $u \in W^{2,p}(\Omega) \cap W_0^{1,2}(\Omega)$ satisfying the equation (6.4) will be called a *solution* of BVP (6.1), (6.2).

<u>6.2. Bounded nonlinearity.</u> First let us suppose that $g : \mathbb{R} \to \mathbb{R}$ is a *continuous* and *bounded* function, and let $b > 0$ be such that

$$|g(s)| \leq b$$

for all $s \in \mathbb{R}$. Then we have

$$\|G(u)\|_p \leqq b(\text{meas } \Omega)^{\frac{1}{p}}$$

for any $u \in L^p(\Omega)$.

Let us suppose that there exist real numbers T_1 and T_2 such that the function g satisfies the following condition:

(g) for any given $R > 0$ there is $t_0 > 0$ such that

$$\int_\Omega g(u)\, \phi \, dx \geqq T_2 , \quad \int_\Omega g(v)\, \phi \, dx \leqq T_1 , \quad T_1 \leqq T_2 ,$$

for all $u, v \in L^2(\Omega)$ with $u \geqq t_0\phi$, $v \leqq - t_0\phi$, $\|Qu\|_2 \leqq R$, $\|Qv\|_2 \leqq R$.

<u>6.3. Theorem</u> *(existence result). Let* A *satisfy the assumptions from* 6.1, *let* g *satisfy the assumptions from* 6.2 *and let* $f \in L^p(\Omega)$, $f = \tau\phi + h$, $p > N$. *Then BVP* (6.1), (6.2) *has a solution* $u \in W^{2,p}(\Omega) \cap W_0^{1,p}(\Omega)$ *for* $p > N$ *provided*

$$\tau \in [T_1, T_2] .$$

<u>*Proof.*</u> The equation (6.4) is equivalent to the system

$$v + KQG(t\phi + v) - KQf = 0 , \tag{6.5}$$

$$PG(t\phi + v) - Pf = 0 , \tag{6.6}$$

$u = t\phi + v$, $v \in \text{Im}(L)$, $t \in \mathbb{R}$. Let $t \in \mathbb{R}$ be arbitrary but fixed. Since $g(t\phi + v) \in L^\infty(\Omega)$, $f \in L^p(\Omega)$, it follows from (6.5) that

$$\|v\|_{2,p} \leqq c_p \left[b(\text{meas } \Omega)^{\frac{1}{p}} + \|Qf\|_p\right]$$

for $p > N$. By the Sobolev imbedding theorem we have $v \in C^1(\bar{\Omega})$ and

$$\|v\|_{C^1} \leqq c \tag{6.7}$$

with a constant $c > 0$ independent of $t \in \mathbb{R}$. By a standard application of the Leray-Schauder degree theory it is possible to prove that for fixed $t \in R$ there is at least one $v \in \text{Im}(L)$ satisfying (6.5) and (6.7).

Let us denote by

$$\sum = \{(t,v) \in \mathbb{R} \times \text{Im}(L); \ t \text{ and } v \text{ satisfy } (6.5)\}$$

the solution set of (6.5). Then the solutions of (6.4) are exactly functions

$u = t\phi + v$ such that $(t,v) \in \Sigma$ and $\psi(t,v) = (f,\phi)_2$, where

$$\psi(t,v) = \int_\Omega g(t\phi + v)\,\phi\,dx$$

is a real function defined on Σ (see (6.6) and the definition of P). By virtue of (g) and (6.7) there exists such a $t_1 > 0$ that

$$\int_\Omega g(t_1\phi + v)\,\phi\,dx \geqq T_2 , \qquad \int_\Omega g(-t_1\phi + w)\,\phi\,dx \leqq T_1 \tag{6.8}$$

for all $(t_1,v) \in \Sigma$ and $(-t_1,w) \in \Sigma$. In the same way as in Lemma 5.5 it is possible to prove the existence of a connected subset Σ_1 of Σ such that $[-t_1,t_1] \subset \mathrm{proj}_{\mathbf{R}}\,\Sigma_1$.

The function ψ is continuous on the connected set Σ_1 . Due to (6.8) we have $\psi(t_1,v) \geqq (f,\phi)_2$ and $\psi(-t_1,w) \leqq (f,\phi)_2$ for all $(t_1,v) \in \Sigma_1$ and $(-t_1,w) \in \Sigma_1$, respectively. This implies that there exist $t \in [-t_1,t_1]$ and $v \in \mathrm{Im}(L)$ such that $u = t\phi + v$ is a solution of (6.4). □

Let us suppose there exist the limits $\lim_{s\to\pm\infty} g(s) = g_\pm$ and

$$g_- \leqq g_+ . \tag{6.9}$$

Set

$$\underline{W} = \inf_{t\in\mathbf{R}} \sup_{(t,v)\in\Sigma} \psi(t,v) ,$$

$$\overline{W} = \sup_{t\in\mathbf{R}} \inf_{(t,v)\in\Sigma} \psi(t,v)$$

and assume that

$$\underline{W} < \overline{W} . \tag{6.10}$$

<u>6.4. Theorem</u> *(multiplicity result). Let us suppose that the assumptions of Theorem* 6.3 *and* (6.9), (6.10) *are satisfied. Then for the right hand side* $f = \tau\phi + h$, *BVP* (6.1), (6.2) *has*

(a) *at least one solution if* $\tau \in (\underline{W},\overline{W})$.

Moreover, the BVP (6.1), (6.2) *has*

(b) *at least two distinct solutions if*

$$\underline{W} < g_- \leqq g_+ < \overline{W} , \quad \tau \in (\underline{W},g_-) \cup (g_+,\overline{W}) .$$

Proof of this theorem follows the same lines as the proof of Theorem 5.7 (cf. also DRÁBEK [86]).

6.5. Examples (i) Let us consider the Dirichlet problem

$$- \Delta u - \lambda_1 u + ue^{-u^2} = f \quad \text{in} \quad \Omega , \tag{6.11}$$

$$u = 0 \quad \text{on} \quad \partial\Omega . \tag{6.12}$$

It follows from Theorem 6.3 that (6.11), (6.12) has a solution for each $f \in L^p(\Omega)$, $p > N$, satisfying $(f,\phi)_2 = 0$, where ϕ is the first eigenfunction of $- \Delta^2$ on Ω . We have $g_+ = g_- = 0$ and for each $h \in \mathrm{Im}(L)$, $Lu = - \Delta u - \lambda_1 u$ we have $\underline{W} < 0 < \overline{W}$. It follows from Theorem 6.4 that for each $h \in \mathrm{Im}(L)$ the problem (6.11), (6.12) has at least two distinct solutions provided

$$f = \tau\phi + h , \quad \tau \in (\underline{W},0) \cup (0,\overline{W}) .$$

(ii) Let us consider the Dirichlet problem

$$- \Delta u - \lambda_1 u - e^{-u^2} = f \quad \text{in} \quad \Omega , \tag{6.13}$$

$$u = 0 \quad \text{on} \quad \partial\Omega . \tag{6.14}$$

Then $g_+ = g_- = 0$, $\underline{W} < 0$, $\overline{W} = 0$ for each $h \in \mathrm{Im}(L)$. Theorem 6.4 implies that the problem (6.13), (6.14) has at least two distinct solutions provided $f = \tau\phi + h$, $\tau \in (\underline{W},0)$.

6.6. Remark. Let us consider a nonlinear function $g : \mathbb{R} \to \mathbb{R}$ satisfying the *sign condition*

$$s \cdot g(s) \geqq 0 \tag{6.15}$$

for all $s \in \mathbb{R}$. Then the assumption (g) is fulfilled with $T_1 = T_2 = 0$. Hence by Theorem 6.3, BVP (6.1), (6.2) with a nonlinearity g satisfying (6.15) has a solution provided

$$(f,\phi)_2 = 0 .$$

6.7. Unbounded nonlinearity. In the following subsections we generalize the results of Theorems 6.3 and 6.4 to unbounded nonlinearities $g = g(x,s)$ satisfying the assumptions from Subsection 6.1 and some additional growth restrictions formulated in the forthcoming lemma.

6.8. Lemma. *Let us consider BVP*

$$Au - \lambda_1 u + \chi_+(x)u^+ - \chi_-(x)u^- = 0 \quad \textit{in} \quad \Omega , \tag{6.16}$$

$$u = 0 \quad \textit{on} \quad \partial\Omega . \tag{6.17}$$

Let $\Gamma_- \in L^p(\Omega)$, $p > N$. *Then there exists a constant* $d = d(\Gamma_-) > 0$ *such that if* $\chi_+, \chi_- \in L^p(\Omega)$ *satisfy*

$$0 \leqq \chi_+(x) \leqq d , \quad 0 \leqq \chi_-(x) \leqq \Gamma_-(x) \tag{6.18}$$

then BVP (6.16), (6.17) *does not have any solution which changes sign in* Ω . *More precisely, if* $u \in W^{2,p}(\Omega)$ *is the solution of BVP* (6.16), (6.17) *then one of the following assertions holds:*

(i) $u = 0$ *on* $\overline{\Omega}$;

(ii) $u(x) > 0$ *for all* $x \in \Omega$ *and* $\frac{\partial u}{\partial \nu} < 0$ *on* $\partial\Omega$;

(iii) $u(x) < 0$ *for all* $x \in \Omega$ *and* $\frac{\partial u}{\partial \nu} > 0$ *on* $\partial\Omega$.

Proof. If $u = 0$ on $\overline{\Omega}$ then the lemma is trivially proved. Let us suppose that the conclusion of the lemma does not hold. Then, for any $n \in \mathbb{N}$, there exist $\chi^n_\pm \in L^p(\Omega)$ and $u_n \in W^{2,p}(\Omega)$ with

$$0 \leqq \chi^n_+(x) \leqq \frac{1}{n} \quad \text{a.e. in} \quad \Omega ,$$

$$0 \leqq \chi^n_-(x) \leqq \Gamma_-(x) \quad \text{a.e. in} \quad \Omega ,$$

$$\|u_n\|_{C^1} = 1$$

verifying

$$Au_n - \lambda_1 u_n + \chi^n_+(x)u^+_n - \chi^n_-(x)u^-_n = 0 \quad \text{in} \quad \Omega , \tag{6.19}$$

$$u_n = 0 \quad \text{on} \quad \partial\Omega , \tag{6.20}$$

and neither the assertion (ii) nor (iii) of the lemma is fulfilled. Since $W^{2,p}(\Omega)$ is a reflexive Banach space compactly imbedded into $C^1(\overline{\Omega})$ there exist $u \in W^{2,p}(\Omega)$, $\chi_- \in L^p(\Omega)$ with

$$\|u\|_{C^1} = 1 , \quad 0 \leqq \chi_-(x) \leqq \Gamma_-(x) \quad \text{a.e. in} \quad \Omega ,$$

such that

$$u_n \rightharpoonup u \quad \text{in} \quad W^{2,p}(\Omega) , \quad u_n \to u \quad \text{in} \quad C^1(\overline{\Omega}) ,$$

$$\chi^n_- \rightharpoonup \chi_- \quad \text{in} \quad L^p(\Omega) , \quad \chi^n_+ \to 0 \quad \text{in} \quad L^\infty(\Omega) ,$$

as $n \to \infty$ (at least for a subsequence). Passing to the limit for $n \to \infty$ in (6.19), (6.20) and using the weak closedness of A and the standard L^p estimate $\|u\|_{2,p} \leqq c\|Au\|_p$ for second order elliptic partial differential equations (see e.g. GILBARG and TRUDINGER [137]) we get

$$Au - \lambda_1 u - \chi_-(x)u^- = 0 \quad \text{in} \quad \Omega , \tag{6.21}$$

$$u = 0 \quad \text{on} \quad \partial\Omega . \tag{6.22}$$

By taking the inner product (in $L^2(\Omega)$) of the equation (6.21) with the eigenfunction ϕ we deduce that $\chi_-(x) = 0$ a.e. in Ω whenever $u(x) < 0$. Therefore (6.21), (6.22) reduce to

$$Au - \lambda_1 u = 0 \quad \text{in} \quad \Omega ,$$

$$u = 0 \quad \text{on} \quad \partial\Omega ,$$

i.e. $u = \pm\phi$. Since $u_n \to u$ in $C^1(\bar{\Omega})$, this implies that there exists a nonnegative integer n_0 such that for each $n \geqq n_0$ either $u_n(x) > 0$ for all $x \in \Omega$ and $\left(\frac{\partial u_n}{\partial \nu}\right)(x) < 0$ for all $x \in \partial\Omega$, or $u_n(x) < 0$ for all $x \in \Omega$ and $\left(\frac{\partial u_n}{\partial \nu}\right)(x) > 0$ for all $x \in \partial\Omega$. We get a contradiction with the fact that for each $n \in \mathbb{N}$, u_n satisfies neither the assertion (ii) nor (iii) of the lemma, and the proof is complete. □

Let us consider a function $g = g(x,s)$ satisfying the assumptions from Subsection 6.1. Then we can assume, without loss of generality, that for the functions $\Gamma_\pm$ defined by

$$\limsup_{s \to +\infty} \frac{g(x,s)}{s} = \Gamma_+(x) , \tag{6.23}$$

$$\limsup_{s \to -\infty} \frac{g(x,s)}{s} = \Gamma_-(x) \tag{6.24}$$

for a.e. $x \in \Omega$, we have $\Gamma_\pm \in L^p(\Omega)$, $p > N$. Let us suppose that g satisfies the *sign condition*

$$g(x,s)\cdot s \geqq 0 \tag{6.25}$$

for a.e. $x \in \Omega$ and all $s \in \mathbb{R}$.

<u>6.9. Theorem.</u> *Let us suppose that* $\Gamma_- \in L^p(\Omega)$, $p > N$, *is the function defined in* (6.24) *and let* $d = d(\Gamma_-)$ *be the constant associated with* Γ_- *by*

Lemma 6.8. *Suppose that the function* Γ_+ *from* (6.23) *is such that*

$$0 \leqq \Gamma_+(x) \leqq d$$

for a.e. $x \in \Omega$. *Moreover, assume that* (6.25) *is valid. Then BVP* (6.1), (6.2) *has at least one solution* $u \in W^{2,p}(\Omega) \cap W_0^{1,2}(\Omega)$, $p > N$, *for any* $f \in L^p(\Omega)$ *satisfying the orthogonality condition* $(f,\phi)_2 = 0$.

The proof of this theorem can be found in the paper by IANNACCI, NKASHAMA and WARD [164].

Let us suppose that in addition to (6.25) the nonlinear function g satisfies at least one of the following two conditions:

(i) there are open sets of positive measure $\Omega_\pm \subset \Omega$, $\partial\Omega_\pm \cap \partial\Omega \neq \emptyset$, and real numbers $s_+ > 0$, $s_- < 0$ such that $g(x,s_+) > 0$ for a.e. $x \in \Omega_+$, $g(x,s_-) < 0$ for a.e. $x \in \Omega_-$;

(ii) there are real numbers $s_+ > 0$, $s_- < 0$ such that $g(x,s) > 0$ for a.e. $x \in \Omega_+(s)$ and all $s \geqq s_+$, $g(x,r) < 0$ for a.e. $x \in \Omega_-(r)$ and all $r \leqq s_-$. Here $\Omega_+(s)$, $\Omega_-(r)$ are subsets of Ω of positive measure.

Note that in the case (ii) it is possible that $\partial\Omega_+(s) \cap \partial\Omega = \emptyset$, $\partial\Omega_-(r) \cap \partial\Omega = \emptyset$. If $g = g(s)$ does not depend on $x \in \Omega$ the previous conditions (i), (ii) have the following simpler form:

(iii) there are $s_1 > 0$ and $s_2 < 0$ such that $g(s_1) > 0$ and $g(s_2) < 0$.

6.10. Theorem *(characterization of the range). In addition to the hypotheses of Theorem* 6.9 *suppose that either* (i) *or* (ii) *(or* (iii)*) is fulfilled. Then for any fixed* $h \in \mathrm{Im}(L) \cap L^p(\Omega)$, $p > N$, *there exist* $\underline{W}(h) < 0 < \overline{W}(h)$ *(where possibly* $\underline{W} = -\infty$ *or* $\overline{W} = +\infty$ *) such that BVP*

$$\begin{aligned} Au - \lambda_1 u + g(x,u) &= \tau\phi + h \quad \text{in } \Omega , \\ u &= 0 \quad \text{on } \partial\Omega \end{aligned}$$

has at least one solution $u \in W^{2,p}(\Omega) \cap W_0^{1,2}(\Omega)$ *provided*

$$\tau \in (\underline{W},\overline{W}) .$$

Proof. Let $f = \tau\phi + h$, $\tau \in \mathbb{R}$, $h \in \mathrm{Im}(L) \cap L^p(\Omega)$, $p > N$, be arbitrary but fixed. We will suppose that g fulfils (6.25) and either (i) or (ii). Let us divide the proof into six steps.

Step 1 (Lyapunov - Schmidt reduction). Using the usual decomposition of (6.4) we obtain an equivalent system

$$v + KQG(t\phi + v) - KQf = 0 , \tag{6.26}$$

$$PG(t\phi + v) - Pf = 0 , \tag{6.27}$$

$u = t\phi + v$, $v \in \mathrm{Im}(L)$, $t \in \mathbb{R}$.

Step 2 (solvability of (6.26)*).* Assume first that g is bounded in the following sense: there exists $b \in L^p(\Omega)$ such that

$$|g(x,s)| \leqq b(x)$$

for a.e. $x \in \Omega$ and for all $s \in \mathbb{R}$. Let $t \in \mathbb{R}$ be fixed. It follows that for any possible solution v of (6.26) we have the estimate

$$\|v\|_{2,p} \leqq c_p\left(\|b\|_p + \|h\|_p\right) , \quad p > N \tag{6.28}$$

(see 6.1 for c_p). Applying the Schauder fixed point theorem and using (6.28) we can prove that for any fixed $t \in \mathbb{R}$ there is at least one $v \in \mathrm{Im}(L)$ satisfying (6.26).

Step 3 (solvability of (6.27)*).* The Sobolev imbedding theorem and (6.28) yield that $v \in C^1(\bar{\Omega})$ and

$$\|v\|_{C^1} \leqq \text{const.} \tag{6.29}$$

for any solution of (6.26) with the constant independent of $t \in \mathbb{R}$. Set

$$\sum = \left\{(t,v) \in \mathbb{R} \times \left[\mathrm{Im}(L) \cap L^p(\Omega)\right] ; \ t \text{ and } v \text{ satisfy (6.26)}\right\}$$

and define a real function $\psi : \sum \rightarrow \mathbb{R}$ by

$$\psi(t,v) = \int_\Omega g\left(x, t\phi(x) + v(x)\right) \phi(x)\, dx ,$$

$(t,v) \in \sum$. Then the solutions of BVP (6.1), (6.2) are such $u = t\phi + v$ that $(t,v) \in \sum$ and

$$\psi(t,v) = \int_\Omega f(x)\, \phi(x)\, dx = \tau .$$

It follows from (6.25), (i) (or (ii)) and (6.29) that there exists $t_1 > 0$ such that

$$\psi(t_1,v) > 0 \quad \text{and} \quad \psi(-t_1,w) < 0 \tag{6.30}$$

for all $(t_1,v) \in \sum$ and $(-t_1,w) \in \sum$. Using the modification of Lemma 5.5 it is possible to prove the existence of a connected subset $\sum_{t_1} \subset \sum$ such that $[-t_1,t_1] \subset \mathrm{proj}_{\mathbb{R}} \sum_{t_1}$. Since ψ is continuous on the connected set $\sum_{t_1}$ there is at least one $t \in (-t_1,t_1)$ and $v \in \mathrm{Im}(L)$ such that $(t,v) \in \sum$ and

$$\psi(t,v) = 0 .$$

This means that $u = t\phi + v$ is a solution of BVP (6.1), (6.2) with the right hand side f satisfying the orthogonality condition $(f,\phi)_2 = 0$. For fixed $h \in \mathrm{Im}(L)$ set

$$\underline{W} = \inf_{t_1} \sup_{(t,w)\in\Sigma_{t_1}} \psi(t,v) , \quad \overline{W} = \sup_{t_1} \inf_{(t,v)\in\Sigma_{t_1}} \psi(t,w) ,$$

where the first "inf" and "sup" are taken over all t_1 satisfying (6.30). Note that $\underline{W} < 0 < \overline{W}$ by (i) and (ii). Then for any $\tau \in (\underline{W},\overline{W})$ we can find $t \in \mathbb{R}$ and $v \in \mathrm{Im}(L)$ such that $(t,v) \in \sum$ and

$$\psi(t,v) = \tau ,$$

i.e. $u = t\phi + v$ is a solution of BVP (6.1), (6.2) with the right hand side $f = \tau\phi + h$. This completes the proof of Theorem 6.10 for a bounded g .

Further, let us suppose that g is not bounded in the sense mentioned above. For fixed $n \in \mathbb{N}$ we define a new function g_n in the following way:

$$g_n(x,s) = \begin{cases} g(x,s) , & x \in \Omega , \quad |s| < n , \\ g(x,n) , & x \in \Omega , \quad s \geqq n , \\ g(x,-n) , & x \in \Omega , \quad s \leqq -n . \end{cases}$$

Then, by virtue of (6.3), for any $n \in \mathbb{N}$ there exists $b_n \in L^p(\Omega)$, $p > N$, such that

$$|g_n(x,s)| \leqq b_n(x)$$

for a.e. $x \in \Omega$ and all $s \in \mathbb{R}$, i.e. g_n is bounded.

Step 4 (apriori estimate). Let us suppose that $(f,\phi)_2 = 0$. We will prove that there exists $n_0 \in \mathbb{N}$ such that $\|u\|_{C^1} < n_0$ for any solution of BVP

$$Au - \lambda_1 u + g_{n_0}(x,u) = f \quad \text{in} \quad \Omega , \tag{6.31}$$

$$u = 0 \quad \text{on} \quad \partial\Omega . \tag{6.32}$$

Suppose the contrary, i.e. there is a sequence of $u_n \in W^{2,p}(\Omega) \cap W_0^{1,2}(\Omega)$

with $\|u_n\|_{C^1} \geq n$ such that

$$Au_n - \lambda_1 u_n + g_n(x,u_n) = f \quad \text{in} \quad \Omega . \tag{6.33}$$

Setting $v_n = \dfrac{u_n}{\|u_n\|_{C^1}}$, we obtain from (6.33)

$$Av_n = \frac{f}{\|u_n\|_{C^1}} - \frac{g_n(x,u_n)}{\|u_n\|_{C^1}} + \lambda_1 v_n \quad \text{in} \quad \Omega , \tag{6.34}$$

$$v_n = 0 \quad \text{on} \quad \partial\Omega . \tag{6.35}$$

The growth condition (6.3) implies that $\left\{\dfrac{g_n(x,u_n)}{\|u_n\|_{C^1}}\right\}$ is bounded in $L^p(\Omega)$.

Hence the right hand side of (6.34) is bounded in $L^p(\Omega)$. Using a standard L^p-estimate and the compact imbedding of $W^{2,p}(\Omega)$ into $C^1(\bar{\Omega})$ (we have $p > N$), we deduce from (6.34), (6.35) that there exists $v \in C^1(\bar{\Omega})$ such that

$$v_n \to v \quad \text{in} \quad C^1(\bar{\Omega}) , \quad \|v\|_{C^1} = 1 , \quad v = 0 \quad \text{on} \quad \partial\Omega$$

(we pass to a subsequence if necessary).

Since $\|Av_n\|_p \leq$ const., $L^p(\Omega)$ is a reflexive Banach space and A is a weakly closed operator, we get that $v \in W^{2,p}(\Omega) \cap W_0^{1,2}(\Omega)$, $Av_n \rightharpoonup Av$ in $L^p(\Omega)$. Hence we can pass to the limit in (6.34), (6.35) obtaining that v solves the problem

$$Av = - P(x) + \lambda_1 v \quad \text{in} \quad \Omega , \tag{6.36}$$

$$v = 0 \qquad \text{on} \quad \partial\Omega . \tag{6.37}$$

The function $P \in L^p(\Omega)$ is the weak limit in $L^p(\Omega)$ of the sequence

$$\left\{ \frac{g_n(x,u_n)}{\|u_n\|_{C^1}} \right\}_{n=1}^{\infty} .$$

Let us define a function $\chi = \chi(x)$ by $\chi(x) = \dfrac{P(x)}{v(x)}$ if $v(x) \neq 0$, $\chi(x) = 0$ if $v(x) = 0$, and set

$$\chi_+(x) = \chi(x) \quad \text{for} \quad x \in \{x \in \Omega;\ v(x) > 0\} ,$$

$$\chi_-(x) = \chi(x) \quad \text{for} \quad x \in \{x \in \Omega;\ v(x) < 0\} .$$

Then with respect to (6.23), (6.24) and (6.25) we have

$$0 \leqq \chi_+(x) \leqq \Gamma_+(x) \ , \quad 0 \leqq \chi_-(x) \leqq \Gamma_-(x)$$

for a.a. $x \in \Omega$. BVP (6.36), (6.37) can be written in an equivalent form

$$Av - \lambda_1 v + \chi_+(x)v^+ - \chi_-(x)v^- = 0 \quad \text{in} \quad \Omega \ ,$$
$$v = 0 \quad \text{on} \quad \partial\Omega \ .$$

It follows from Lemma 6.8 that either $v > 0$ in Ω , $\frac{\partial v}{\partial \nu} < 0$ on $\partial\Omega$ or $v < 0$ in Ω , $\frac{\partial v}{\partial \nu} > 0$ on $\partial\Omega$.

Let us assume that $v > 0$ (the case $v < 0$ can be treated similarly). Since $v_n \to v$ in $C^1(\bar{\Omega})$, $v > 0$ in Ω , $\frac{\partial v}{\partial \nu} < 0$ on $\partial\Omega$, we have $u_n(x) \to +\infty$ uniformly on each compact subset of Ω and $u_n(x) > 0$ for all $x \in \Omega$ and n sufficiently large. Multiplying the equation (6.33) by the eigenfunction ϕ and integrating over Ω , we get

$$\int_\Omega g_n\big(x,u_n(x)\big) \ \phi(x) \ dx = 0 \ .$$

On the other hand, our hypotheses (6.25) and (i) (or (ii)) imply

$$\int_\Omega g_n\big(x,u_n(x)\big) \ \phi(x) \ dx > 0$$

for n large enough, which is a contradiction. The apriori estimate just proved yields that any solution of the problem (6.31), (6.32) is simultaneously the solution of BVP (6.1), (6.2).

Step 5. Take $f \in L^p(\Omega)$, $p > N$, $(f,\phi)_2 = 0$. Define g_{n_0} with n_0 so large that g_{n_0} satisfies (i) or (ii) and any solution of (6.31), (6.32) satisfies the apriori estimate $\|u\|_{C^1} \leqq n_0$. Since g_{n_0} is bounded, BVP (6.31), (6.32) has at least one solution by Step 3. It is the solution of BVP (6.1), (6.2) as well (cf. Step 4).

Step 6 (proof of Theorem 6.10 *for unbounded* g *).* Let $h \in \mathrm{Im}(L) \cap L^p(\Omega)$, $p > N$, be fixed. Let us consider BVP

$$Au - \lambda_1 u + g_{n_0}(x,u) = \tau\phi + h \quad \text{in} \quad \Omega \ , \qquad (6.38)$$

$$u = 0 \qquad \text{on} \quad \partial\Omega \ , \qquad (6.39)$$

where g_{n_0} was defined in Step 5 for $f \equiv h$. Then any solution u_0 of BVP (6.38), (6.39) with $\tau = 0$ satisfies

$$\|u_0\|_{C^1} < n_0 \; . \tag{6.40}$$

It can be also written in the form $u_0 = t_0\phi + v_0$, where

$$\psi_{n_0}(t_0,v_0) = \int_\Omega g_{n_0}\big(x,\ t_0\phi(x) + v_0(x)\big)\ \phi(x)\ dx = 0 \ ,$$

$(t_0,v_0) \in \sum^{n_0}$ (see Step 3). Moreover, there exists $t_1 > 0$ (which depends only on h but not on s) and a connected set $\sum_{t_1}^{n_0} \subset \sum^{n_0}$ such that $[-t_1,t_1] \subset \mathrm{proj}_{\mathbb{R}} \sum_{t_1}^{n_0}$,

$$\psi_{n_0}(t_1,v) > 0 \ , \quad \psi_{n_0}(-t_1,w) < 0 \tag{6.41}$$

for any $(t_1,v) \in \sum_{t_1}^{n_0}$, $(-t_1,w) \in \sum_{t_1}^{n_0}$. Since ψ_{n_0} is continuous on a connected set $\sum_{t_1}^{n_0}$, it follows from (6.40) and (6.41) that for any $\tau \in \big(\underline{W}(h), \overline{W}(h)\big)$, $\underline{W}(h) < 0 < \overline{W}(h)$, $|\underline{W}(h)|$, $\overline{W}(h)$ sufficiently small (see Step 3 for the definition of $\underline{W}$, $\overline{W}$), there exists at least one solution u of BVP (6.38), (6.39) such that $\|u\|_{C^1} < n_0$. According to Step 4 u is also a solution of BVP (6.1), (6.2). This completes the proof. □

<u>6.11. Example.</u> Let us consider BVP

$$-\ \Delta u - \lambda_1 u + g\big(u(x)\big) = f \quad \text{in} \quad \Omega \ , \tag{6.42}$$

$$u = 0 \quad \text{on} \quad \partial\Omega \ , \tag{6.43}$$

where

$$g(s) = \begin{cases} \ln(1+s)(1-\cos s) \ , & s \geqq 0 \ , \\ s(1-\cos s) \ , & s < 0 \ . \end{cases}$$

The function verifies (6.25), (iii) and $\Gamma_+(x) \equiv 0$, $\Gamma_-(x) \equiv 1$ in Ω . According to Theorem 6.10, BVP (6.42), (6.43) has a solution for all $f = \tau\phi + h$ for all $\tau \in \big(\underline{W}(h), \overline{W}(h)\big)$ with some $\underline{W}(h) < 0 < \overline{W}(h)$.

<u>6.12. Dual formulation.</u> It is possible to prove a dual version of Lemma 6.8 with an arbitrary $\Gamma_+ \in L^p(\Omega)$, $p > N$, a constant $d = d(\Gamma_+) > 0$ and functions $\chi_\pm$ satisfying $0 \leqq \chi_+(x) \leqq \Gamma_+(x)$, $0 \leqq \chi_-(x) \leqq d$. Then we also obtain dual version of Theorems 6.9 and 6.10 where the function $\Gamma_+ \in L^p(\Omega)$, $p > N$ given by (6.23) may be arbitrary and Γ_- given by (6.24) must be such that

$$0 \leq \Gamma_-(x) \leq d$$

for a.a. $x \in \Omega$, where $d = d(\Gamma_+)$ is the constant associated with Γ_+ by the dual version of Lemma 6.8.

6.13. Remarks. (i) In the one-dimensional case ($N = 1$), the relationship between Γ_- and $d(\Gamma_-)$ was explicitly calculated in Section 1 (cf. also DRÁBEK [90]) using the shooting argument.

(ii) If $g(x,u) \equiv 0$, the Fredholm alternative implies that BVP

$$\begin{aligned} Au - \lambda_1 u &= f \quad \text{in} \quad \Omega , \\ u &= 0 \quad \text{on} \quad \partial\Omega \end{aligned}$$

has a solution for f satisfying $(f,\phi)_2 = 0$. Theorem 6.10 asserts that if the nonlinearity g is in some sense nontrivial (see conditions (i), (ii), (iii)) then the right hand sides f satisfying $(f,\phi)_2 = 0$ form a proper subset of the set of all right hand sides for which BVP (6.1), (6.2) has a solution. Moreover, the orthogonal decomposition of f gives more precise information about the structure of the range of the operator defined by the left hand side of BVP (6.1), (6.2) (see the definition of $\underline{W}(h)$, $\overline{W}(h)$ in the proof of Theorem 6.10).

(iii) Theorem 6.10 completes Theorems 1 and 2 in IANNACCI, NKASHAMA and WARD [164]. It is also a generalization of the result of de FIGUEIREDO and NI [114], GUPTA [142] and DRÁBEK [86].

(iv) Let

$$g^{-\infty}(x) = \limsup_{s \to -\infty} g(x,s) , \quad g_{+\infty}(x) = \liminf_{s \to +\infty} g(x,s)$$

be well defined functions bounded from above and from below, respectively, and instead of (6.25) assume that

$$\int_\Omega g^{-\infty}(x)\, \phi(x)\, dx < \int_\Omega g_{+\infty}(x)\, \phi(x)\, dx .$$

Then BVP (6.1), (6.2) has at least one solution $u \in W^{2,p}(\Omega) \cap W_0^{1,2}(\Omega)$ for any $f \in L^p(\Omega)$, $p > N$, satisfying

$$\int_\Omega g^{-\infty}(x)\, \phi(x)\, dx < \int_\Omega f(x)\, \phi(x)\, dx < \int_\Omega g_{+\infty}(x)\, \phi(x)\, dx . \tag{6.44}$$

Let us give a *sketch of the proof*. We can derive an apriori estimate similarly to Step 4 for any right hand side f satisfying the Landesman - Lazer type condition (6.44). Then using a truncation of g outside of a sufficiently large interval we prove the solvability of BVP (6.1), (6.2). We proceed in the same way as in Steps 1 - 3.

CHAPTER 3

Weakly nonlinear problems with oscillating nonlinearity

7. NEUMANN PROBLEM FOR SECOND ORDER PARTIAL DIFFERENTIAL EQUATIONS

7.1. Subsolutions and supersolutions. Let us consider BVP (5.1), (5.2) with the same hypotheses as in Subsection 5.1. A function $u \in C^2(\Omega) \cap C^1(\bar{\Omega})$ is called *a subsolution* of BVP (5.1), (5.2) if

$$\begin{aligned} Au + g(u) &\leq f \quad \text{in} \quad \Omega , \\ Bu &\leq 0 \quad \text{on} \quad \partial\Omega , \end{aligned}$$

and u is called *a supersolution* if the above inequalities are reversed. It is known that BVP (5.1), (5.2) has at least one classical solution provided there exist a subsolution v and a supersolution w such that $v \leq w$ (see FUČÍK [125]).

Let $f \in C^{\alpha}(\bar{\Omega})$, $0 < \alpha < 1$, and write $f = \bar{f} + \tilde{f}$, where

$$\bar{f} = \frac{1}{\text{meas } \Omega} \int_{\Omega} f(x) \, dx , \quad \int_{\Omega} \tilde{f}(x) \, dx = 0 .$$

Let us denote by $R(\tilde{f})$ the set of all $\bar{f} \in \mathbb{R}$ for which BVP (5.1), (5.2) (with $f = \bar{f} + \tilde{f}$) has at least one classical solution $u \in C^2(\Omega)$.

With respect to the results of Section 5 this means

$$R(\tilde{f}) = \{ \frac{1}{\text{meas } \Omega} \int_{\Omega} g(\bar{u} + \tilde{u}(x)) \, dx ; \ \tilde{u} \in C^2(\Omega) \text{ and } \bar{u} \in \mathbb{R} \text{ satisfy } (5.6) \} .$$

Let us suppose that $g : \mathbb{R} \to \mathbb{R}$ is Hölder continuous and T-periodic function, $T > 0$.

7.2. Lemma. *Let* $\bar{f}_1 \leq \bar{f}_2$ *be real numbers and* $\bar{f} \in [\bar{f}_1, \bar{f}_2]$. *If the problems*

$$Au + g(u) = \bar{f}_j + \tilde{f} \quad \textit{in} \quad \Omega , \tag{7.1}$$

$$Bu = 0 \quad \textit{on} \quad \partial\Omega , \tag{7.2}$$

$j = 1,2$ *have classical solutions then the problem*

$$Au + g(u) = \bar{f} + \tilde{f} \quad \textit{in} \quad \Omega , \tag{7.3}$$

$$Bu = 0 \quad \textit{on} \quad \partial\Omega \tag{7.4}$$

also has a classical solution.

Proof. Let u_j , $j = 1,2$, be classical solutions of BVP (7.1), (7.2). Then it follows from $\bar{f}_1 \leqq \bar{f} \leqq \bar{f}_2$ that u_1 is a subsolution and u_2 is a supersolution of BVP (7.3), (7.4). By periodicity of g there exists $n_0 \in \mathbb{N}$ such that $v = u_1 - n_0 T$ is a subsolution and $w = u_2 + n_0 T$ is a supersolution of BVP (7.3), (7.4) and $v \leqq w$. Then BVP (7.3), (7.4) has at least one classical solution u such that $v \leqq u \leqq w$ (see FUČÍK [125]). □

Let us define

$$d(\tilde{f}) = \min_u \max_{x\in\bar{\Omega}} \{Au + g(u) - \tilde{f}\} , \tag{7.5}$$

$$D(\tilde{f}) = \max_u \min_{x\in\bar{\Omega}} \{Au + g(u) - \tilde{f}\} , \tag{7.6}$$

where the minimum and maximum are taken over all $u \in C^2(\Omega) \cap C^1(\bar{\Omega})$ satisfying $Bu = 0$. Set $\underline{G} = \min_{s\in\mathbb{R}} g(s)$, $\bar{G} = \max_{s\in\mathbb{R}} g(s)$.

7.3. Theorem. *Let* A *and* g *be as above,* $f \in C^\alpha(\bar{\Omega})$ *with* $0 < \alpha < 1$, $f = \bar{f} + \tilde{f}$. *Then* $R(\tilde{f})$ *is a nonempty closed subinterval of* $[\underline{G},\bar{G}]$, *moreover* $R(\tilde{f}) = [d(\tilde{f}), D(\tilde{f})]$.

Proof. It follows from Lemma 7.2 that $R(\tilde{f})$ is a nonempty subinterval of $[\underline{G},\bar{G}]$. To prove that $R(\tilde{f})$ is closed, let $\{\bar{f}_k\}$ be a sequence in $R(\tilde{f})$ which converges to $\bar{f}$, and let u_k be a solution of BVP (5.1), (5.2) with $f_k = \bar{f}_k + \tilde{f}$. By the T-periodicity of g , we can assume without loss of generality that $\bar{u}_k \in [0,T]$. The compactness of $[0,T]$ implies that there is a subsequence of $\{\bar{u}_k\}$ (which will be denoted again by $\{\bar{u}_k\}$) such that $\bar{u}_k \to \bar{u} \in [0,T]$. It follows from

$$\tilde{u}_k + TG(\bar{u}_k + \tilde{u}_k) - TPG(\bar{u}_k + \tilde{u}_k) - T\tilde{f} = 0 ,$$

together with the boundedness of G and the compactness of T that there is a subsequence of $\{\tilde{u}_k\}$ (denoted again by $\{\tilde{u}_k\}$) such that $\tilde{u}_k \to \tilde{u}$ in $L^p(\Omega)$ and

$$\tilde{u} + TG(\bar{u} + \tilde{u}) - TPG(\bar{u} + \tilde{u}) - T\tilde{f} = 0 ,$$
$$PG(\bar{u} + \tilde{u}) = \bar{f} .$$

The regularity results mentioned in Section 5 imply that $u = \bar{u} + \tilde{u}$ is a classical solution of BVP (5.1), (5.2) with the right hand side $f = \overline{f} + \tilde{f}$. Hence $R(\tilde{f})$ is a closed interval $[\alpha,\beta]$. We will prove that $\alpha = d(\tilde{f})$, $\beta = D(\tilde{f})$, where $d(\tilde{f})$ and $D(\tilde{f})$ are given by (7.5) and (7.6), respectively. Let us denote by $u \in C^2(\Omega) \cap C^1(\overline{\Omega})$ the solution of BVP

$$Au + g(u) = \alpha + \tilde{f} \quad \text{in} \quad \Omega , \tag{7.7}$$

$$Bu = 0 \quad \text{on} \quad \partial\Omega , \tag{7.8}$$

and suppose that

$$\alpha > d' = \inf_{w} \max_{x \in \overline{\Omega}} \{Aw + g(w) - \tilde{f}\}$$

for $w \in C^2(\Omega) \cap C^1(\overline{\Omega})$ satisfying $Bw = 0$. Then there is d'' with $d' < d'' < \alpha$ and $v \in C^2(\Omega) \cap C^1(\overline{\Omega})$ satisfying $Bv = 0$ and such that

$$Av + g(v) - \tilde{f} \leqq d'' .$$

Consequently, v is a subsolution of BVP

$$Au + g(u) = d'' + \tilde{f} \quad \text{in} \quad \Omega , \tag{7.9}$$

$$Bu = 0 \quad \text{on} \quad \partial\Omega . \tag{7.10}$$

On the other hand, due to (7.7), u is a supersolution of BVP (7.9), (7.10). By periodicity of g we may suppose that $v \leqq u$ on Ω (cf. the proof of Lemma 7.2). Hence BVP (7.9), (7.10) has a solution, which is a contradiction with the definition of $R(\tilde{f})$, i.e. $\alpha = d(\tilde{f})$. The case $\beta = D(\tilde{f})$ is treated similarly. □

<u>7.4. Example.</u> Let us consider BVP

$$-\Delta u + \sin u = \overline{f} + \tilde{f} \quad \text{in} \quad \Omega ,$$

$$\frac{\partial u}{\partial \nu} = 0 \quad \text{on} \quad \partial\Omega .$$

Then the corresponding set $R(\tilde{f})$ is a nonempty closed subinterval $[d(\tilde{f}),D(\tilde{f})] \subset [-1,1]$, where

$$d(\tilde{f}) = \min_{u} \max_{x \in \overline{\Omega}} \{-\Delta u + \sin u - \tilde{f}\} ,$$

$$D(\tilde{f}) = \max_{u} \min_{x \in \overline{\Omega}} \{-\Delta u + \sin u - \tilde{f}\} ,$$

and the minimum and maximum are taken over all $u \in C^2(\Omega)$ with $\frac{\partial u}{\partial \nu} = 0$.

7.5. Remarks. (i) Let us suppose that the periodic function g satisfies

$$\int_0^T g(s)\, ds = 0 . \tag{7.11}$$

This implies

$$0 \in [d(\tilde{f}), D(\tilde{f})] . \tag{7.12}$$

In particular, it follows from (7.12) that BVP

$$- \Delta u + \sin u = f \quad \text{in} \quad \Omega ,$$

$$\frac{\partial u}{\partial \nu} = 0 \quad \text{on} \quad \partial\Omega$$

has at least one classical solution for $f \in C^{\alpha}(\bar{\Omega})$, $0 < \alpha < 1$, satisfying

$$\int_\Omega f(x)\, dx = 0 . \tag{7.13}$$

In order to prove (7.12) we use the variational approach. Let us define a C^1-functional $\Phi : W^{1,2}(\Omega) \to \mathbf{R}$ by

$$\Phi(u) = \frac{1}{2} \int_\Omega \sum_{i,j=1}^{N} a_{ij}(x) \frac{\partial u}{\partial x_i} \frac{\partial u}{\partial x_j}\, dx + \int_\Omega \int_0^{u(x)} g(s)\, ds\, dx -$$

$$- \int_\Omega \tilde{f}(x)\, u(x)\, dx .$$

It follows from (7.11) and (7.13) that Φ is bounded from below and $\Phi(u) \to +\infty$ if $\|\tilde{u}\|_{1,2} \to \infty$. On the other hand, we have

$$\Phi(u + T) = \Phi(u) .$$

Hence there is a bounded minimizing sequence $\{u_k\}$ of Φ . The existence of at least one critical point u_0 of Φ now follows from the weak lower semicontinuity of Φ on $W^{1,2}(\Omega)$. An elementary calculation yields that u_0 is a weak solution of BVP (5.1), (5.2), and the regularity result implies that it is a classical solution.

(ii) Let us denote

$$S_- = \{\tilde{f} \in C^{\alpha}(\bar{\Omega}) \cap \operatorname{Ker} P ; \quad d(\tilde{f}) < 0\} ,$$

$$S_+ = \{\tilde{f} \in C^{\alpha}(\bar{\Omega}) \cap \operatorname{Ker} P ; \quad D(\tilde{f}) > 0\}$$

and suppose that the nodes of g are *isolated*. Then the sets S_- and

S_+ are *dense* in $C^{\alpha}(\bar{\Omega}) \cap \text{Ker } P$ with respect to the L^{∞}-norm. In other words, this means that the set of all $\tilde{f}$ for which zero is an interior point of the interval $[d(\tilde{f}), D(\tilde{f})]$ is dense in $C^{\alpha}(\bar{\Omega}) \cap \text{Ker } P$ with respect to the L^{∞}-norm. The proof of this assertion is the same as that of Theorem 5 in MAWHIN and WILLEM [218].

8. PERIODIC PROBLEM FOR SECOND ORDER ORDINARY DIFFERENTIAL EQUATION

8.1. Let $T > 0$ and let us denote by C_T^0 the Banach space of all continuous and T-periodic functions defined on the real line $\mathbb{R}$ with the norm

$$\|u\|_{C_T^0} = \max_{t \in \mathbb{R}} |u(t)| .$$

Further, let g be a continuous function such that g' exists a.e. in $\mathbb{R}$ and there exist constants $M > 0$, $K > 0$, $s_0 > 0$ such that

$$|g(s)| \leq M , \quad |g'(s)| \leq K < \frac{\pi^2}{T^2} \tag{8.1}$$

for all $|s| \geq s_0$. Assume in addition that g is not a constant function.

We will study the periodic BVP

$$u''(t) + g(u(t)) = f(t) , \quad t \in [0,T] , \tag{8.2}$$

$$u(0) = u(T) , \quad u'(0) = u'(T) , \tag{8.3}$$

where $f \in C_T^0$. We say that u is *a solution* of the periodic BVP (8.2), (8.3) if $u \in C^2([0,T])$ and u satisfies (8.2), (8.3).

For p, q such that

$$\underline{G} = \inf_{s \in \mathbb{R}} g(s) < q \leq p < \sup_{s \in \mathbb{R}} g(s) = \overline{G} \tag{8.4}$$

we set

$$M_{p,q} = M_{p,q}^1 \cup M_{p,q}^2 ,$$

where

$$M_{p,q}^1 = \{d \in \mathbb{R} ; \exists c_1, c_2 \in \mathbb{R} , \ 0 \leq c_1 < c_2 , \ s \in [c_1, c_2] \Rightarrow$$
$$\Rightarrow g(s) > p , \ s \in [-c_2, -c_1] \Rightarrow g(s) < q , \ d \leq c_2 - c_1\} ,$$

$$M_{p,q}^2 = \{d \in \mathbb{R} ; \exists c_1, c_2 \in \mathbb{R} , \ 0 \leq c_1 < c_2 , \ s \in [c_1, c_2] \Rightarrow$$

$\Rightarrow g(s) < q \ , \quad s \in [-c_2,-c_1] \Rightarrow g(s) > p \ , \quad d \leqq c_2 - c_1\} \ .$

If $\sup M_{p,q} = \infty$ for each p, q satisfying (8.4), then g is called *an expansive function* (see Fig. 3).

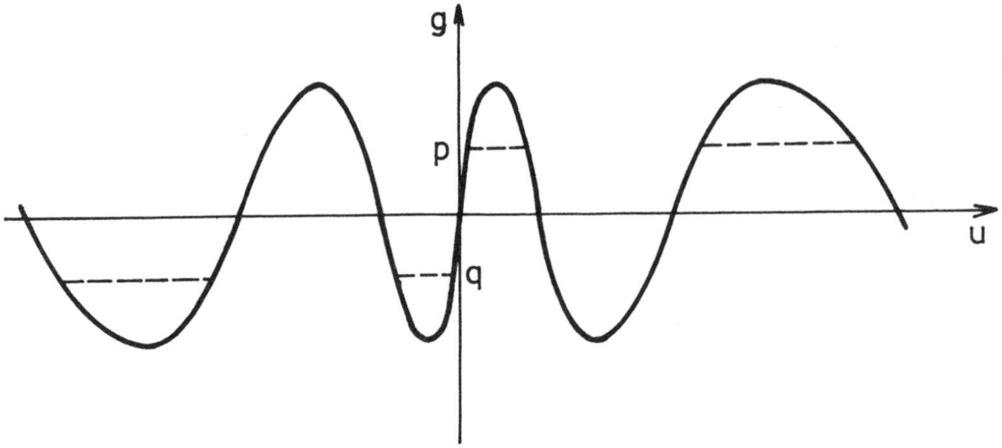

Fig. 3

Let us assume that the sets $g^{-1}(\underline{G})$, $g^{-1}(\overline{G})$ contain no nondegenerate interval.

<u>8.2. Lemma.</u> *Let* $f \in C_T^0$, $t_0 \in \mathbb{R}$ *and* (8.1) *be fulfilled. If* u_1, u_2 *are solutions of the periodic BVP* (8.2), (8.3) *such that*

$$u_1(t_0) = u_2(t_0)$$

then u_1 *and* u_2 *coincide on* $\mathbb{R}$.

For the proof see FUČÍK [125, Section 26.8].

<u>8.3. Lemma.</u> *Let* $f \in C_T^0$ *and* (8.1) *be fulfilled. Then the Dirichlet BVP*

$$u''(t) + g(c + u(t)) = f(t) \ , \quad t \in [0,T] \ , \tag{8.5}$$

$$u(0) = u(T) = 0 \tag{8.6}$$

has a unique solution $u \in C^2([0,T])$ *for arbitrary* $c \in \mathbb{R}$.

For the proof see FUČÍK [125, Section 26.9].

8.4. Theorem. *Let* $f \in C_T^0$ *and* (8.1) *be fulfilled. Then the periodic BVP* (8.2), (8.3) *has at least one solution if*

$$\underline{G} < q \leq \frac{1}{T}\int_0^T f(t)\,dt \leq p < \overline{G}\ ,$$

$$T^2M + T\int_0^T |f(t)|\,dt < \sup M_{p,q}\ .$$

Proof. Let us denote by $\tilde{v}_{c,f}$ a solution of BVP (8.5), (8.6) and set

$$v_{c,f}(t) = c + \tilde{v}_{c,f}(t - kT)$$

for $t \in [kT, (k+1)T]$, $k \in \mathbb{Z}$. Then $v_{c,f}$ is a T-periodic solution of BVP (8.2), (8.3) if and only if

$$\int_0^T g\big(v_{c,f}(t)\big)\,dt = \int_0^T f(t)\,dt\ .$$

Let us define a function $\Phi_f : \mathbb{R} \to \mathbb{R}$ by

$$\Phi_f : c \mapsto \int_0^T g\big(v_{c,f}(t)\big)\,dt\ .$$

Rolle's theorem implies the existence of such a $t_c \in (0,T)$ that $v'_{c,f}(t_c) = 0$. Consequently,

$$|v'_{c,f}(t)| \leq \left|\int_{t_c}^{t} g\big(c + \tilde{v}_{c,f}(\tau)\big)\,d\tau\right| + \left|\int_{t_c}^{t} f(\tau)\,d\tau\right| \leq$$

$$\leq TM + \int_0^T |f(\tau)|\,d\tau\ , \quad t \in [0,T]\ , \quad c \in \mathbb{R}\ ; \tag{8.7}$$

$$|\tilde{v}_{c,f}(t_1) - \tilde{v}_{c,f}(t_2)| \leq \sup_{t\in[0,T]} |v'_{c,f}(t)|\ |t_1 - t_2| \leq$$

$$\leq T^2M + T\int_0^T |f(\tau)|\,d\tau\ , \quad t_1, t_2 \in [0,T]\ , \quad c \in \mathbb{R}\ . \tag{8.8}$$

From (8.8) and from the assumption

$$T^2M + T\int_0^T |f(t)|\,dt < \sup M_{p,q}$$

we obtain $c_1, c_2 \in \mathbb{R}$ such that

$$\Phi_f(c_1) < Tq \quad\text{and}\quad \Phi_f(c_2) > Tp\ . \tag{8.9}$$

Let us suppose that $\lim_{n\to\infty} d_n = d_0$. Then according to (8.7), (8.8) the set $\{\tilde{v}_{d_n,f}\}_{n=1}^{\infty}$ is relatively compact in the space $C^2([0,T])$ (see KUFNER, JOHN and FUČÍK [183]). This fact together with Lemma 2 implies that there exists exactly one $\tilde{v}_{d_0,f}$ which is the solution of BVP (8.5), (8.6) and $\Phi_f(d_0) = \lim_{n\to\infty} \Phi_f(d_n)$. Hence Φ_f is a continuous function and (8.9) yields $c_3 \in (c_1,c_2)$ such that

$$\Phi_f(c_3) = \int_0^T f(t)\,dt\ .$$

Then $v_{c_3,f}$ is a solution of the periodic BVP (8.2), (8.3). □

<u>8.5. Corollary</u> *(expansive nonlinearity). Let* $f \in C_T^0$, (8.1) *be fulfilled. Suppose, moreover, that* g *is an expansive function,* $\sup M_{p,q}^i = \infty$, $i = 1,2$, *and* $g^{-1}(\underline{G})$, $g^{-1}(\overline{G})$ *are either both empty or both infinite. Then the problem* (8.2), (8.3) *has infinitely many distinct solutions if and only if*

$$\underline{G} < \frac{1}{T}\int_0^T f(t)\,dt < \overline{G}\ ,\ \textit{provided}\ \ g^{-1}(\underline{G}) = g^{-1}(\overline{G}) = \emptyset\ ;$$

$$\underline{G} < \frac{1}{T}\int_0^T f(t)\,dt < \overline{G}\ ,\quad f \equiv \underline{G}\ ,\quad f \equiv \overline{G}$$

provided $g^{-1}(\underline{G}) \neq \emptyset$, $g^{-1}(\overline{G}) \neq \emptyset$.

<u>Proof.</u> There are $p, q \in \mathbb{R}$ such that

$$\underline{G} < q \leq \frac{1}{T}\int_0^T f(t)\,dt \leq p < \overline{G}$$

provided $g^{-1}(\underline{G}) = g^{-1}(\overline{G}) = \emptyset$. Because of $\sup M_{p,q}^i = \infty$, $i=1,2$, we obtain

$\{c_n\}_{n=1}^{\infty} \subset \mathbb{R}$, $c_n \neq c_m$ for $n \neq m$, $\Phi_f(c_n) = \int_0^T f(t)\,dt$. If $g^{-1}(\underline{G}) \neq \emptyset$, $g^{-1}(\overline{G}) \neq \emptyset$ then for each $k_1 \in g^{-1}(\underline{G})$ and $k_2 \in g^{-1}(\overline{G})$, the functions $u \equiv k_1$ and $u \equiv k_2$ are solutions of BVP (8.2), (8.3) with $f \equiv \underline{G}$ and $f \equiv \overline{G}$, respectively. The necessity of the condition follows from the fact that each periodic solution u of (8.2), (8.3) must satisfy

$$\int_0^T g(u(t))\,dt = \int_0^T f(t)\,dt . \qquad \square$$

<u>8.6. Corollary</u> *(periodic nonlinearity). Let* $f \in C_T^0$, (8.1) *be fulfilled and, moreover, let* g *be a* τ*-periodic function. Then BVP* (8.2), (8.3) *has at least two distinct solutions* u_1 , u_2 *such that* $|u_i(0)| \leq \tau$, $i = 1,2$, *if*

$$-1 < -p \leq \frac{1}{T}\int_0^T f(t)\,dt \leq p < 1$$

and

$$T^2M + T\int_0^T |f(t)|\,dt < \sup M_{p,q} .$$

Proof. All assumptions of Theorem 8.4 are fulfilled and, moreover, Φ_f is a τ-periodic function. There are $c_1, c_2 \in \mathbb{R}$, $c_1 < c_2 < c_1 + \tau$ such that

$$\Phi_f(c_1) = \Phi_f(c_1 + \tau) < -Tp , \quad \Phi_f(c_2) > Tp .$$

Hence we obtain $c_3 \in (c_1, c_2)$ and $c_4 \in (c_2, c_1 + \tau)$ such that

$$\Phi_f(c_3) = \Phi_f(c_4) = \int_0^T f(t)\,dt . \qquad \square$$

<u>8.7. Examples.</u> (i) *Expansive nonlinearity.* Corollary 8.5 implies that the equation

$$u''(t) + \sin \ln \left(1 + |u(t)|\right) = f(t)$$

possesses an infinite number of T-periodic solutions with a period $T < \pi$ if and only if

$$- 1 < \frac{1}{T} \int_0^T f(t)\, dt < 1 \quad \text{or} \quad f \equiv \pm 1 .$$

(ii) *Periodic nonlinearity.* Corollary 8.6 implies that the equation of mathematical pendulum

$$u''(t) + \sin u(t) = f(t)$$

has at least two distinct T-periodic solutions u_1, u_2, $T < \pi$, such that $|u_i(0)| \leqq 2\pi$, $i = 1,2$, if

$$- 1 < - p \leqq \frac{1}{T} \int_0^T f(t)\, dt \leqq p < 1 ,$$

$$T^2 + T \int_0^T |f(t)|\, dt < \pi - 2 \arcsin p .$$

8.8. Remark. The results of Theorem 8.4 and of Corollaries 8.5, 8.6 were generalized in various directions in the following works: DING [79], FOURNIER and MAWHIN [124], INVERNIZZI [166], KANNAN and ORTEGA [170,171], MAWHIN [213], MAWHIN and WARD [215], MAWHIN and WILLEM [217,218], ORTEGA [249], PETRYSHIN and YU [255], TARANTONELLO [282].

9. PERIODIC PROBLEM FOR SYSTEM OF SECOND ORDER ORDINARY DIFFERENTIAL EQUATIONS

9.1. Let $T > 0$ be a real number and $N \geqq 2$ an integer. In this section the symbol $u(t) = \big(u_1(t),\dots,u_N(t)\big)$ will denote the vector function. We will study the existence of solutions for the periodic BVP

$$u'' + \sigma u' + Au + g\big(u(t)\big) + h\big(u(t)\big) = f , \quad 0 \leqq t \leqq T , \tag{9.1}$$

$$u(0) = u(T) , \quad u'(0) = u'(T) . \tag{9.2}$$

We will suppose that σ is a real number and A is a real $N \times N$ *constant matrix* such that

(H1) 0 *is an eigenvalue of* A *with geometric multiplicity* 1, *and no other eigenvalue of* A *has the form* $m^2\omega^2 - im\omega\sigma$ *with* $m \in \mathbb{Z}$ *and*

$\omega = \frac{2\pi}{T}$ *(where* i *is imaginary unit).*

Moreover, we assume that

(H2) (g) $g : \mathbb{R}^N \to \mathbb{R}^N$ *is continuous and bounded, say* $|g| \leq M_g$ *, and there are functions* $g_j : \mathbb{R} \to \mathbb{R}$, $j = 1,\ldots,N$ *, such that*

$$g(u) = \big(g_1(u_1), g_2(u_2), \ldots, g_N(u_N)\big)$$

for all $u = (u_1, u_2, \ldots, u_N) \in \mathbb{R}^N$;

(h) $h : \mathbb{R}^N \to \mathbb{R}^N$ *is continuous and bounded, say* $|h| \leq M_h$;

(f) $f \in L^\infty \equiv L^\infty\big([0,T], \mathbb{R}^N\big)$.

Let us note that (9.1), (9.2) represents the periodic BVP for the *system* of N ordinary differential equations of the second order.

9.2. Example. The symmetric tridiagonal matrix

$$A = N^2 \begin{bmatrix} 1 & -1 & & & & \\ -1 & 2 & -1 & & & \\ & -1 & 2 & -1 & & \\ & & \ddots & \ddots & \ddots & \\ & & & -1 & 2 & -1 \\ & & & & -1 & 1 \end{bmatrix} \tag{9.3}$$

verifies (H1) (assuming T small enough when $\sigma = 0$).

The field g defined by

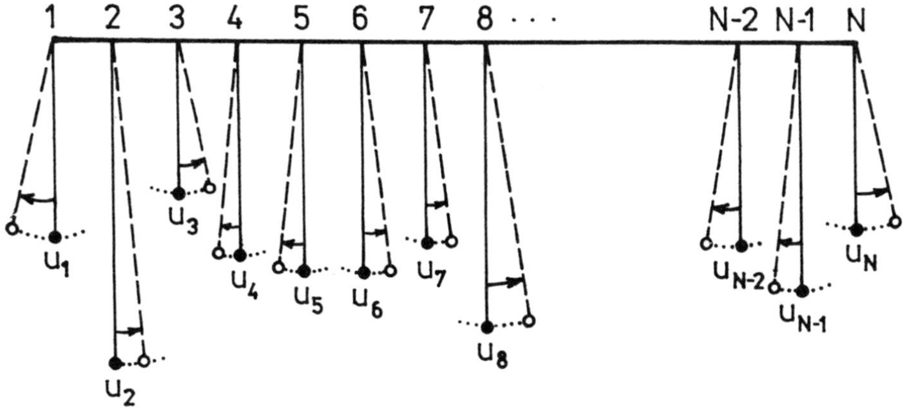

Fig. 4

$$g(u) = (\sin u_1, \sin u_2, \dots, \sin u_N) \tag{9.4}$$

verifies (H2) (g). We remark that if (9.3), (9.4) hold and $h \equiv 0$, then (9.1), (9.2) is a model for the motion of a *system of* N *linearly coupled pendulums* with external disturbances and possibly with a viscous damping (see Fig. 4). The periodic BVP (9.1), (9.2) with (9.3), (9.4) is also a model for the dynamics of an N-*coupled point Josephson junction*, which is important in the theory of *superconductivity* (see e.g. LEVI, HOPPENSTEADT and MIRANKER [197]).

9.3. Linear part of the problem. On

$$\mathrm{dom}(L) = \{u \in W^{2,\infty}([0,T], \mathbb{R}^N);\ u^{(k)}(0) = u^{(k)}(T),\ k = 0,1\}$$

we define a vector differential operator

$$L : \mathrm{dom}(L) \subset L^\infty \to L^\infty$$

by

$$Lu = u'' + \sigma u + Au .$$

The classical linear theory (see e.g. HALE [147]) shows that L is a linear Fredholm operator with index 0, and that $\mathrm{Ker}\, L = \mathrm{Ker}\, A$, $\mathrm{Ker}\, L^* = \mathrm{Ker}\, A^*$. Since $\dim \mathrm{Ker}\, A = 1$ (and $\dim \mathrm{Ker}\, A^* = 1$) we find a unit vector $\phi \in \mathbb{R}^N$ ($\phi^* \in \mathbb{R}^N$) spanning $\mathrm{Ker}\, A$ ($\mathrm{Ker}\, A^*$, respectively). Let us choose projectors P, Q in L^∞ :

$$Pu = \left(\frac{1}{T}\int_0^T (u,\phi)_N\right)\phi, \quad Qv = \left(\frac{1}{T}\int_0^T (v,\phi^*)_N\right)\phi^* ,$$

where $(\cdot,\cdot)_N$ denotes the inner product in $\mathbb{R}^N$, i.e.

$$(u,\phi)_N = \phi_1 u_1(t) + \phi_2 u_2(t) + \dots + \phi_N u_N(t) .$$

Hence

$$Pu = \left(\frac{1}{T}\int_0^T \big(\phi_1 u_1(t) + \dots + \phi_N u_N(t)\big)\, dt\cdot\phi_1 , \dots ,\right.$$

$$\left.\frac{1}{T}\int_0^T \big(\phi_1 u_1(t) + \dots + \phi_N u_N(t)\big)\, dt\cdot\phi_N\right) ,$$

and similarly Qu. We denote by $K_{P,Q} : L^\infty \to L^\infty$ the generalized (right) inverse of L relative to P and Q (see e.g. FUČÍK [125]). Then $K_{P,Q}$ is a compact operator.

Let us fix $u \in \mathrm{dom}(L) \cap \mathrm{Ker}\, P$ and $v \in L^\infty$ such that $u = K_{P,Q} v$. Let A^+ be the (Moore - Penrose) pseudoinverse of A , and let L_m^{-1} be the (two-sided) inverse of

$$L_m = (-m^2\omega^2 + im\omega\sigma)I + A ,$$

$m \in \mathbb{Z} \setminus \{0\}$. Then a well-known technique based on the Fourier series and the Parseval identity yields

$$\|u\|_\infty \leqq \Big(\|A^+\|^2 + \sum_{m\neq 0} \|L_m^{-1}\|^2\Big)^{1/2} \|v\|_\infty ,$$

i.e.

$$\|K_{P,Q}\| \leqq \sqrt{\|A^+\|^2 + \sum_{m\neq 0} \|L_m^{-1}\|^2} . \tag{9.5}$$

Indeed, let $\sum_{m\in\mathbb{Z}} \hat{u}_m e^{im\omega t}$ and $\sum_{m\in\mathbb{Z}} \hat{z}_m e^{im\omega t}$ be the Fourier series associated with u and $z = (I - Q)v$, respectively. Then $(\hat{z}_0, \phi^*)_N = 0$, $A\hat{u}_0 = \hat{z}_0$ with $(\hat{u}_0, \phi)_N = 0$, i.e. $\hat{u}_0 = A^+\hat{z}_0$, and $\hat{u}_m = L_m^{-1}\hat{z}_m$ for $m \neq 0$. Therefore,

$$\|u\|_\infty \leqq |\hat{u}_0| + \Big\|\sum_{m\neq 0} \hat{u}_m e^{im\omega t}\Big\|_\infty \leqq |A^+\hat{z}_0| + \sum_{m\neq 0} \|L_m^{-1}\|\, |\hat{z}_m| \leqq$$

$$\leqq \|A^+\|\, |\hat{z}_0| + \Big(\sum_{m\neq 0} \|L_m^{-1}\|^2\Big)^{1/2}\Big(\sum_{m\neq 0} |\hat{z}_m|^2\Big)^{1/2} \leqq$$

$$\leqq \Big(\|A^+\|^2 + \sum_{m\neq 0} \|L_m^{-1}\|^2\Big)^{1/2} \left(\frac{1}{T}\int_0^T |(I - Q)v|^2\right)^{1/2} \leqq$$

$$\leqq \Big(\|A^+\|^2 + \sum_{m\neq 0} \|L_m^{-1}\|^2\Big)^{1/2} \left(\frac{1}{T}\int_0^T |v|^2\right)^{1/2} ,$$

$I - Q$, Q being a pair of L^2-orthogonal projectors.

<u>9.4. Lemma.</u> *We have* $\sum_{m\neq 0} \|L_m^{-1}\|^2 \to 0$ *as* $T \to 0$.

Proof. For $m \neq 0$, $\omega > 0$, define $z(m,\omega) = -m^2\omega^2 + im\omega\sigma$. Fix ω_0 so large that

$$\|A\| \leqq \frac{|z(1,\omega)|}{4} \tag{9.6}$$

for $\omega \geqq \omega_0$. We have

$$\|L_m^{-1}\|^2 = [\lambda_1(L_m^* L_m)]^{-1} =$$

$$= \left(|z(m,\omega)|^2 + \lambda_1\left(\overline{z(m,\omega)}\ A + z(m,\omega)A^* + A^*A\right)\right)^{-1} \leqq$$

$$\leqq \left(|z(m,\omega)|^2 + \lambda_1\left(\overline{z(m,\omega)}\ A + z(m,\omega)A^*\right)\right)^{-1} \leqq$$

$$\leqq \left(|z(m,\omega)|^2 - 2|z(m,\omega)|\ \|A\|\right)^{-1} \leqq 2|z(m,\omega)|^{-2} =$$

$$= 2(m^4\omega^4 + m^2\omega^2\sigma^2)^{-1} , \tag{9.7}$$

where $\lambda_1(H)$ denotes the first eigenvalue of a selfadjoint matrix H . □

<u>9.5. Remark.</u> When A is symmetric and positive semidefinite, as in (9.3), then (9.6) is not needed. Indeed, in this case

$$\lambda_1\left(\overline{z(m,\omega)}\ A + z(m,\omega)A^*\right) = 2\ \mathrm{Re}\ z(m,\omega)\lambda_1(A) = 0$$

and so

$$\|L_m^{-1}\|^2 \leqq (m^4\omega^4 + m^2\omega^2\sigma^2)^{-1} . \tag{9.8}$$

<u>9.6. Remark.</u> An explicit upper bound for

$$\sum_{m\neq 0} \|L_m^{-1}\|^2$$

can be easily derived from (9.7) or (9.8). Let $\rho_m = m^4\omega^4 + m^2\omega^2\sigma^2$, and fix a positive integer m_0 . Then

$$\sum_{m\neq 0} \frac{1}{\rho_m} \leqq \frac{2}{\omega^4} \sum_{m>0} m^{-4} - \frac{2\sigma^2}{\omega^2} \sum_{1\leqq m\leqq m_0} m^{-2}\ \rho_m^{-1} \leqq$$

$$\leqq \frac{\pi^4}{45\omega^4} - \frac{2\sigma^2}{\omega^2} \sum_{1\leqq m\leqq m_0} m^{-2}\ \rho_m^{-1} . \tag{9.9}$$

<u>9.7. Bounded perturbations of the linear equation.</u> Let S be a continuous bounded operator $L^\infty \to L^\infty$ such that

$$\|S(u)\|_\infty \leqq M$$

for all $u \in L^\infty$ with a constant $M > 0$. We will consider the *operator equation*

$$Lu + S(u) = f \ , \quad u \in \mathrm{dom}(L) \ , \tag{9.10}$$

where L is defined in 9.3, and $f \in L^\infty$ is fixed. It is obvious that (9.10) is equivalent to the system

$$v + K_{P,Q}\, S(r\phi + v) = K_{P,Q}\, f \ , \tag{9.11}$$

$$QS(r\phi + v) = Qf \ , \tag{9.12}$$

where $r = (Pu,\phi)_N$, $v = u - r\phi$. Recall that $(I - Q)f_1 = (I - Q)f_2$ implies $K_{P,Q}f_1 = K_{P,Q}f_2$ by the definition of $K_{P,Q}$.

<u>9.8. Lemma.</u> *Let*

$$\Sigma = \{(r,v) \in \mathbf{R} \times \mathrm{Ker}\, P \ ; \quad r \ , v \ \textit{fulfil}\ (9.11)\} \ .$$

Then

(i) $\mathrm{proj}_{\mathbf{R}}\, \Sigma = \mathbf{R}$;

(ii) *for each* $e \in \mathrm{Ker}\, Q$ *there exists at least one* ρ , $- M \leqq \rho \leqq M$ *such that* (9.10) *with* $f = \rho\phi^* + e$ *is solvable.*

<u>*Proof.*</u> It follows from Schauder's fixed point theorem. □

Let us define a map $\psi : \Sigma \to \mathbf{R}$ by

$$\psi(r,v) = \left(QS(r\phi + v) - Qf,\ \phi^*\right)_N \ .$$

<u>9.9. Theorem.</u> *Let us suppose that there are real numbers* r_- , r_+ *such that*

$$\psi(r_-,v) \leqq 0 \leqq \psi(r_+,w) \tag{9.13}$$

for all $v, w \in \mathrm{Ker}\, P$ *with* $(r_-,v), (r_+,w) \in \Sigma$. *Then* (9.10) *is solvable.*

<u>*Proof.*</u> Set $\alpha = \max\{|r_-|, |r_+|\}$. In the same way as in Lemma 5.5 it is possible to prove the existence of a connected subset Σ_α of Σ such that

$$[-\alpha,\alpha] \subset \mathrm{proj}_{\mathbf{R}}\, \Sigma_\alpha \ .$$

The continuity of ψ , the connectedness of Σ_α and the inequalities (9.13) imply the existence of a point $(r,v) \in \Sigma$ for which $\psi(r,v) = 0$, i.e. $u = r\phi + v$ is a solution of (9.10). □

9.10. Periodic perturbations of the linear equation. Now we suppose that A, g, h, f verify (H1), (H2). If we define $S : L^\infty \to L^\infty$ as Nemytskiĭ's operator induced by $g + h$, then the periodic BVP (9.1), (9.2) is clearly equivalent to the abstract equation (9.10). To apply Theorem 9.9, that is to verify (9.13), we impose the following sign condition on the components g_j with respect to the components ϕ_j and ϕ_j^*, $j = 1,\dots,N$:

(H3) *there are real numbers* r_+, r_-, $\delta > 0$ *and* $\tau \geq 0$ *such that*

$$|s - r_\pm \phi_j| \leq \delta \quad \textit{implies} \quad \pm\, g_j(s) \geq \tau$$

for all indices $j \in J_+ = \{j;\ 1 \leq j \leq N,\ \phi_j^* > 0\}$, *and*

$$|s - r_\mp \phi_j| \leq \delta \quad \textit{implies} \quad \pm\, g_j(s) \geq \tau$$

for all indices $j \in J_- = \{j;\ 1 \leq j \leq N,\ \phi_j^* < 0\}$.

Let us remark that the hypothesis (H3) does not concern indices in the set $\{1,2,\dots,N\} \setminus (J_+ \cup J_-)$.

9.11. Theorem. *Assume* (H1), (H2), (H3). *Moreover, suppose that*

(i) $\|K_{P,Q}\| \left(M_g + M_h + \|(I - Q)h\|_\infty\right) \leq \delta$,

(ii) $M_h \leq \tau$,

(iii) $Qf = 0$.

Then the periodic BVP (9.1), (9.2) *is solvable.*

Proof. We only have to show that (9.13) is fulfilled. The assumption (iii) implies that

$$\psi(r,v) = \left(QS(r\phi + v),\ \phi^*\right) = \frac{1}{T}\int_0^T \sum_{j=1}^N \left(g_j(r\phi_j + v_j) + h_j(r\phi + v)\right)\phi_j^* .$$

If we take $r_\pm$ from (H3), then it is easy to check (using (i) and (ii)) that

$$\psi(r_-,v) \leq 0 \leq \psi(r_+,w)$$

for all v and w in $\operatorname{Ker} P$ with (r_-,v) and (r_+,w) in the set Σ. □

9.12. Remark. Theorem 9.11 is a natural one. It states that the range of L

is contained in the range of $L + S$ when some a priori estimates and some sign conditions hold. Note that trivial generalizations of Theorem 9.11 can be obtained by assuming, for example, that the map h depends also on t, $0 \leqq t \leqq T$, and on u' : $h = h\big(t, u(t), u'(t)\big)$. In this case we only have to assume that $h = h(t,x,y)$ is Carathéodory and bounded, and to work in $W^{1,\infty}$ instead of L^{∞}. Indeed, Nemytskiĭ's operator induced by h can be substituted by any continuous operator $L^{\infty} \to L^{\infty}$ or $W^{1,\infty} \to L^{\infty}$, with its range contained in the ball centered at 0 with radius M_h.

However, in spite of its generality, Theorem 9.11 can provide more precise information on the range of $u \mapsto Lu + g(u)$ if h is viewed as a perturbation of $f \in \operatorname{Im} L$ instead of a perturbation of g.

<u>9.13. Special matrices and nonlinearities.</u> In the forthcoming subsections we restrict the classes of the matrices A and of the fields g under consideration assuming that

(H1') $A = (a_{ij})$ *verifies* (H1); *moreover, for* $i = 1,2,\ldots,N$,

$$\sum_{j=1}^{N} a_{ij} = 0 \,, \tag{9.14}$$

$$\phi_i^* \geqq 0 \,. \tag{9.15}$$

(H2') *there are numbers* $b_j > 0$, $j = 1,2,\ldots,N$, *and a* p-*periodic* $(p > 0)$ *continuous map* $\Psi : \mathbb{R} \to \mathbb{R}$ *such that*

$$|\Psi(s)| \leqq 1 \quad \textit{for all} \quad s \in \mathbb{R} \,,$$

$\Psi(s) > 0$ *(or* < 0*) for* $p_0 < s < p_1$ $(p_1 < s < p_0 + p$, *respectively),* $p_0 < p_1 < p_0 + p$, *and* $g(u) = \big(b_1\Psi(u_1),\, b_2\Psi(u_2),\, \ldots,\, b_N\Psi(u_N)\big)$ *for all* $u = (u_1,u_2,\ldots,u_N) \in \mathbb{R}^N$.

Obviously (9.14) implies (9.15) provided A is symmetric, because (9.14) implies that $\operatorname{Ker} A$ is spanned by $\phi = \frac{1}{\sqrt{N}}(1,1,\ldots,1)$. A model example for Ψ is $\Psi = \sin$ with $p_0 = 0$, $p_1 = \frac{p}{2} = \pi$, like in the pendulum-type equations, but other periodic maps can be considered as well.

<u>9.14. Theorem.</u> *Assume* (H1'), (H2'). *Let* $e \in L^{\infty}$ *be given. Suppose that there exists a number* δ *such that*

$$0 < \delta < \min\left\{ \frac{p_1 - p_0}{2} , \frac{p_0 + p - p_1}{2} \right\} , \tag{9.16}$$

$$\|A^+\| \left(\sqrt{\sum_{j=1}^{N} b_j^2} + \|(I - Q)e\|_\infty \right) < \delta , \tag{9.17}$$

and that

$$|(Qe)_j| < \tau \tag{9.18}$$

for all $j = 1,\dots,N$, *where* τ *is a positive number defined by*

$$\tau = \min\left(\{\Psi(s);\ |s - r_1| \leq \delta\} \cup \{-\Psi(s);\ |s - r_2| \leq \delta\}\right) \cdot$$

$$\cdot \min\{b_j;\ j = 1,\dots,N\}$$

with $r_1 = \dfrac{p_0 + p_1}{2}$, $r_2 = r_1 + \dfrac{p}{2}$.

Then there exists an explicitly computable number $T_0 > 0$ *such that, for* $T \leq T_0$, *the periodic BVP*

$$u_i'' + \sigma u_i' + \sum_{j=1}^{N} a_{ij} u_j + b_i \Psi(u_i) = e_i , \quad 0 \leq t \leq T , \tag{9.19}$$

$$u_i(0) = u_i(T) , \quad u_i'(0) = u_i'(T) , \quad i = 1,\dots,N , \tag{9.20}$$

has at least two solutions which do not differ by an integer multiple of the vector $p(1,1,\dots,1) = (p,p,\dots,p)$.

Proof. We use twice Theorem 9.11 setting

$$h = -Qe , \quad f = (I - Q)e .$$

Note that in this case Theorem 9.11 holds even if (i) is substituted by the weaker assumption

(i') $\|K_{P,Q}\|\left(M_g + \|(I - Q)f\|_\infty\right) \leq \delta$,

and (ii) by

(ii') $\sup\{|h_i(x)|;\ i = 1,\dots,N ,\ x \in \mathbb{R}^N\} \leq \tau$.

By (9.17) and Lemma 9.4 there is $T_0 > 0$ such that

$$\left(\|A^+\|^2 + \sum_{m\neq 0} \|L_m^{-1}\|^2\right)^{1/2} \left(\sqrt{\sum_{j=1}^{N} b_j^2} + \|(I - Q)e\|_\infty \right) \leq \delta \tag{9.21}$$

whenever $T \leq T_0$. Using (9.5) we see that (9.21) implies the inequality (i').

The inequality (9.18) implies that the assumption (ii') holds with strict inequality sign. The assumption (iii) holds by the definition of f. It remains only to check (H3). Set $r_0 = r_1 - \frac{p}{2}$ and

$$r_+ = r_1 \sqrt{N} , \quad r_- \in \{r_0 \sqrt{N} , r_2 \sqrt{N}\} .$$

We immediately get that

$$\left| s - \frac{r_\pm}{\sqrt{N}} \right| \leqq \delta \quad \text{implies} \quad \pm b_j \Psi(s) \geqq \tau$$

for all $j \in J_+$ (recall that $J_- = \emptyset$ by (9.15)). Thus (H3) holds in two different settings, namely $(r_+,r_-) = (r_1\sqrt{N}, r_0\sqrt{N})$ and $(r_+,r_-) = (r_1\sqrt{N}, r_2\sqrt{N})$. Moreover, by virtue of the strict inequality sign in (ii') we have

$$(-1)^\ell \psi(r_\ell \sqrt{N}, v) < 0$$

for all $(r_\ell\sqrt{N}, v) \in \Sigma$, $\ell = 0,1,2$. Thus Theorem 9.11 yields the existence of solutions

$$u^{(\ell)} = r^{(\ell)}(1,1,\dots,1) + v^{(\ell)} , \quad \ell = 0,1 ,$$

of the periodic BVP (9.19), (9.20) with $v^{(0)}$ and $v^{(1)}$ in $\operatorname{Ker} P$ and $r_0 < r^{(0)} < r_1 < r^{(1)} < r_2$. If $u^{(1)} - u^{(0)} = kp(1,1,\dots,1)$ for some $k \in \mathbb{Z}$, then $v^{(1)} - v^{(0)} \equiv 0$ and $r^{(1)} - r^{(0)} = kp$. Since $r^{(1)} - r^{(0)} < r_2 - r_0 = p$, we necessarily have $k = 0$. □

<u>9.15. Mechanical model.</u> Let us consider the periodic BVP on $[0,T]$ for the 2-dimensional system

$$\begin{aligned} u_1'' + \sigma u_1' + a_1(u_1 - u_2) + b_1 \sin u_1 &= e_1 , \\ u_2'' + \sigma u_2' + a_2(u_2 - u_1) + b_2 \sin u_2 &= e_2 , \end{aligned} \tag{9.22}$$

where a_i, b_i $(i = 1,2)$ are strictly positive numbers and $e = (e_1,e_2)$ is in L^∞. The system (9.22) is a model for the motion of a system of 2 linearly coupled pendulums with external disturbances and a viscous damping given by a constant σ (see MARLIN [207] for details). The matrix

$$A = \begin{bmatrix} a_1 & -a_1 \\ -a_2 & a_2 \end{bmatrix}$$

verifies (H1'). Indeed, its eigenvalues are $\lambda_1 = 0$, $\lambda_2 = a_1 + a_2$. If $\sigma = 0$ we have to choose T so small that $\lambda_2 < \omega^2$. The kernel of A (or of A^*) is spanned by $\phi = \frac{1}{\sqrt{2}}(1,1)$ (by $\phi^* = \frac{1}{\sqrt{a_1^2 + a_2^2}}(a_2,a_1)$, respectively). The norm of A is

$$\|A\| = \sqrt{2(a_1^2 + a_2^2)} \ .$$

The pseudoinverse of A is $A^+ = \frac{1}{2(a_1^2 + a_2^2)} A^*$ so that

$$\|A^+\| = \frac{1}{\sqrt{2(a_1^2 + a_2^2)}} \ .$$

The inequality (9.16) is $0 < \delta < \frac{\pi}{2}$ and $\tau = \cos\delta \cdot \min\{b_1,b_2\}$. Set

$$\bar{e} = \frac{1}{T}\int_0^T e \ .$$

Thus $Qe = (\bar{e},\phi^*)_N\phi^*$, $N = 2$. A direct application of Theorem 9.14 gives the following assertion.

<u>9.16. Corollary.</u> *Let us suppose that there is a number* δ , $0 < \delta < \frac{\pi}{2}$ *such that*

$$\frac{1}{\sqrt{2(a_1^2 + a_2^2)}}\left(\sqrt{b_1^2 + b_2^2} + \sup_{0\leq t\leq T}\sqrt{\tilde{e}_1^2 + \tilde{e}_2^2}\right) < \delta \ ,$$

$$\frac{\max\{a_1,a_2\}}{a_1^2 + a_2^2}\,|a_2\bar{e}_1 + a_1\bar{e}_2| < \cos\delta \cdot \min\{b_1,b_2\} \ , \tag{9.23}$$

where

$$\bar{e}_i = \frac{1}{T}\int_0^T e_i \ , \quad i = 1,2 \ ,$$

$$\tilde{e}_i = e_i - \frac{\bar{e}_i a_j^2 + \bar{e}_j a_i a_j}{a_i^2 + a_j^2} \ , \quad \{i,j\} = \{1,2\} \ .$$

Then the periodic BVP (9.22) *on* $[0,T]$ *has at least two solutions which do not differ by an integer multiple of* $2\pi(1,1)$, *provided* T *is small enough, say* $T \leq T_0$.

9.17. Remarks. (i) *The computation* of T_0 is easy. Here, and in any other particular case of Theorem 9.14, we have only to recall the upper bound of $\sum_{m\neq 0} \|L_m^{-1}\|^2$ derived in Remark 9.6 in terms of integer powers of T, and apply it in (9.21).

(ii) If e is the restriction on the interval $[0,T]$ of an *odd* T-*periodic function*, then $\bar{e} = 0$, $\tilde{e} = e$. More generally, when $\bar{e} = 0$ then the inequality (9.23) holds for any δ, $0 < \delta < \frac{\pi}{2}$, and so the conclusion of Corollary 9.16 still holds with the only assumption

$$\frac{1}{\sqrt{2(a_1^2 + a_2^2)}} \left(\sqrt{b_1^2 + b_2^2} + \sup_{0\leq t\leq T} \sqrt{\tilde{e}_1^2 + \tilde{e}_2^2} \right) < \frac{\pi}{2} .$$

9.18. Model of discrete Josephson junction. Let us suppose that $A = (a_{ij})$ is defined by (9.3), $\Psi = \sin$, $b_j = 1$, $j = 1,2,\ldots,N$. Then the periodic BVP (9.19), (9.20) has the following form:

$$\begin{aligned}
&u_1'' + \sigma u_1' + N^2 u_1 - N^2 u_2 + \sin u_1 = e_1 ,\\
&u_2'' + \sigma u_2' - N^2 u_1 + 2N^2 u_2 - N^2 u_3 + \sin u_2 = e_2 ,\\
&\cdots\cdots\cdots\cdots\cdots\cdots\cdots\\
&u_N'' + \sigma u_N' - N^2 u_{N-1} + N^2 u_N + \sin u_N = e_N ,
\end{aligned} \tag{9.24}$$

$$u_i(0) = u_i(T) , \quad u_i'(0) = u_i'(T) , \quad i = 1,2,\ldots,N . \tag{9.25}$$

We have recalled at the beginning of this section that this particular form of BVP (9.19), (9.20) represents, for example, the oscillations of an N-coupled point Josephson junction with external time-dependent disturbances. The matrix A is symmetric, and $\phi = \phi^* = \frac{1}{\sqrt{N}}(1,1,\ldots,1)$. The inequality (9.16) has the form $0 < \delta < \frac{\pi}{2}$, and $\tau = \cos\delta$. Moreover,

$$Qe = \left(\sum_{j=1}^{N} \frac{1}{\sqrt{N}} \bar{e}_j \right) \phi^* = \left(\frac{1}{N} \sum_{j=1}^{N} \bar{e}_j \right) (1,1,\ldots,1) ,$$

and

$$(I - Q)e = e - \left(\frac{1}{N} \sum_{j=1}^{N} \bar{e}_j \right) (1,1,\ldots,1) .$$

From Theorem 9.14 we therefore obtain the following assertion.

9.19. Corollary. *The BVP* (9.24), (9.25) *has at least two solutions which do not differ by an integer multiple of the vector* $2\pi(1,1,\dots,1)'$ *provided* T *is sufficiently small and the inequalities*

$$\|A^+\| \left(1 + \sup_{0\leq t\leq T} \sqrt{\left(\sum_{j=1}^{N} \tilde{e}_j^2\right)}\right) < \delta \ , \tag{9.26}$$

$$|\bar{\bar{e}}| < \cos\delta$$

hold for some δ, $0 < \delta < \frac{\pi}{2}$, *with*

$$\bar{\bar{e}} := \frac{1}{N}\sum_{j=1}^{N} \frac{1}{T}\int_0^T e_j(t)\,dt \ ,$$

$$\tilde{e}_j := e_j - \bar{\bar{e}} \ , \quad j = 1,\dots,N \ .$$

9.20. Remarks. (i) Obviously (9.26) would be inconsistent if $\|A^+\| \geq \frac{\pi}{2}$. Let us compute $\|A^+\|$. Define $J = \frac{1}{N^2} A$. By elementary algebraic tools we get

(1) $\|A^+\| = \|(N^2J)^+\| = \|\frac{1}{N^2} J^+\| = \frac{1}{N^2} \|J^+\|$,

(2) the eigenvalues of J^+ are $0 < \lambda_N^{-1} < \lambda_{N-1}^{-1} < \dots < \lambda_2^{-1}$, where $0 = \lambda_1 < \lambda_2 < \dots < \lambda_N$ are the eigenvalues of J,

(3) J^+ is symmetric so that $\|J^+\| = \lambda_2^{-1}$.

Now, J being symmetric and tridiagonal, its first nonzero eigenvalue λ_2 can be computed with high accuracy by the bisection method (see e.g. BARTH, MARTIN and WILKINSON [26]). We do not give numerical details here, like error estimates. We only present the following results, obtained by the bisection method:

N	1	3	4	5	10	20
$\|A^+\|$	0.125	0.111111	0.106694	0.104741	0.102158	0.101529

Recall that $\frac{\pi}{2} = 1,570\dots$ and hence the condition (9.26) is reasonable.

(ii) Let us remark that the solvability of the periodic BVP for the *scalar* forced ordinary differential equation of pendulum type has been studied by several authors, see e.g. DRÁBEK [83], FOURNIER and MAWHIN [124], INVERNIZZI [166], KANNAN and ORTEGA [170,171], MAWHIN [210], MAWHIN and WILLEM [218], PETRYSHYN and YU [256], FUČÍK [125] and the bibliography therein, and Section 8 of this book. The periodic BVP for a *system* of linearly or nonlinearly coupled pendulums with external time-dependent disturbances was considered in MARLIN [207], but assuming the existence of particular symmetries. His results were generalized by MAWHIN [208], but nevertheles some symmetry of the forcing terms was still required. These symmetries reduce the kernel of the linear part of the system. Therefore they can be viewed as *nonresonance conditions* (see also MAWHIN [208] for a discussion of their role) while the BVPs studied in this section are *resonance* problems. Note also that more general results for conservative systems (damping σ is equal to zero) were obtained in the recent work by MAWHIN [212] using the variational approach.

(iii) Periodic problems for systems of ordinary differential equations were recently published in papers by CAÑADA and MARTINES - AMORES [39,40], CARISTI [44,45], CONTI, IANNACCI and NKASHAMA [66], DING [79], DRÁBEK and INVERNIZZI [96], HABETS and NKASHAMA [144], MAWHIN [212], NKASHAMA [236,237], ZANOLIN [298].

PART II
Strongly nonlinear problems

CHAPTER 4

Solvability of strongly nonlinear problems

10. RANGES OF HOMOGENEOUS OPERATORS

10.1. Abstract operator equation. Let X, Y, Z be Banach spaces with zero elements 0_X, 0_Y, 0_Z and with norms $\|\cdot\|_X$, $\|\cdot\|_Y$, $\|\cdot\|_Z$, respectively. A subset C of Z is called a *cone* if it is closed, convex, invariant under multiplication by nonnegative real numbers, and if $C \cap (-C) = \{0_Z\}$. We suppose that a given fixed cone C in Z has the following properties:

(Z1) If $z \in Z$ then there exists a uniquely determined couple $z^+, z^- \in C$ such that

$$z = z^+ - z^- .$$

Moreover, for each $z_1^+, z_1^- \in C$ such that $z = z_1^+ - z_1^-$ we have $z_1^+ - z^+ \in C$, $z_1^- - z^- \in C$, and for any $t \geq 0$ $(tz)^+ = tz^+$, $(tz)^- = tz^-$, $(-z)^+ = z^-$.

(Z2) The mapping $z \mapsto z^+$ is continuous.

We will suppose that also the following condition holds:

(Z3) $X \subset Z$ and the imbedding $X \hookrightarrow Z$ is continuous.

Let $a > 0$ be fixed and let J be a mapping defined on X with values in the space Y, and suppose that the following assumptions are fulfilled:

(J1) J is positively a-*homogeneous;*

(J2) J is *one-to-one,* J is *continuous* in 0_X and J^{-1} is *continuous;*

(J3) J is *odd.*

Let S be an operator defined on Z, acting into Y and satisfying

(S1) S is positively a-*homogeneous;*

(S2) S is *continuous;*

(S3) the mappings $x \mapsto S(x^+)$, $x \mapsto S(x^-)$ are *compact* operators from X into Y.

Suppose that $G : X \to Y$ is a *compact* operator. Denote

$$\mathcal{R}_{(\mu,\nu)}(J,S,G) = \{f \in Y; \exists\, x_0 \in X : J(x_0) - \mu S(x_0^+) + \nu S(x_0^-) + G(x_0) = f\}$$

and set

$$A_{-1} = \{(\mu,\nu) \in \mathbb{R}^2;\ \exists\, x_0 \neq 0_X : J(x_0) - \mu S(x_0^+) + \nu S(x_0^-) = 0_Y\} ,$$

$$A_0 = \mathbb{R}^2 \setminus A_{-1} ,$$

$$A_1 = \{(\mu,\nu) \in A_0;\ \deg[\tilde{F};\ B_1,\ 0_Y] \neq 0\} ,$$

where $\tilde{F} : y \mapsto y - \mu S(J^{-1}(y))^+ + \nu S(J^{-1}(y))^-$, $y \in Y$,

$$A_2 = \{(\mu,\nu) \in A_0;\ \mathcal{R}_{(\mu,\nu)}(J,S,0) \neq Y\} ,$$

$$A_3 = \{(\mu,\nu) \in \mathbb{R}^2;\ \mathcal{R}_{(\mu,\nu)}(J,S,0) = Y\} .$$

Then the sets A_i , $i = -1,0,1,2,3$ are *symmetric* subsets of $\mathbb{R}^2$ with respect to the diagonal $\mu = \nu$, and the following assertions are valid:

(i) A_0 *is open in* $\mathbb{R}^2$ *and moreover, if* $(\alpha,\beta) \in \mathbb{R}^2$, $|\alpha| + |\beta| < \dfrac{c_1(\mu,\nu)}{s}$, $(\mu,\nu) \in A_0$, *then* $(\mu + \alpha,\ \nu + \beta) \in A_0$ *where*

$$c_1(\mu,\nu) = \inf_{\|x\|_X = 1} \|J(x) - \mu S(x^+) + \nu S(x^-)\|_Y > 0$$

and

$$s = \max\left\{ \sup_{\|x\|_X=1} \|S(x^+)\|_Y ,\ \sup_{\|x\|_X=1} \|S(x^-)\|_Y\right\} < +\infty .$$

(ii) *For* $(\mu,\nu) \in A_0$ *the set* $\mathcal{R}_{(\mu,\nu)}(J,S,0)$ *is closed in* Y .

(iii) $A_1 \subset A_3$.

(iv) A_1 *is an open subset of* $\mathbb{R}^2$.

(v) A_1 *is a union of some components of* A_0 .

(vi) *Let* T *be a component of* A_0 *containing the point* (λ,λ) *for a real number* λ . *Then* $T \subset A_1$.

(vii) *Let* $(\mu,\nu) \in A_1$ *and suppose that*

$$\limsup_{\|x\|_X \to \infty} \frac{\|G(x)\|_Y}{\|x\|_X^a} < c_1(\mu,\nu) .$$

Then $\mathcal{R}_{(\mu,\nu)}(J,S,G) = Y$.

(viii) *For a given* $(\mu,\nu) \in A_2$ *there exists* $c_2(\mu,\nu) > 0$ *such that if*

$$\limsup_{\|x\|_X \to \infty} \frac{\|G(x)\|_Y}{\|x\|_X^a} \leq c_2(\mu,\nu)$$

then $\mathcal{R}_{(\mu,\nu)}(J,S,G) \neq Y$.

(ix) A_2 *is an open set in* $\mathbf{R}^2$.

Proof. The symmetry of the sets A_i , $i = -1,0,1,2,3$ follows directly from the definition.

Ad (i). Let us suppose that $c_1(\mu,\nu) = 0$. Then there exists a sequence $\{x_n\}_{n=1}^{\infty}$, $\|x_n\|_X = 1$, $n = 1,2,\ldots$, such that

$$\lim_{n\to\infty} \|J(x_n) - \mu S(x_n^+) + \nu S(x_n^-)\|_Y = 0 .$$

Due to (J2) and (S3) there exists a subsequence (denoted again by $\{x_n\}_{n=1}^{\infty}$) and $x_0 \in X$ such that

$$\mu S(x_n^+) - \nu S(x_n^-) \longrightarrow J(x_0) \quad \text{in} \quad Y$$

and hence

$$J(x_n) \longrightarrow J(x_0) \quad \text{in} \quad Y \quad \text{and} \quad x_n \longrightarrow x_0 \quad \text{in} \quad X .$$

This implies that

$$\|x_0\|_X = 1 \quad \text{and} \quad J(x_0) - \mu S(x_0^+) + \nu S(x_0^-) = 0_Y ,$$

a contradiction. Let $(\mu,\nu) \in A_0$ and $(\alpha,\beta) \in \mathbf{R}^2$ be such that

$$|\alpha| + |\beta| < \frac{c_1(\mu,\nu)}{s} .$$

Then

$$\|J(x) - (\mu + \alpha)S(x^+) + (\nu + \beta)S(x^-)\|_Y \geq$$

$$\geq \|J(x) - \mu S(x^+) + \nu S(x^-)\|_Y - \|\alpha S(x^+) - \beta S(x^-)\|_Y \geq$$

$$\geq c_1(\mu,\nu)\|x\|_X^a - (|\alpha| + |\beta|)s\ \|x\|_X^a > 0$$

for $x \neq 0_X$. Hence $(\mu + \alpha,\ \nu + \beta) \in A_0$.

Ad (ii). Let

$$J(x_n) - \mu S(x_n^+) + \nu S(x_n^-) = f_n$$

and

$$f_n \to f \quad \text{in} \quad Y .$$

Due to (i) we have

$$c_1(\mu,\nu)\|x_n\|_X^a \leqq \|f_n\|_Y ,$$

that is $\{x_n\}_{n=1}^{\infty}$ is bounded in X. There exists a subsequence (denoted again by $\{x_n\}_{n=1}^{\infty}$) and $x_0 \in X$ such that

$$\mu S(x_n^+) - \nu S(x_n^-) \to J(x_0) + f \quad \text{in} \quad Y$$

and hence

$$J(x_n) \to J(x_0) \quad \text{in} \quad Y .$$

Consequently,

$$x_n \to x_0 \quad \text{in} \quad X \quad \text{and} \quad J(x_0) - \mu S(x_0^+) + \nu S(x_0^-) = f ,$$

i.e. $f \in \mathcal{R}_{(\mu,\nu)}(J,S,0)$.

Ad (iii). Let $(\mu,\nu) \in A_1$ and $f \in Y$ be arbitrary but fixed. It is sufficient to prove that the equation

$$y - \mu S\big(J^{-1}(y)\big)^+ + \nu S\big(J^{-1}(y)\big)^- = f$$

has a solution in Y. In virtue of (i) there exists $\rho > 0$ such that

$$\|y - \mu S\big(J^{-1}(y)\big)^+ + \nu S\big(J^{-1}(y)\big)^-\|_Y > \|f\|_Y$$

for any $y \in Y$, $\|y\|_Y = \rho$. It follows from the homotopy invariance property of the degree and from the definition of A_1 that

$$\begin{aligned}
&\deg\big[I - \mu S\big(J^{-1}(\cdot)\big)^+ + \nu S\big(J^{-1}(\cdot)\big)^- - f;\ B_\rho,\ 0_Y\big] = \\
&= \deg\big[I - \mu S\big(J^{-1}(\cdot)\big)^+ + \nu S\big(J^{-1}(\cdot)\big)^-;\ B_\rho,\ 0_Y\big] = \\
&= \operatorname{def}\big[I - \mu S\big(J^{-1}(\cdot)\big)^+ + \nu S\big(J^{-1}(\cdot)\big)^-;\ B_1,\ 0_Y\big] \neq 0 ,
\end{aligned}$$

i.e. $(\mu,\nu) \in A_3$.

The assertions (iv) and (v) follow directly from the definition of A_1 . The assertion (vi) follows from the homotopy invariance property of the Leray - Schauder degree because due to the Borsuk theorem (see e.g. FUČÍK, NEČAS, SOUČEK and SOUČEK [129]) we have

$$\deg\big[I - \lambda S\big(J^{-1}(\cdot)\big)^+ + \lambda S\big(J^{-1}(\cdot)\big)^-;\ B_1,\ 0_Y\big] \neq 0 .$$

Ad (vii). Let $f \in Y$ be arbitrary but fixed. Let us suppose that $(\mu,\nu) \in A_1$.

There are $\varepsilon > 0$ and $\rho > 0$ such that

$$\|y - \mu S(J^{-1}(y))^+ + \nu S(J^{-1}(y))^-\|_Y - (c_1(\mu,\nu) - \varepsilon)\|J^{-1}(y)\|_X^a > \|f\|_Y$$

for any $y \in Y$, $\|y\|_Y = \rho$ (see the definition of $c_1(\mu,\nu) > 0$). Hence

$$\|y - \mu S(J^{-1}(y))^+ + \nu S(J^{-1}(y))^-\|_Y > \|G(J^{-1}(y))\|_Y + \|f\|_Y$$

for any $y \in Y$, $\|y\|_Y = \rho$ and the assertion follows from the homotopy invariance property of the Leray - Schauder degree.

Ad (viii). Due to the assumption $(\mu,\nu) \in A_2$ there exists $y \in Y$, $\|y\|_Y = 1$ such that

$$J(x) - \mu S(x^+) + \nu S(x^-) \neq y$$

for arbitrary $x \in X$. Since $\mathcal{R}_{(\mu,\nu)}(J,S,0)$ is closed, we have

$$\inf_{x \in X} \|J(x) - \mu S(x^+) + \nu S(x^-) - y\|_Y = 2\sigma > 0 .$$

Set

$$c_2(\mu,\nu) = \frac{\sigma}{\sigma + 2} c_1(\mu,\nu) .$$

Let us choose $r > 0$ such that

$$\|G(x)\|_Y < \frac{\sigma}{\sigma + 1} c_1(\mu,\nu)\|x\|_X^a$$

for any $\|x\|_X \geq r$. The mapping

$$x \mapsto J(x) - \mu S(x^+) + \nu S(x^-) + G(x)$$

maps bounded sets in X onto bounded sets in Y. Moreover, there exists $b > 0$ such that

$$\|x\|_X \geq r$$

provided

$$J(x) - \mu S(x^+) + \nu S(x^-) + G(x) = tf$$

for $t \geq b$ with $f \in Y$, $\|f\|_Y = 1$. We will prove that if $f \in Y$, $\|f\|_Y = 1$, $\|f - y\|_Y \leq \sigma$, $t \geq b$ then $tf \notin \mathcal{R}_{(\mu,\nu)}(J,S,G)$. Let us suppose the contrary, i.e. there exists $x \in X$ such that

$$J(x) - \mu S(x^+) + \nu S(x^-) + G(x) = tf .$$

Then

$$t = \|J(x) - \mu S(x^+) + \nu S(x^-) + G(x)\|_Y \geq$$

$$\geq \|J(x) - \mu S(x^+) + \nu S(x^-)\|_Y - \|G(x)\|_Y \geq \frac{c_1(\mu,\nu)}{\sigma + 1} \|x\|_X^a . \tag{10.1}$$

On the other hand, we have

$$t\sigma = 2t\sigma - t\sigma \leq$$

$$\leq t\left\| y - J\left(\frac{x}{t^{1/a}}\right) + \mu S\left(\frac{x}{t^{1/a}}\right)^+ - \nu S\left(\frac{x}{t^{1/a}}\right)^-\right\|_Y - t\|y - f\|_Y =$$

$$= \|ty - J(x) + \mu S(x^+) - \nu S(x^-)\|_Y - t\|y - f\|_Y \leq$$

$$\leq \|tf - J(x) + \mu S(x^+) - \nu S(x^-)\|_Y =$$

$$= \|G(x)\|_Y < \frac{\sigma}{\sigma + 1} c_1(\mu,\nu)\|x\|_X^a . \tag{10.2}$$

It follows from (10.1) and (10.2) that

$$t\sigma < \frac{\sigma}{\sigma + 1} c_1(\mu,\nu)\|x\|_X^a \leq t\sigma ,$$

which is a contradiction.

Ad (ix). Let $(\mu,\nu) \in A_2$, $(\alpha,\beta) \in \mathbb{R}^2$ and

$$|\alpha| + |\beta| < \frac{c_2(\mu,\nu)}{s}$$

with $c_2(\mu,\nu)$ defined above. Set

$$G(x) = \alpha S(x^+) - \beta S(x^-) .$$

It follows from (viii) that $\mathcal{R}_{(\mu,\nu)}(J,S,G) \neq Y$, i.e. $(\mu + \alpha,\ \nu + \beta) \in A_2$.

□

<u>10.2. Ordinary differential operators of second order.</u> Let V be a subspace of the Sobolev space $W^{1,p}(0,\pi)$, $p \geq 2$, which fulfils one and only one from the following conditions:

(i) $V = W^{1,p}(0,\pi)$;

(ii) $V = \{u \in W^{1,p}(0,\pi);\ u(0) = 0\}$;

(ii') $V = \{u \in W^{1,p}(0,\pi);\ u(\pi) = 0\}$;

(iii) $V = W_0^{1,p}(0,\pi)$.

In the case (i) the norm $\|\cdot\|_V$ is defined by

$$\|u\|_V^2 = \int_0^\pi [(u'(t))^2 + (u(t))^2]\, dt ;$$

in the cases (ii), (ii') and (iii) the norm $\|\cdot\|_V$ is defined by

$$\|u\|_V^2 = \int_0^\pi (u'(t))^2\, dt .$$

Set $X = Z = V$, $Y = X^*$ and $C = \{u \in X;\ u(t) \geq 0$ for all $t \in [0,\pi]\}$. Let a , b , c be real functions defined on $[0,\pi]$. Suppose that $a(t) > 0$ for all $t \in [0,\pi]$ and $a \in C^1([0,\pi])$, $b(t) \geq 0$, $c(t) > 0$ for all $t \in [0,\pi]$ and $b,\ c \in C([0,\pi])$. Let a_0 , a_1 , b_0 , b_1 are supposed to be nonnegative reals. In the cases (i), (ii) and (ii') we assume, moreover, $b(t) \neq 0$ for all $t \in [0,\pi]$ or $a_0 + a_1 > 0$. Let $\lambda_1 c(t) - b(t) > 0$ for all $t \in [0,\pi]$, where $\lambda_1 > 0$ is the least eigenvalue of the problem

$$J(u) - \lambda S(u) = 0_Y \tag{10.3}$$

(the existence of $\lambda_1 > 0$ is proved in FUČÍK, NEČAS, SOUČEK and SOUČEK [129]). In the case (i) suppose that

$$b_0 = b_1 = 0 \quad \text{and} \quad a_0 + a_1 > 0$$

or

$$\lambda_1 b_0 - a_0 \geq 0 , \quad \lambda_1 b_1 - a_1 \geq 0 ,$$

$$\lambda_1 b_0 - a_0 + \lambda_1 b_1 - a_1 > 0 .$$

Denote

$$(J(u),v)_X = \int_0^\pi [a(t)\, |u'(t)|^{p-2} u'(t)\, v'(t) + b(t)\, |u(t)|^{p-2} u(t)\, v(t)]\, dt + {} $$
$$+ a_0 |u(0)|^{p-2} u(0)\, v(0) + a_1 |u(\pi)|^{p-2} u(\pi)\, v(\pi) , \tag{10.4}$$

$$(S(u),v)_X = \int_0^\pi c(t)\, |u(t)|^{p-2} u(t)\, v(t)\, dt + {}$$
$$+ b_0 |u(0)|^{p-2} u(0)\, v(0) + b_1 |u(\pi)|^{p-2} u(\pi)\, v(\pi) , \tag{10.5}$$

$$(f^*,v)_X = \int_0^\pi f(t)\, v(t)\, dt , \tag{10.6}$$

where the symbol $(\cdot,\cdot)_X$ is used for the duality between X^* and X, $f \in L^1(0,\pi)$.

The function $u \in X$ is called *a weak solution* of the nonlinear Sturm - Liouville problem of the second order if

$$\big(J(u),v\big)_X - \mu\big(S(u^+),v\big)_X + \nu\big(S(u^-),v\big)_X = (f^*,v)_X \tag{10.7}$$

holds for each $v \in X$.

10.3. Lemma. *The operators* J *and* S *satisfy the conditions* (J1) - (J3) *and* (S1) - (S3), *respectively.*

Proof. The conditions (J1) and (J3) can be easily verified. The continuity of Němyckiĭ's operator acting from $L^p(0,\pi)$ into $L^q(0,\pi)$ ($q = \frac{p}{p-1}$) and the continuity of the imbedding from $W^{1,p}(0,\pi)$ into $C([0,\pi])$ imply that the operator J is continuous. There exists $c > 0$ such that

$$\big(J(u) - J(v),\ u - v\big)_X \geqq c\|u - v\|_X^p \tag{10.8}$$

holds for all $u, v \in X$ (because the inequality

$$\big(|x|^{p-2}x - |y|^{p-2}y\big)(x - y) \geqq \tilde{c}|x - y|^p$$

holds for any real numbers x and y with a suitable constant $\tilde{c} > 0$). From a theorem of Minty - Browder (see e.g. BROWDER [33]) we conclude the surjectivity of J^{-1}. Hence (J2) is verified. The conditions (S1) and (S2) can be verified directly, while (S3) follows from the compact imbedding of $W^{1,p}(0,\pi)$ into $C([0,\pi])$. □

10.4. Theorem. *Let* u *be a weak solution of the nonlinear Sturm - Liouville problem satisfying* (10.7). *Then* $u \in C^1([0,\pi])$. *Moreover, if* $f \in C([0,\pi])$ *then* $a(t)|u'(t)|^{p-2}u'(t) \in C^1([0,\pi])$.

Proof. Using (10.4) - (10.7) and integrating by parts we obtain

$$\int_0^\pi M(t)\, v'(t)\, dt = 0\ , \tag{10.9}$$

where

$$M(t) = a(t)|u'(t)|^{p-2}\, u'(t) - \int_0^t \Big\{ b(\tau)|u(\tau)|^{p-2}\, u(\tau) -$$

$$- \mu c(\tau)|u^+(\tau)|^{p-2} u^+(\tau) + \nu c(\tau)|u^-(\tau)|^{p-2} u^-(\tau) - f(\tau)\Big\} d\tau \; .$$

The function $M(t)$ is an element of $L^q(0,\pi)$ ($q = \frac{p}{p-1}$) and the identity (10.9) holds for each $v \in C_0^\infty(0,\pi)$ (where $C_0^\infty(0,\pi)$ is the set of all infinitely differentiable functions with compact supports in $(0,\pi)$). We have

$$\int_0^\pi \frac{dM(t)}{dt} v(t)\, dt = 0 \qquad (10.10)$$

for each $v \in C_0^\infty(0,\pi)$, where $\frac{dM(t)}{dt}$ denotes the derivative of $M(t)$ in the sense of distributions. The expression (10.10) implies $M(t) = \bar{c}$ a.e. in $[0,\pi]$, where $\bar{c}$ is a constant. Let us denote

$$F(t,z) = a(t)\; |z|^{p-2} z - \int_0^t \Big\{ b(\tau)\; |u(\tau)|^{p-2} u(\tau) -$$

$$- \mu c(\tau)|u^+(\tau)|^{p-2} u^+(\tau) + \nu c(\tau)|u^-(\tau)|^{p-2} u^-(\tau) - f(\tau)\Big\} d\tau - \bar{c} \; ,$$

$t \in [0,\pi]$, $z \in \mathbb{R}$. By the same argument as in the proof of Lemma 10.3 there exists a constant $c_1 > 0$ such that

$$\big(F(t,z_1) - F(t,z_2)\big)(z_1 - z_2) \geqq c_1 |z_1 - z_2|^p$$

for each $t \in [0,\pi]$, $z_1, z_2 \in \mathbb{R}$. This inequality implies for each $t \in [0,\pi]$ the existence of $z = z(t)$ which is uniquely determined and satisfies

$$F\big(t,z(t)\big) = 0 \; . \qquad (10.11)$$

Moreover, the function $z(t)$ is continuous on $[0,\pi]$. However, from (10.11) we obtain $z(t) = u'(t)$ a.e. in $[0,\pi]$. Hence $u \in C^1([0,\pi])$. The proof of the second part of the theorem is similar to the first. □

10.5. Remark. Let us remark that many other interesting properties can be proved for the solution of (10.7). Let us mention for instance that if a function u is a weak solution of (10.7) and $f \equiv 0$ then u and its derivative u' have only a finite number of nodes in $[0,\pi]$ and $|u(t)| + |u'(t)| > 0$ for any $t \in [0,\pi]$.

It is also proved in NEČAS [231] that the eigenvalues of (10.3) form a countable set

$$0 < \lambda_1 < \lambda_2 < \ldots < \lambda_n < \ldots$$

such that $\lim_{n\to\infty} \lambda_n = \infty$. The corresponding eigenfunctions form an isolated set in X . To any eigenvalue λ_n , $n = 1,2,\dots$, there corresponds a finite number of isolated eigenfunctions u such that $\|u\|_X = 1$.

Using the assertions in Subsection 10.1 and Theorem 10.4 it is possible to prove the following theorem.

10.6. Theorem *(homogeneous problem). Let* $(\mu,\nu) = (\lambda + \alpha, \lambda + \beta)$ *, where* $|\alpha| + |\beta| < \frac{c_1(\lambda,\lambda)}{s}$ *(for the definition of* $c_1(\lambda,\lambda)$ *and* s *see Subsection* 10.1 (i) *). Then the problem* (10.7) *has at least one weak solution* $u \in X$ *for an arbitrary right hand side* $f \in L^1(0,\pi)$ *. If* $f \in C([0,\pi])$ *then the problem* (10.7) *has at least one classical solution in the sense of Theorem* 10.4.

Let a function $g : [0,\pi] \times \mathbf{R} \to \mathbf{R}$ satisfy the Carathéodory conditions and let there exist a function $m(t) \in L^q(0,\pi)$, with an arbitrary $q > 1$, such that

$$|g(t,s)| \leq m(t)\left(1 + |s|^{p-1}\right) \tag{10.12}$$

holds for each $s \in \mathbf{R}$ and for a.a. $t \in (0,\pi)$. Let us define an operator $G : X \to X^*$ by

$$\left(G(u),v\right)_X = \int_0^\pi g\left(t,u(t)\right)\, v(t)\, dt\ , \quad u,\ v \in X\ .$$

Similarly as above we can prove the following assertion.

10.7. Theorem *(perturbed homogeneous case). Let* $(\mu,\nu) \in A_1$ *and let* $|m(t)| \leq c_1(\mu,\nu)$ *for a.a.* $t \in [0,\pi]$ *. Then the problem*

$$\left(J(u),v\right)_X - \mu\left(S(u^+),v\right)_X + \nu\left(S(u^-),v\right)_X + \left(G(u),v\right)_X = (f^*,v)_X \tag{10.13}$$

has at least one weak solution $u \in X$ *for an arbitrary right hand side* $f \in L^1(0,\pi)$ *. If we suppose* $g(t,s) \in C([0,\pi] \times \mathbf{R})$ *and* $f \in C([0,\pi])$ *, the problem* (10.13) *has at least one classical solution in the sense of Theorem* 10.4.

10.8. Remark. The geometrical interpretation of Theorem 10.6 is sketched in Fig. 5.

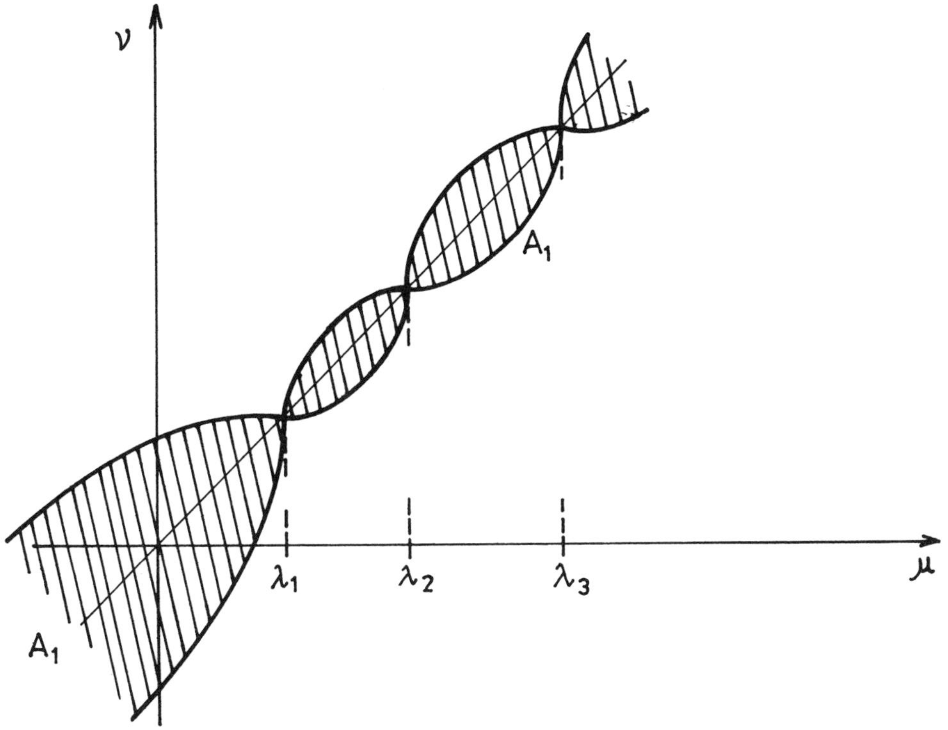

Fig. 5

<u>10.9. Ordinary differential operators of fourth order.</u> Let $X = W_0^{2,p}(0,\pi)$, $Y = X^*$, $Z = C([0,\pi])$, $C = \{z \in Z;\ z(t) \geqq 0$ for all $t \in [0,\pi]\}$. Then (Z1), (Z2), (Z3) are fulfilled. Let us suppose $a \in C^1([0,\pi])$, $b, c \in C([0,\pi])$, $a(t) > 0$, $b(t) \geqq 0$, $c(t) > 0$ for all $t \in [0,\pi]$. Let us denote

$$\left(J(u),v\right)_X = \int_0^\pi \left[a(t)\,|u''(t)|^{p-2}\, u''(t)\, v''(t) + b(t)\,|u(t)|^{p-2}\, u(t)\, v(t)\right] dt\,, \tag{10.14}$$

$$\left(S(u),v\right)_X = \int_0^\pi c(t)\,|u(t)|^{p-2}\, u(t)\, v(t)\, dt\,. \tag{10.15}$$

Moreover, let us suppose that

$$\lambda_1 c(t) - b(t) > 0$$

for all $t \in [0,\pi]$, where $\lambda_1 > 0$ is the least eigenvalue of the problem (10.3) (where J and S are defined by (10.14), (10.15)).

Then the assertion of Lemma 10.3 remains true. The equation (10.13) with J and S defined by (10.14), (10.15) is the weak formulation of the strongly nonlinear Dirichlet BVP

$$\left(a(t)|u''(t)|^{p-2} u''(t)\right)'' + b(t)|u(t)|^{p-2} u(t) - \mu c(t)|u^+(t)|^{p-2} u^+(t) + \\ + \nu c(t)|u^-(t)|^{p-2} u^-(t) + g\left(t,u(t)\right) = f(t) , \quad t \in [0,\pi] , \tag{10.16}$$

$$u(0) = u'(0) = u(\pi) = u'(\pi) = 0 . \tag{10.17}$$

Applying the abstract results of Subsection 10.1 we obtain analogous *existence theorems* as in Subsections 10.6 and 10.7 concerning *the weak solvability* of (10.16), (10.17). Also the eigenvalues and the corresponding eigenfunctions of (10.3) with J and S defined by (10.14), (10.15) have the properties formulated in Remark 10.5 (see KRATOCHVÍL and NEČAS [180]).

<u>10.10. Partial differential equations.</u> Let $\Omega \subset \mathbf{R}^N$ be a bounded domain with a lipschitzian boundary $\partial\Omega$. Set $X = W_0^{1,p}(\Omega)$, $Y = X^*$, $Z = L^p(\Omega)$, $C = \{f \in L^p(\Omega);\ f(x) \geqq 0 \text{ for a.a. } x \in \Omega\}$. Let us denote

$$p^* = \frac{pN}{N - p}$$

for $p < N$ and $p^* = +\infty$ for $p = N$. Let $\alpha < p^*$ be arbitrary if $p \leqq N$. Set $\alpha' = \frac{\alpha}{\alpha - 1}$ for $p \leqq N$, $\alpha' = 1$ for $p > N$. We will suppose that a Carathéodory function $g : \Omega \times \mathbf{R} \to \mathbf{R}$ satisfies

$$|g(x,s)| \leqq m(x) + c|s|^{p-1} \tag{10.18}$$

with $m(x) \in L^{\alpha'}(\Omega)$ and a constant $c > 0$. Let us define operators $J, S, G : X \to X^*$ and an element $f^* \in X^*$ by

$$\left(J(u),v\right)_X = \int_\Omega |\nabla u(x)|^{p-2} \nabla u(x) \nabla v(x)\, dx ,$$

$$\left(S(u),v\right)_X = \int_\Omega |u(x)|^{p-2} u(x) v(x)\, dx ,$$

$$\left(G(u),v\right)_X = \int_\Omega g\left(x,u(x)\right) v(x)\, dx ,$$

$$(f^*,v)_X = \int_\Omega f(x)\, v(x)\, dx$$

for $u, v \in X$ and $f \in L^{\alpha'}(\Omega)$. The operator equation (10.13) is the *weak formulation* of the Dirichlet BVP

$$- \operatorname{div} \left(|\nabla u(x)|^{p-2} \nabla u(x)\right) - \mu |u^+(x)|^{p-2} u^+(x) + \nu |u^-(x)|^{p-2} u^-(x) + \\ + g\left(x,u(x)\right) = f(x) , \quad x \in \Omega , \tag{10.19}$$

$$u = 0 \quad \text{on} \quad \partial\Omega . \tag{10.20}$$

Let us suppose $(\mu,\nu) \in A_1$ and

$$\limsup_{s \to \pm\infty} \frac{|g(x,s)|}{|s|^{p-1}} < c_1(\mu,\nu)$$

for a.a. $x \in \Omega$. Then it follows from the assertion 10.1 (vii) that BVP (10.19), (10.20) has at least one weak solution for arbitrary $f \in L^{\alpha'}(\Omega)$.

However, the description of the set A_{-1} and hence also the description of A_0, A_1, A_2 and A_3 is a very difficult problem in the case of partial differential operators. Even the complete description of the set of all eigenvalues of the problem (10.3) with J and S defined in this subsection, i.e. the desription of the set of all eigenvalues of

$$- \operatorname{div} \left(|\nabla u|^{p-2} \nabla u\right) - \lambda |u|^{p-2} u = 0 \quad \text{in} \quad \Omega ,$$

$$u = 0 \quad \text{on} \quad \partial\Omega$$

is an open problem. It is well known that the Ljusternik - Schnirelmann theory ensures the existence of an infinite sequence of positive eigenvalues of (10.3) but in general this theory does not provide all eigenvalues. The set of all eigenvalues can be more complicated and we cannot speak about the i-th eigenvalue of the problem (10.3). Nevertheless, there exists the least eigenvalue $\lambda_1 > 0$ (see e.g. ANANE [12], BARLES [25], LINDQVIST [202], ÔTANI and TESHIMA [253]). Hence in the case of partial differential operators we can formulate relatively general existence results only near the first eigenvalue λ_1, using its variational characterization

$$\lambda_1 = \min_{\substack{u \in X \\ u \neq 0}} \frac{\left(J(u),u\right)_X}{\left(S(u),u\right)_X} \tag{10.21}$$

(see Section 12 for details).

11. FUČÍK'S SPECTRUM OF STRONGLY NONLINEAR HOMOGENEOUS PROBLEMS

11.1. We will deal with the solvability of the homogeneous Dirichlet BVP for the Sturm - Liouville equation of the second order with constant coefficients. First we will be concerned with the *initial value problem* (IVP)

$$- \left(|u'(t)|^{p-2} u'(t)\right)' - \mu |u^+(t)|^{p-2} u^+(t) + \\ + \nu |u^-(t)|^{p-2} u^-(t) = f(t) , \tag{11.1}$$

$$u(t_0) = \alpha_1 , \quad u'(t_0) = \alpha_2 , \quad t \in \mathbb{R} , \tag{11.2}$$

where α_1 , α_2 , t_0 are real numbers, $f \in L^1_{loc}(\mathbb{R})$.

Let u be a real function of real variable, suppose u' to be continuous and $|u'|^{p-2} u'$ absolutely continuous on each compact interval in $\mathbb{R}$. If the function u fulfils the initial conditions (11.2) and the equation (11.1) holds a.e. in $\mathbb{R}$ then u is called *a solution of IVP* (11.1), (11.2).

11.2. Remarks. (i) If $f \in C(I)$ for an interval $I \subset \mathbb{R}$ then $|u'|^{p-2} u' \in C^1(I)$ and the equation (11.1) holds for each $t \in I$ (cf. Theorem 10.4).

(ii) Suppose $\mu > 0$ and $\nu > 0$. It is possible to prove that the condition $f \in L^1_{loc}(\mathbb{R})$ guarantees the existence of *a unique solution* of IVP (11.1), (11.2).

(iii) Elementary properties of the equation

$$- \left(|u'|^{p-2} u'\right)' - \mu |u^+|^{p-2} u^+ + \nu |u^-|^{p-2} u^- = k , \tag{11.3}$$

where k is a constant, yields the following assertions.

If the function u satisfies (11.3) and the initial conditions $u(0) = 0$, $u'(0) = \alpha_2 > 0$ then $t_0 = \inf \{t > 0;\ u'(t) = 0\}$ is a finite number, and

$$u^+(t_0 + t) = u^+(t_0 - t)$$

for all $t \in [0,t_0]$. If $\alpha_2 < 0$, it is possible to prove that t_0 is finite and

$$u^-(t_0 + t) = u^-(t_0 - t)$$

holds for each $t \in [0,t_0]$.

If the function u is a solution of (11.3) with $k = 0$ and $u(0) = 0$, $u'(0) = \alpha_2 \neq 0$ then u is a *periodic function* with the period

$$\left[\left(\frac{\lambda_1}{\mu}\right)^{\frac{1}{p}} + \left(\frac{\lambda_1}{\nu}\right)^{\frac{1}{p}} \right] \pi ,$$

where λ_1 is the least eigenvalue of BVP

$$-\left(|u'|^{p-2}\, u'\right)' - \lambda |u|^{p-2}\, u = 0 \quad \text{in} \quad [0,\pi] , \tag{11.4}$$

$$u(0) = u(\pi) = 0 . \tag{11.5}$$

11.3. Theorem. *All eigenvalues* λ_k, $k = 2,3,\ldots,$ *of BVP* (11.4), (11.5) *are of the form* $\lambda_k = k^p \lambda_1$, *where* $\lambda_1 > 0$ *is the first eigenvalue. To every eigenvalue* λ_k, $k = 1,2,\ldots,$ *there corresponds exactly one eigenfunction* v_k *such that* $v_k'(0) = 1$. *The eigenfunction* v_k *has exactly* $k - 1$ *nodes in* $(0,\pi)$.

Proof. Let $\lambda \in \mathbb{R}$ be an eigenvalue of BVP (11.4), (11.5) and let v be the corresponding eigenfunction. Assume $v(t) > 0$ in a right reduced neighbourhood of zero. For $\lambda < 0$ we obtain directly from the equation (11.4) that $\{t \in (0,\pi];\ v(t) = 0\} = \emptyset$. For $\lambda = 0$ we obtain $v \equiv 0$ in $[0,\pi]$. Hence $\lambda > 0$ for each eigenvalue of the problem (11.4), (11.5). Denote $\lambda_1 = \inf\{\lambda > 0;\ \lambda$ is an eigenvalue of BVP (11.4), (11.5)$\}$. Let us assume for a moment that $\lambda_1 > 0$. We prove that λ_1 is the eigenvalue of BVP (11.4), (11.5). Taking into account the definition of λ_1 we conclude that there exists a sequence of eigenvalues $\{\tau_m\}_{m=1}^{\infty}$, a sequence of the corresponding eigenfunctions $\{w_m\}_{m=1}^{\infty}$ and a sequence of real numbers $\{t_m\}_{m=1}^{\infty}$ such that

$$\lim_{m \to \infty} \tau_m = \lambda_1 \quad \text{and} \quad \|t_m w_m\|_X = 1 , \quad m = 1,2,\ldots .$$

It follows from the reflexivity of X that there is a subsequence $\{t_{m_k} w_{m_k}\}_{k=1}^{\infty}$ and $w_0 \in X$ such that $t_{m_k} w_{m_k} \rightharpoonup w_0$ in X. The compactness of S yields $\tau_{m_k} S(w_{m_k}) \to \lambda_1 S(w_0)$ in X^*. Thus we have

$$J(t_{m_k} w_{m_k}) \to \lambda_1 S(w_0) \quad \text{in} \quad X^* .$$

In virtue of the continuity of the operator J^{-1}, we have $t_{m_k} w_{m_k} \to w_0$ in

X and hence

$$J(w_0) - \lambda_1 S(w_0) = 0 .$$

We have proved that λ_1 is an eigenvalue. Going back to the beginning of this proof we find that necessarily $\lambda_1 > 0$. Let u_1 be the eigenfunction corresponding to λ_1 . Suppose there exists $t \in (0,\pi)$ such that $u(t) = 0$. Choose $t_0 \in (0,\pi)$ such that $t_0 = \min \{t \in (0,\pi);\ u(t) = 0\}$ (this makes sense due to Remark 10.5). Define

$$\tilde{u}(t) = u\left(\frac{t_0}{\pi} t\right) , \quad t \in [0,\pi] .$$

Then

$$- \left(|\tilde{u}'|^{p-2} \tilde{u}'\right)' - \left(\frac{t_0}{\pi}\right)^p \lambda_1 \left(|\tilde{u}|^{p-2} \tilde{u}\right) = 0 ,$$
$$\tilde{u}(0) = \tilde{u}(\pi) = 0 ,$$

which contradicts the fact that λ_1 is the least eigenvalue. We have proved that no eigenfunction corresponding to λ_1 changes its sign. It follows directly from the equation (11.4) that to each eigenvalue λ there corresponds one and only one eigenfunction v . Denote $\lambda_k = k^p \lambda_1$, $k \geqq 2$, k an integer. Define a function v_k in the following way:

$$v_k : t \longmapsto \begin{cases} \frac{1}{k} u_1(kt) , & t \in \left[2\ell \frac{\pi}{k} , (2\ell + 1) \frac{\pi}{k}\right) , \\ -\frac{1}{k} u_1(kt) , & t \in [0,\pi] \setminus \left[2\ell \frac{\pi}{k} , (2\ell + 1) \frac{\pi}{k}\right) \end{cases}$$

where $\ell = 1,2,\dots,\frac{1}{2} k$ if k is even, $\ell = 1,2,\dots,\left[\frac{1}{2} k\right] + 1$ if k is an odd number (the symbol $[t]$ denotes the integer part of a real number t). In this way we obtain eigenfunctions v_k which correspond to the eigenvalues λ_k for all $k \geqq 2$. On the other hand, if v is an eigenfunction corresponding to λ_k for some $k \geqq 2$ then we have $v = v_k$ in $[0,\pi]$ (see Remarks 11.2). Finally, if $\lambda \neq \lambda_1$ is an eigenvalue of BVP (11.4), (11.5) and v is the corresponding eigenfunction then there exists $t \in (0,\pi)$ such that $v(t) = 0$. Put $t_0 = \inf \{t \in (0,\pi];\ v(t) = 0\}$. According to 11.2 (ii) we have

$$v(t) = \frac{t_0}{\pi} u\left(\frac{\pi}{t_0} t\right) , \quad t \in [0,t_0] .$$

Similarly, if $t_1 = \inf \{t \in (t_0,\pi];\ v(t) = 0\}$ then

$$v(t) = -\frac{t_1 - t}{\pi}\, u\left(\frac{\pi}{t_1 - t_0}(t - t_0)\right), \quad t \in [t_0, t_1] .$$

This fact implies the existence of $k \geqq 2$ such that $\lambda = k^p \lambda_1 = \lambda_k$. □

11.4. Remark. Let us mention that all *nodes* of the eigenfunctions of BVP (11.4), (11.5) are *simple*, i.e. $u'(t_0) \neq 0$ whenever $u(t_0) = 0$ and u is an eigenfunction of (11.4), (11.5).

In the next assertion we give an analytic description of *Fučík's spectrum of the homogeneous BVP*

$$-\left(|u'|^{p-2} u'\right)' - \mu |u^+|^{p-2} u^+ + \nu |u^-|^{p-2} u^- = 0 , \tag{11.6}$$

$$u(0) = u(\pi) = 0 . \tag{11.7}$$

11.5. Theorem. *The Dirichlet BVP* (11.6), (11.7) *has a nontrivial weak solution if and only if* $(\mu,\nu) \in A_{-1}$, *where* $A_{-1} = \bigcup_{n=1}^{\infty} C_n$,

$$C_1 = \{(\mu,\nu) \in \mathbf{R}^2;\ (\mu - \lambda_1)(\nu - \lambda_1) = 0\} ,$$

$$C_{2k} = \left\{(\mu,\nu) \in \mathbf{R}^2;\ \frac{(\lambda_1)^{1/p}}{(\mu)^{1/p}} + \frac{(\lambda_1)^{1/p}}{(\nu)^{1/p}} = \frac{1}{k}\right\},$$

$$C_{2k+1} = \left\{(\mu,\nu) \in \mathbf{R}^2;\ \frac{(\lambda_1)^{1/p}}{(\mu)^{1/p}} + \frac{(\lambda_1)^{1/p}}{(\nu)^{1/p}} = \frac{1}{k} - \frac{(\lambda_1)^{1/p}}{k(\mu)^{1/p}}\right\} \cup$$

$$\cup \left\{(\mu,\nu) \in \mathbf{R}^2;\ \frac{(\lambda_1)^{1/p}}{(\mu)^{1/p}} + \frac{(\lambda_1)^{1/p}}{(\nu)^{1/p}} = \frac{1}{k} - \frac{(\lambda_1)^{1/p}}{k(\nu)^{1/p}}\right\} ,$$

$k = 1,2,\ldots$.

Proof. Let u be a nontrivial weak solution of BVP (11.6), (11.7). Then $u \in C^1([0,\pi])$ according to Theorem 10.4, and according to Remark 10.5 the function u has only a finite number of nodes in $[0,\pi]$. If the function u has no node in $(0,\pi)$ then due to Remark 11.2 (iii) we have either $\mu = \lambda_1$ (ν arbitrary) or $\nu = \lambda_1$ (μ arbitrary). In the opposite case it is possible to divide the interval $[0,\pi]$ into a finite number of subintervals so that on each of them either $u(t) \geqq 0$ or $u(t) \leqq 0$ holds. In accordance with Remark 11.2 (iii) we have

$$u(t) = K_1 u_1\left(\left(\frac{\mu}{\lambda_1}\right)^{1/p}(t-\alpha)\right), \quad t \in \left[\alpha, \alpha + \left(\frac{\lambda_1}{\mu}\right)^{1/p}\pi\right]$$

if $u(t) > 0$ on $\left(\alpha, \alpha + \left(\frac{\lambda_1}{\mu}\right)^{1/p}\pi\right)$;

$$u(t) = -K_2 u_1\left(\left(\frac{\nu}{\lambda_1}\right)^{1/p}(t-\beta)\right), \quad t \in \left[\beta, \beta + \left(\frac{\lambda_1}{\nu}\right)^{1/p}\pi\right]$$

if $u(t) < 0$ on $\left(\beta, \beta + \left(\frac{\lambda_1}{\nu}\right)^{1/p}\pi\right)$, where $K_1 > 0$, $K_2 > 0$ are suitable constants such that $u \in C^1([0,\pi])$. If $u \in C^1([0,\pi])$, $u(0) = u(\pi) = 0$, then necessarily either $(\mu,\nu) \in C_{2k}$ or $(\mu,\nu) \in C_{2k+1}$ for some $k \in \mathbb{N}$.

On the other hand, if $(\mu,\nu) \in A_{-1}$ then in the same way as in the first part of the proof it is possible to construct a nontrivial weak solution of BVP (11.6), (11.7) (see Fig. 6). □

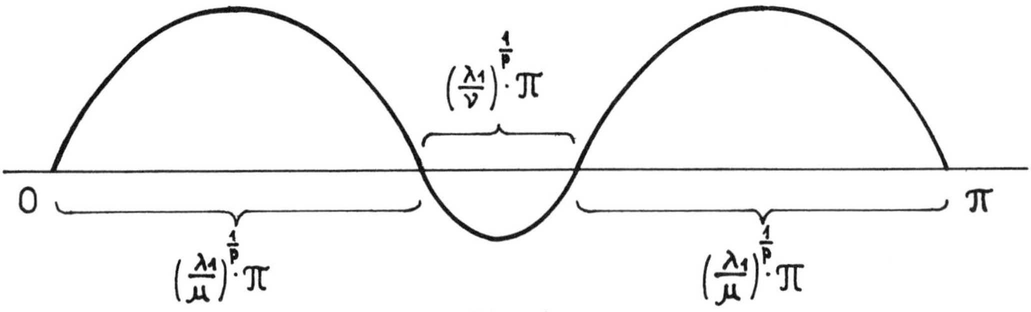

Fig. 6

11.6. Theorem. *Let the parameters* μ *and* ν *fulfil one of the conditions*

(i) $\mu < \lambda_1$, $\nu < \lambda_1$;

(ii) $\mu > \lambda_1$, $\nu > \lambda_1$ *and*

$$\frac{(\lambda_1)^{1/p}}{(\mu)^{1/p}} + \frac{(\lambda_1)^{1/p}}{(\nu)^{1/p}} > 1 - \frac{(\lambda_1)^{1/p}}{(\mu)^{1/p}} , \quad \frac{(\lambda_1)^{1/p}}{(\mu)^{1/p}} + \frac{(\lambda_1)^{1/p}}{(\nu)^{1/p}} > 1 - \frac{(\lambda_1)^{1/p}}{(\nu)^{1/p}} ;$$

$$\frac{1}{k+1} - \frac{(\lambda_1)^{1/p}}{(k+1)(\mu)^{1/p}} < \frac{(\lambda_1)^{1/p}}{(\mu)^{1/P}} + \frac{(\lambda_1)^{1/p}}{(\nu)^{1/p}} < \frac{1}{k} - \frac{(\lambda_1)^{1/p}}{k(\mu)^{1/p}} ,$$

$$\frac{1}{k+1} - \frac{(\lambda_1)^{1/p}}{(k+1)(\nu)^{1/p}} < \frac{(\lambda_1)^{1/p}}{(\mu)^{1/p}} + \frac{(\lambda_1)^{1/p}}{(\nu)^{1/p}} < \frac{1}{k} - \frac{(\lambda_1)^{1/p}}{k(\nu)^{1/p}} ;$$

$k \in \mathbb{N}$. *Then the Dirichlet BVP*

$$- \left(|u'|^{p-2} u'\right)' - \mu|u^+|^{p-2} u^+ + \nu|u^-|^{p-2} u^- = f , \qquad (11.8)$$

$$u(0) = u(\pi) = 0 \qquad (11.9)$$

has at least one weak solution for an arbitrary right hand side $f \in L^1(0,\pi)$.

Proof. Let us suppose that μ and ν satisfy the hypotheses of Theorem 11.6. Then (μ,ν) belongs to the component of $\mathbb{R}^2 \setminus A_{-1}$ containing the point (λ,λ) , where λ is not an eigenvalue of BVP (11.4), (11.5). Hence $(\mu,\nu) \in A_1$ and the assertion follows from 10.1 (iii) (see Subsection 10.1 for A_{-1} and A_1). □

11.7. Remark. In this section we intend to give the classification of parameters $(\mu,\nu) \in \mathbb{R}^2$ shown in Fig. 7. The set A_{-1} is described by Theorem 11.5, the set A_1 is described by Theorem 11.6 (see Fig. 7). It remains to prove that the "white parts" in Fig. 7 belong to A_2 . In order to prove this result we use the properties of the solution of IVP.

11.8. Solutions of IVP. Denote by $\Phi^{\mu,\nu}_{+1}$ and $\Phi^{\mu,\nu}_{-1}$ (if there is no danger of misunderstanding, we write Φ_{+1} and Φ_{-1} only) the solutions of IVP

$$- \left(|u'|^{p-2} u'\right)' - \mu|u^+|^{p-2} u^+ + \nu|u^-|^{p-2} u^- = 0 , \qquad (11.10)$$

$$u(0) = 0 , \quad u'(0) = 1 \quad \text{and} \quad u(0) = 0 , \quad u'(0) = -1 ,$$

respectively. It follows from the elementary properties of the solution of (11.10) that

$$\{(\mu,\nu) \in \mathbb{R}^2;\ \mu \leqq 0,\ \nu > \lambda_1\} \cup \{(\mu,\nu) \in \mathbb{R}^2;\ \mu > \lambda_1,\ \nu \leqq 0\} \subset A_2 .$$

11.9. Lemma. *Let the parameters* μ *and* ν *fulfil one of the conditions*

(i) $\mu > \lambda_1$, $\nu < \lambda_1$;

(ii) $\mu < \lambda_1$, $\nu > \lambda_1$;

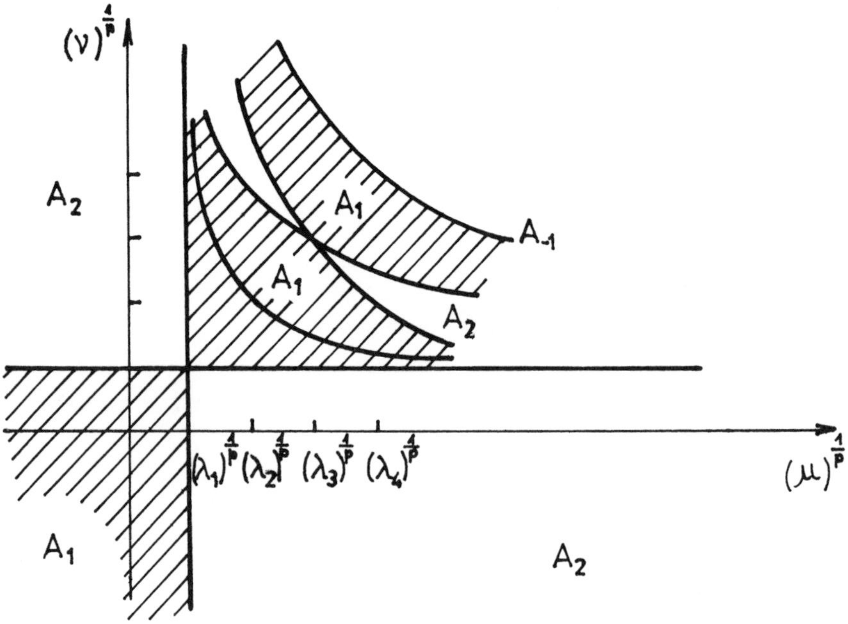

Fig. 7

(iii) $$\frac{(\lambda_1)^{1/p}}{(\mu)^{1/p}} + \frac{(\lambda_1)^{1/p}}{(\nu)^{1/p}} > \frac{1}{k} - \frac{(\lambda_1)^{1/p}}{k(\mu)^{1/p}} ,$$

$$\frac{(\lambda_1)^{1/p}}{(\mu)^{1/p}} + \frac{(\lambda_1)^{1/p}}{(\nu)^{1/p}} < \frac{1}{k} - \frac{(\lambda_1)^{1/p}}{k(\nu)^{1/p}} ;$$

(iv) $$\frac{(\lambda_1)^{1/p}}{(\mu)^{1/p}} + \frac{(\lambda_1)^{1/p}}{(\nu)^{1/p}} < \frac{1}{k} - \frac{(\lambda_1)^{1/p}}{k(\mu)^{1/p}} ,$$

$$\frac{(\lambda_1)^{1/p}}{(\mu)^{1/p}} + \frac{(\lambda_1)^{1/p}}{(\nu)^{1/p}} > \frac{1}{k} - \frac{(\lambda_1)^{1/p}}{k(\nu)^{1/p}} ,$$

$k \in \mathbb{N}$. *Then*

$$\Phi_{+1}(\pi)\ \Phi_{-1}(\pi) > 0 . \tag{11.11}$$

Proof. Similarly as in the proof of Theorem 11.5 we can compare the nodes of $\Phi_{+1}(t)$ and $\Phi_{-1}(t)$ in $(0,\pi]$. The conditions (i) - (iv) yield (11.11) (see Fig. 8). □

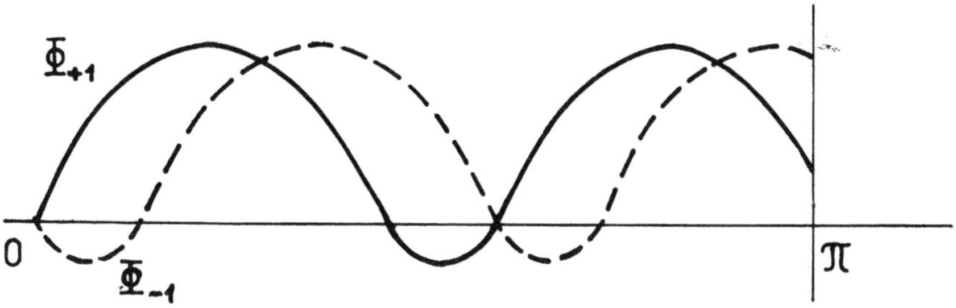

Fig. 8

11.10. Lemma. *Let us suppose that there exists* $t_0 \in (0,\pi)$ *such that*

$$\Phi_{\pm 1}(t) > 0 , \quad \Phi'_{\pm 1}(t) < 0 \quad \textit{for all} \quad t \in [t_0,\pi] .$$

Then there exists a right hand side $f \in L^1(0,\pi)$ *such that BVP* (11.8), (11.9) *has no weak solution.*

Proof. Let $f : \mathbb{R} \to \mathbb{R}$ be such a function that $f \in L^1(\mathbb{R})$, $f(t) = 0$ for all $t \in (-\infty,t_0] \cup (\pi,+\infty)$ and $f(t) < 0$ for $t \in (t_0,\pi]$. We have $f \in L^1(0,\pi)$. Let Φ_α be the weak solution of BVP (11.8), (11.9) with the right hand side f and suppose $\Phi_\alpha(0) = 0$, $\Phi'_\alpha(0) = \alpha$. For $\alpha > 0$ we have by Remark 11.2 (ii)

$$\Phi_\alpha(t) = \alpha\Phi_{+1}(t) , \quad t \in [0,t_0] .$$

Put $t_1 = \inf \{t \in (t_0,\pi];\ \Phi_\alpha(t) = 0\}$. The interval (t_0,t_1) contains a point τ_1 such that

$$\left(\frac{\Phi_\alpha}{\Phi_{+1}}\right)'(\tau_1) < 0 . \tag{11.12}$$

In the opposite case

$$\frac{\Phi_\alpha(\tau)}{\Phi_{+1}(\tau)} \geqq \frac{\Phi_\alpha(t_0)}{\Phi_{+1}(t_0)} = \alpha > 0 , \quad \tau \in (t_0,t_1)$$

which is impossible. From (11.12) we obtain

$$(\Phi'_\alpha \, \Phi_{+1} - \Phi_\alpha \, \Phi'_{+1})(\tau_1) < 0 \, . \tag{11.13}$$

Hence $F(\tau_1) < 0$, where

$$F : \tau \mapsto \left(|\Phi'_\alpha|^{p-2} \, \Phi'_\alpha (\Phi_{+1})^{p-1} - (\Phi_\alpha)^{p-1} \, |\Phi'_{+1}|^{p-2} \, \Phi'_{+1}\right)(\tau) \, ,$$

because the function $s \mapsto |s|^{p-2} \, s$ is increasing on $\mathbf{R}^1$. We will prove the existence of a set $\mathcal{A} \subset (t_0, \tau_1)$ with meas $\mathcal{A} > 0$ such that the following conditions are fulfilled:

(i) $\Phi'_\alpha(t) < 0$; (ii) $F(t) < 0$; (iii) $F'(t) < 0$ for all $t \in \mathcal{A}$.
Indeed, if $\Phi'_\alpha(t) < 0$ for all $t \in (t_0, \tau_1)$ then (ii) and (iii) are fulfilled because $F(t_0) = 0$, $F(\tau_1) < 0$ and F is absolutely continuous on (t_0, τ_1). In the opposite case denote $\tau_2 = \sup \{\tau < \tau_1 ; \, \Phi'_\alpha(\tau) = 0\}$. Then $\tau_2 < \tau_1$ (see Remark 10.5) and by virtue of (11.13) we have $\Phi'_\alpha(\tau_1) < 0$. We conclude $\Phi'_\alpha(t) < 0$, $t \in (\tau_2, \tau_1)$. Since $F(\tau_2) > 0$, $F(\tau_1) < 0$, the conditions (i) - (iii) are fulfilled. Hence we have

$$F'(t) = F_1(t) + F_2(t) < 0 \quad \text{for all} \quad t \in \mathcal{A} \, , \tag{11.14}$$

where

$$F_1(t) = \left[\left(|\Phi'_\alpha|^{p-2} \, \Phi'_\alpha\right)' (\Phi_{+1})^{p-1} - (\Phi_\alpha)^{p-1}\left(|\Phi'_{+1}|^{p-2} \, \Phi'_{+1}\right)'\right](t) \, ,$$

$$F_2(t) = \left[\left(|\Phi'_\alpha|^{p-2} \, \Phi'_\alpha\right)(\Phi_{+1}^{p-1})' - (\Phi_\alpha^{p-1})'\left(|\Phi'_{+1}|^{p-2} \, \Phi'_{+1}\right)\right](t) =$$

$$= (p - 1)\Phi'_\alpha \, \Phi'_{+1}\left[|\Phi'_\alpha|^{p-2} \, \Phi_{+1}^{p-2} - \Phi_\alpha^{p-2}|\Phi'_{+1}|^{p-2}\right](t) \, .$$

The condition (ii) implies

$$\left(|\Phi'_\alpha|^{p-2} \, \Phi_{+1}^{p-2} - \Phi_\alpha^{p-2} \, |\Phi'_{+1}|^{p-2}\right)(t) > 0$$

for all $t \in \mathcal{A}$. So we have

$$F_2(t) > 0 \, , \quad t \in \mathcal{A} \, . \tag{11.15}$$

From the relations (11.14), (11.15) we conclude

$$F_1(t) < 0 \, , \quad t \in \mathcal{A} \, . \tag{11.16}$$

On the other hand, the equation (11.10) implies

$$F_1(t) = - f(t)\left[\Phi_{+1}(t)\right]^{p-1} > 0 \, , \quad t \in \tilde{\mathcal{A}} \, ,$$

where $\tilde{\mathcal{A}} \subset \mathcal{A}$, meas $\tilde{\mathcal{A}} > 0$. This fact contradicts (11.16).

For $\alpha = 0$ we have $\Phi_0(t) = 0$ for all $t \in [0,t_0]$. Denoting

$$t_1 = \inf \{t \in (t_0,\pi);\ \Phi_0(t) = 0\} ,$$

we obtain the existence of $z_0 \in (t_0,t_1)$ such that $\Phi_0'(z_0) = 0$. Suppose that z_0 is chosen as follows:

$$z_0 = \sup \{z \in (t_0,t_1);\ \Phi_0'(z) = 0\} .$$

There exists a point $\tau_1 \in (z_0,t_1)$ such that the conditions (i) - (iii) are fulfilled if we write Φ_0 instead of Φ_α , $\alpha > 0$. The rest of the proof is similar to that for $\alpha > 0$.

For $\alpha < 0$ we have

$$\Phi_\alpha(t) = |\alpha|\ \Phi_{-1}(t) , \quad t \in [0,t_0]$$

and the proof is quite anlogous to that for $\alpha > 0$. It means that for the right hand side f defined above there exists no weak solution of BVP (11.8), (11.9). □

<u>11.11. Remark.</u> Modifying the proof it is possible to replace the assumptions of Lemma 11.10 by

$$\Phi_{\pm 1}(t) > 0 , \quad \Phi_{+1}'(t) < 0 , \quad \Phi_{-1}'(t) \geqq 0 ,$$

$$\Phi_{\pm 1}(t) > 0 , \quad \Phi_{+1}'(t) \geqq 0 , \quad \Phi_{-1}'(t) < 0 ,$$

$$\Phi_{\pm 1}(t) > 0 , \quad \Phi_{+1}'(t) \geqq 0 , \quad \Phi_{-1}'(t) \geqq 0 ,$$

and analogously for $\Phi_{\pm 1}(t) < 0$, $t \in [t_0,\pi]$. Hence the assertion of Lemma 11.10 remains true if Φ_{+1} and Φ_{-1} satisfy (11.11).

The proof of the following theorem follows directly from Lemma 11.9 and Remark 11.11.

<u>11.12. Theorem.</u> *Let the parameters* μ *and* ν *fulfil one of the conditions* (i) - (iv) *from Lemma* 11.9. *Then* $(\mu,\nu) \in A_2$.

12.1. Ordinary differential equations of second order. We will consider BVP

$$-\left(|u'(t)|^{p-2}\,u'(t)\right)' = g\left(t,u(t)\right) + f(t)\ , \quad t \in [0,\pi]\ , \tag{12.1}$$

$$u(0) = u(\pi) = 0\ . \tag{12.2}$$

We will prove that if the values

$$\liminf_{s \to \pm\infty} \frac{g(t,s)}{|s|^{p-2}s}\ , \quad \limsup_{s \to \pm\infty} \frac{g(t,s)}{|s|^{p-2}s}$$

lie (roughly speaking) for a.a. $t \in [0,\pi]$ in the set A_1 (see Subsection 11.7) then BVP (12.1), (12.2) is solvable for any $f \in L^1(0,\pi)$. This result represents (in a special case of differential operators) a generalization of *the abstract Fredholm alternative* for nonlinear operators (see NEČAS [230], POCHOŽAJEV [259]).

12.2. Assumptions. Let $p \geqq 2$ be a real number and let the Carathéodory function g satisfy the *growth condition* (10.12). Let us denote by λ_n, $n = 1,2,\ldots$, the eigenvalues of BVP (11.4), (11.5).

By *a solution* of BVP (12.1), (12.2) we will always mean a function $u \in C^1([0,\pi])$ satisfying boundary conditions (12.2) and such that $|u'|^{p-2}u'$ is absolutely continuous on $[0,\pi]$ and the equation (12.1) holds a.e. in $(0,\pi)$.

12.3. Theorem. *Let* g *satisfy* (10.12) *and one of the following estimates:*

$$\limsup_{s \to \pm\infty} \frac{g(t,s)}{|s|^{p-2}s} \leqq \lambda_1 - \delta\ , \tag{12.3}$$

$$\lambda_i + \delta \leqq \liminf_{s \to \pm\infty} \frac{g(t,s)}{|s|^{p-2}s} \leqq \limsup_{s \to \pm\infty} \frac{g(t,s)}{|s|^{p-2}s} \leqq \lambda_{i+1} - \delta \tag{12.4$_i$}$$

for a.a. $t \in (0,\pi)$ *with some* $\delta > 0$ *and* $i \geqq 1$. *Then BVP* (12.1), (12.2) *has for each* $f \in L^1(0,\pi)$ *at least one solution.*

12.4. Remark. Let K be the square from Fig. 9 or Fig. 10. Then (12.3) and (12.4), respectively, can be written as

$$\left.\begin{array}{l}\left(\limsup\limits_{s\to+\infty}\dfrac{g(t,s)}{|s|^{p-2}s}\ ,\ \limsup\limits_{s\to-\infty}\dfrac{g(t,s)}{|s|^{p-2}s}\right)\in K\ ,\\[2ex] \left(\liminf\limits_{s\to+\infty}\dfrac{g(t,s)}{|s|^{p-2}s}\ ,\ \liminf\limits_{s\to-\infty}\dfrac{g(t,s)}{|s|^{p-2}s}\right)\in K\end{array}\right\}\qquad(12.5)$$

for a.a. $t\in(0,\pi)$.

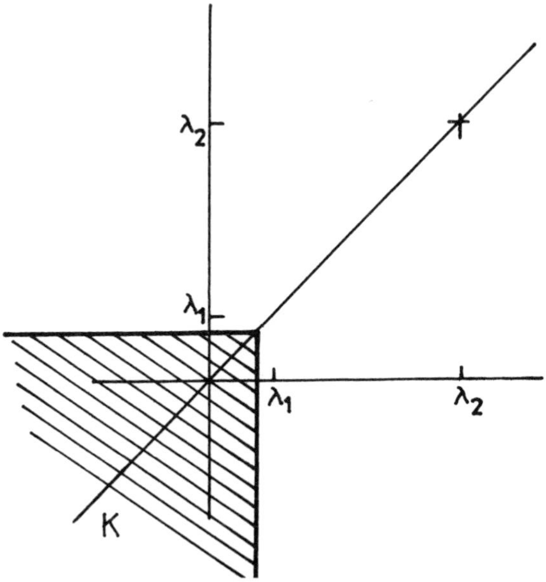

Fig. 9

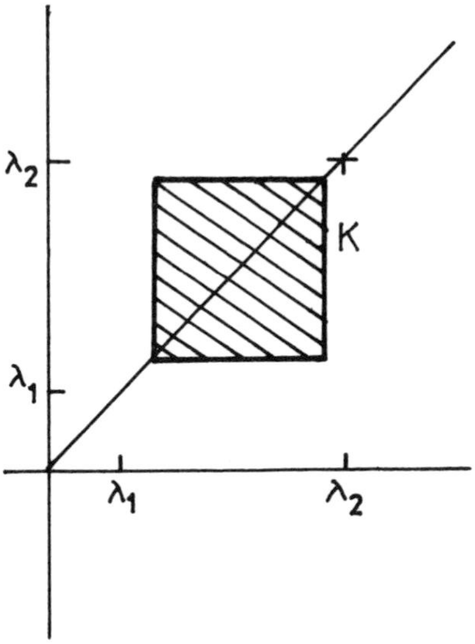

Fig. 10

In the sequel we will describe a more general set K such that (12.5) guarantees the solvability of BVP (12.1), (12.2).

<u>12.5. Theorem.</u> *Suppose that* g *satisfies* (10.12) *and that there exists a component* A_1^i *of the set* A_1 *(see Subsection* 11.7 *for* A_1 *) and points* (μ_i,ν_i), $(\mu_{i+1},\nu_{i+1})\in A_1^i$ *such that*

$$\mu_i\leq\liminf_{s\to+\infty}\frac{g(t,s)}{|s|^{p-2}s}\leq\limsup_{s\to+\infty}\frac{g(t,s)}{|s|^{p-2}s}\leq\mu_{i+1}\ ,\qquad(12.6_i)$$

$$\nu_i\leq\liminf_{s\to-\infty}\frac{g(t,s)}{|s|^{p-2}s}\leq\limsup_{s\to-\infty}\frac{g(t,s)}{|s|^{p-2}s}\leq\nu_{i+1}\qquad(12.7_i)$$

for a.a. $t\in(0,\pi)$. *Then BVP* (12.1), (12.2) *has for any* $f\in L^1(0,\pi)$ *at least one solution.*

12.6. Remark. The index i in Theorem 12.5 has a precise meaning if we denote by A_1^0 and A_1^i $(i = 1,2,\dots)$ the components of A_1 containing a point (λ,λ) with $\lambda < \lambda_1$ and $\lambda \in (\lambda_i,\lambda_{i+1})$, respectively. In the case $i = 0$ the estimate from below in (12.6_0), (12.7_0) is not necessary (i.e. we can formally put $\mu_0 = \nu_0 = -\infty$); this case is the same as (12.3) in Theorem 12.3. The conditions (12.6_i), (12.7_i) for $i \geq 1$ are a generalization of (12.4_i) which corresponds to the case $\mu_i = \nu_i = \lambda_i + \delta$, $\mu_{i+1} = \nu_{i+1} = \lambda_{i+1} - \delta$. The condition (12.6_i), (12.7_i) is equivalent to (12.5) from Remark 12.4 with the rectangle $K = \{(\mu,\nu) \in \mathbb{R}^2;\ \mu \in [\mu_i,\mu_{i+1}],\ \nu \in [\nu_i,\nu_{i+1}]\}$ (see Fig. 11).

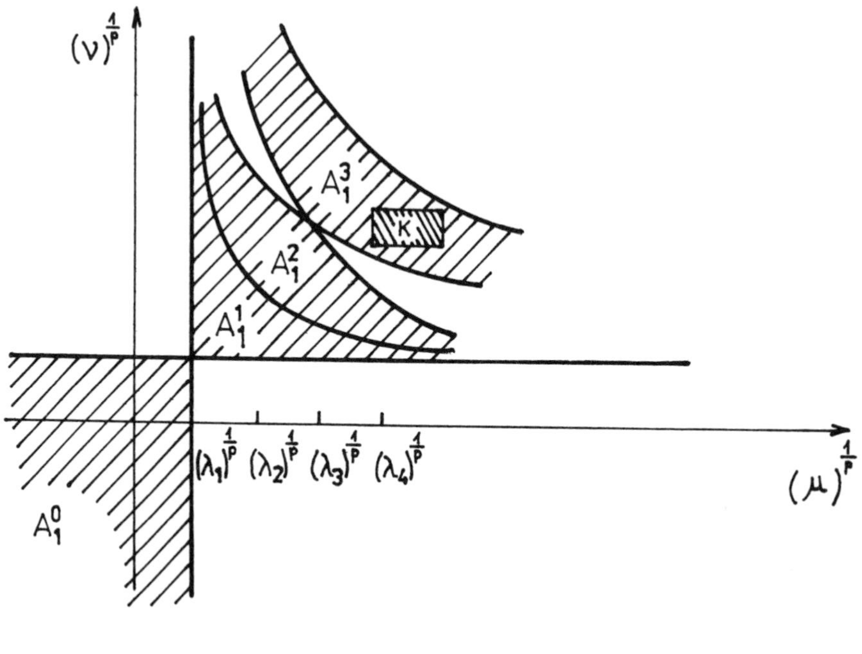

Fig. 11

12.7. Quasihomogeneous operators. Let $T_0 : X \to X^*$ be an a-homogeneous operator $(a \geqq 1)$ acting from the Banach space X into its dual X^*, i.e. $T_0(tx) = t^a T_0(x)$ for all $t > 0$, $x \in X$. Then $T : X \to X^*$ is said to be *a-quasihomogeneous with respect to* T_0 if the relations

$$t_n \to 0 , \quad x_n \rightharpoonup x , \quad t_n^a \, T\left(\frac{x_n}{t_n}\right) \to y^* \quad \text{in } X^*$$

imply $y^* = T_0(x)$.

The operator T is called an *a-homeomorphism of* X *onto* X^* if it is a homeomorphism of X onto X^* and there exist $C_1, C_2 > 0$ such that

$$C_1 \|x\|_X^a \leqq \|T(x)\|_{X^*} \leqq C_2 \|x\|_X^a$$

for all $x \in X$.

Further, we will suppose that *the limits*

$$\lim_{s \to \pm\infty} \frac{g(t,s)}{|s|^{p-2}s}$$

exist. Using the estimates

$$\lim_{s \to +\infty} \frac{g(t,s)}{|s|^{p-2}s} \leqq \lambda_1 - \delta , \qquad \lim_{s \to -\infty} \frac{g(t,s)}{|s|^{p-2}s} \leqq \lambda_1 - \delta , \tag{12.8}$$

$$\left.\begin{aligned} \lambda_i + \delta \leqq \lim_{s \to +\infty} \frac{g(t,s)}{|s|^{p-2}s} \leqq \lambda_{i+1} - \delta , \\ \lambda_i + \delta \leqq \lim_{s \to -\infty} \frac{g(t,s)}{|s|^{p-2}s} \leqq \lambda_{i+1} - \delta ; \end{aligned}\right\} \tag{12.9$_i$}$$

$$\mu_i \leqq \lim_{s \to +\infty} \frac{g(t,s)}{|s|^{p-2}s} \leqq \mu_{i+1} , \quad \nu_i \leqq \lim_{s \to -\infty} \frac{g(t,s)}{|s|^{p-2}s} \leqq \nu_{i+1} \tag{12.10$_i$}$$

a.e. in $(0,\pi)$, we can formulate the following two existence results (for the definition of J and G see Section 10).

12.8. Theorem. *Consider the situation from Theorems* 12.3 *and* 12.5 *but replace* (12.3), (12.4$_i$) *and* (12.6$_i$), (12.7$_i$) *by* (12.8), (12.9$_i$) *and* (12.10$_i$), *respectively. Let* T *be an odd* (p-1)*-homeomorphism of* $X = W_0^{1,p}(0,\pi)$ *onto its dual* X^* *and let* T *be* (p-1)*-quasihomogeneous with respect to* J. *Then for any* $f^* \in X^*$ *there exists at least one solution of*

$$T(u) - G(u) = f^* . \tag{12.11}$$

12.9. Theorem. *Let us suppose that* $q = p'$ *in the growth condition* (10.12), *where* $\frac{1}{p} + \frac{1}{p'} = 1$. *Let* (12.3), (12.4_i) *and* (12.6_i), (12.7_i) *hold. Then the assertion of Theorem* 12.8 *remains true.*

The proofs of Theorems 12.3, 12.5, 12.8 and 12.9 are based on the Leray - Schauder degree theory (see below) and in order to justify its application we need the following results concerning *homogeneous problems.*

12.10. Theorem. *Let* $\chi \in L^1(0,\pi)$ *satisfy one of the following estimates:*

$$\chi(t) \leqq \lambda_1 - \delta \quad a.e.\ in \quad (0,\pi) , \tag{12.12}$$

$$\lambda_i + \delta \leqq \chi(t) \leqq \lambda_{i+1} - \delta \quad a.e.\ in \quad (0,\pi) \tag{12.13$_i$}$$

with some $\delta > 0$, *where* λ_n *are the eigenvalues of BVP* (11.4), (11.5). *Then there is no nontrivial solution of BVP*

$$- \left(|v'|^{p-2}\, v'\right)' = \chi |v|^{p-2}\, v \quad in \quad (0,\pi) , \tag{12.14}$$

$$v(0) = v(\pi) = 0 . \tag{12.15}$$

12.11. Theorem. *Let* $\chi_+, \chi_- \in L^1(0,\pi)$ *and let there exist a component* A_1^i *of* A_1 *containing points* (μ_i,ν_i) , (μ_{i+1},ν_{i+1}) *such that*

$$\mu_i \leqq \chi_+(t) \leqq \mu_{i+1} , \quad \nu_i \leqq \chi_-(t) \leqq \nu_{i+1} \quad a.e.\ on \quad (0,\pi) . \tag{12.16$_i$}$$

Then there is no nontrivial solution of BVP

$$- \left(|v'|^{p-2}\, v'\right)' = \chi_+ |v|^{p-2}\, v^+ - \chi_- |v|^{p-2}\, v^- \quad in \quad (0,\pi) , \tag{12.17}$$

$$v(0) = v(\pi) = 0 . \tag{12.18}$$

12.12. Remark. In the case (12.16_0) the estimate from below is not necessary. We can set formally $\mu_0 = \nu_0 = -\infty$ (cf. Remark 12.6).

The proof of Theorem 12.10 in the case (12.12) is based on the variational characterization of λ_1 . This method can be used also for partial differential equations (see below). An analogous approach for $i \geqq 1$ can be used only in the linear case $p = 2$, and only for this special case we are able to prove the complete analogue of Theorem 12.10 for partial differential equations.

The proofs of Theorems 12.10 and 12.11 in the cases (12.13_i) and (12.16_i), $i \geqq 1$, respectively, are for $p > 2$ based on a *comparison lemma* which will be proved by the *shooting method*. We will use the properties of the following two IVPs :

$$-\left(|u'|^{p-2}\,u'\right)' = \lambda|u|^{p-2}\,u\,, \qquad (12.19_\lambda)$$

$$u(t_0) = 0\,, \quad u'(t_0) = \alpha\,, \qquad (12.20)$$

and

$$-\left(|w'|^{p-2}\,w'\right)' = \chi|w|^{p-2}\,w\,, \qquad (12.21)$$

$$w(t_0) = 0\,, \quad w'(t_0) = \beta\,, \qquad (12.22)$$

where t_0, $\lambda \in \mathbb{R}$ and $\chi \in L^1(t_0,T)$ for some $T > t_0$, $\chi(t) \geqq r > 0$ a.e. in (t_0,T).

It follows directly from the equation (12.21) that the solution is concave and convex on the intervals where $w > 0$ and $w < 0$, respectively. In particular, this is true for (12.19_λ) with $\lambda > 0$.

<u>12.13. Comparison Lemma.</u> *Let* u_1 *and* u_2 *be solutions of IVP* (12.19_{λ_1}), (12.20) *and IVP* (12.19_{λ_2}), (12.20), *respectively, with some* $t_0, \lambda_1, \lambda_2, \alpha \in \mathbb{R}$, $\lambda_1, \lambda_2 > 0$. *Set*

$$t_{\lambda_i} = \inf\{t > t_0\ ;\ u_i(t) = 0\}\,.$$

Suppose that $\chi \in L^1(t_0,T)$, w *is a solution of IVP* (12.21), (12.22) *on* $[t_0,T)$ *with* $\beta \in \mathbb{R}$, $\alpha\beta > 0$, *and* $t_\chi \in (t_0,T)$, *where*

$$t_\chi = \inf\{t \in (t_0,T)\ ;\ w(t) = 0\}\,.$$

If $\lambda_1 \leqq \chi(t) \leqq \lambda_2$ *a.e. on* (t_0,T) *then* $t_{\lambda_1} \geqq t_\chi \geqq t_{\lambda_2}$.

<u>*Proof.*</u> We can suppose $\alpha > 0$, $\beta > 0$ without loss of generality. Let us prove $t_\chi \geqq t_{\lambda_2}$. For the sake of brevity we will write λ and u instead of λ_2 and u_2. There are uniquely determined points $t'_\lambda \in (t_0,t_\lambda)$, $t'_\chi \in (t_0,t_\chi)$ such that

$$u'(t'_\lambda) = 0 \ , \quad w'(t'_\chi) = 0 \ , \quad u'(t) < 0 \ \text{ in } \ (t'_\lambda, t_\lambda) \ ,$$
$$w'(t) < 0 \ \text{ in } \ (t'_\chi, t_\chi) \tag{12.33}$$

(see Remark 12.12). The function $\bar{u}(t) = u(t - t'_\chi + t'_\lambda)$ is a solution of

$$-\left(|\bar{u}'|^{p-2}\,\bar{u}'\right)' = \lambda|\bar{u}|^{p-2}\,\bar{u} \ , \tag{12.24}$$

$$\bar{u}(t_0 + t'_\chi - t'_\lambda) = 0 \ , \quad \bar{u}'(t_0 + t'_\chi - t'_\lambda) = \alpha \ . \tag{12.25}$$

We will prove that

$$t_\lambda + t'_\chi - t'_\lambda \leqq t_\chi \ . \tag{12.26}$$

Suppose the contrary (see Fig. 12).

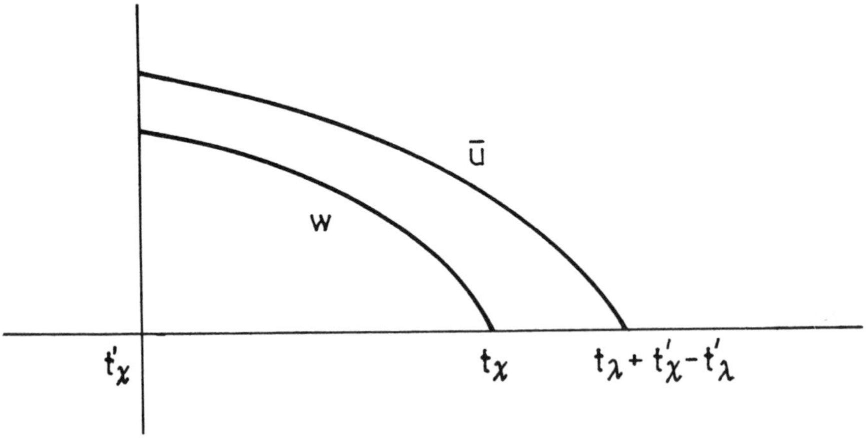

Fig. 12

We have $\left(\frac{w}{\bar{u}}\right)(t'_\chi) > 0$, $\left(\frac{w}{\bar{u}}\right)(t_\chi) = 0$ and therefore there exists $\tau \in (t'_\chi, t_\chi)$ such that $\left(\frac{w}{\bar{u}}\right)'(\tau) < 0$, i.e. $(w'\bar{u} - w\bar{u}')(\tau) < 0$, hence also $F(\tau) < 0$, where

$$F(\tau) = \left(|w'|^{p-2}\,w'(\bar{u})^{p-1} - (w)^{p-1}\,|\bar{u}'|^{p-2}\,\bar{u}'\right)(t)$$

(we use the fact that $\bar{u}(t), w(t) > 0$ in (t'_χ, t_χ) and the function $s \mapsto |s|^{p-2}\,s$ is increasing). Simultaneously, $F(t'_\chi) = 0$ because $w'(t'_\chi) = \bar{u}'(t'_\chi) = 0$, and therefore there exists a set $\mathcal{A}$ of positive measure such that

$$F(t) < 0 \ , \quad F'(t) < 0 \ \text{ on } \ \mathcal{A} \ . \tag{12.27}$$

The remaining part of the proof is the same as that of Lemma 11.10. Namely, we can write $F'(t) = F_1(t) + F_2(t)$, where

$$F_1(t) = [(|w'|^{p-2} w')'(\bar{u})^{p-1} - (w)^{p-1}(|\bar{u}'|^{p-2} \bar{u}')'](t) ,$$

$$F_2(t) = (p - 1)[w'\bar{u}'(|w'|^{p-2} \bar{u}^{p-2} - |\bar{u}'|^{p-2} w^{p-2})](t) .$$

It follows from (12.27) that $(w'\bar{u} - w\,\bar{u}')(t) < 0$ in $\mathcal{A}$ and this together with (12.23) gives

$$F_2(t) > 0 , \quad t \in \mathcal{A} . \tag{12.28}$$

Further, (12.19$_\lambda$), (12.20), (12.21), (12.22) imply

$$F_1(t) = (\lambda - \chi(t))w(t)^{p-1} \bar{u}(t)^{p-1} \geqq 0 \quad \text{a.e. in} \quad (0,\pi) . \tag{12.29}$$

The relations (12.28) and (12.29) contradict (12.27). Hence (12.26) is proved. Now, by an analogous argument as above but on the interval $[t_0 + t'_\chi - t'_\lambda, t'_\chi]$ instead of $[t'_\chi, t_\lambda + t'_\chi - t'_\lambda]$ we can prove $t_0 \leqq t_0 + t'_\chi - t'_\lambda$, which together with (12.26) implies $t_\chi \geqq t_\lambda = t_{\lambda_2}$. The inequality $t_\chi \leqq t_{\lambda_1}$ can be proved analogously. □

<u>12.14. Proof of Theorem 12.10.</u> Consider the case (12.12). If w is a non-trivial solution of BVP (12.14), (12.15) then we obtain (multiplying (12.14) by w and integrating by parts)

$$1 = \frac{\int_0^\pi |w'|^p \, dt}{\int_0^\pi \chi |w|^p \, dt} . \tag{12.30}$$

It is well known that

$$\lambda_1 = \min_{\substack{u \in W_0^{1,p}(0,\pi) \\ u \neq 0}} \frac{\int_0^\pi |u'|^p \, dt}{\int_0^\pi |u|^p \, dt} , \tag{12.31}$$

and this is a contradiction because (12.30), (12.31) cannot hold simultaneously under the assumption (12.12).

Consider the case (12.13_i), $i \geqq 1$. Let v_i and v_{i+1} be a solution of (12.19_λ), (12.20) with $\lambda = \lambda_i + \delta$ and $\lambda = \lambda_{i+1} - \delta$, respectively, and with $\alpha = 1$. Denote by

$$t_j^i = j\left(\frac{\lambda_1}{\lambda_i + \delta}\right)^{\frac{1}{p}} \pi , \qquad t_j^{i+1} = j\left(\frac{\lambda_1}{\lambda_{i+1} - \delta}\right)^{\frac{1}{p}} \pi$$

($j = 1,2,\dots$) the nodes of v_i and v_{i+1}, respectively (it follows from the elementary properties of (12.19_λ) that if u_λ is a solution of IVP (12.19_λ), (12.20) with $\alpha > 0$, $\lambda > 0$ then u_λ is a $2\left(\frac{\lambda_1}{\lambda}\right)^{1/p}\pi$-periodic function having isolated nodes

$$t_j^\lambda = t_0 + j\left(\frac{\lambda_1}{\lambda}\right)^{\frac{1}{p}} \pi , \qquad j = 0,1,2,\dots ,$$

and $|u_\lambda'(t_j^\lambda)| = \alpha$). If w is a nontrivial solution of BVP (12.14), (12.15) then we can suppose $w'(0) > 0$ due to the uniqueness of the solution of IVP (12.21), (12.22) (see Section 11). Hence w is the solution of IVP (12.21), (12.22) with $t_0 = 0$, $\beta > 0$, and it is easy to see (using Comparison Lemma 12.13) that

$$t_j^{i+1} \leqq t_j^w \leqq t_j^i < \pi , \qquad j = 1,2,\dots,i ,$$

where t_j^w denotes the j-th (from the left) node of w. More precisely, this follows directly for $j = 1$; further, we can use Comparison Lemma 12.13 at $t_0 = t_j^w$ successively for $j = 1,2,\dots,i-1$ for the comparison of nodes of $u_i(t) = v_i(t - t_j^w + t_j^i)$, w, $u_{i+1}(t) = v_{i+1}(t - t_j^w + t_j^{i+1})$. Now it follows from Lemma 12.13 that w has no further node in $(t_i^w, \pi]$ because $t_{i+1}^{i+1} > \pi$ (see Section 11). Therefore $w(\pi) \neq 0$, which contradicts the boundary conditions (12.15). This completes the proof of Theorem 12.10. □

12.15. Proof of Theorem 12.11. We will consider IVP

$$-\left(|u'|^{p-2} u'\right)' = \mu|u|^{p-2} u^+ - \nu|u|^{p-2} u^- , \tag{12.32}$$

$$u(0) = 0 , \quad u'(0) = \gamma \tag{12.33}$$

with $\mu, \nu, \gamma \in \mathbb{R}$, $\gamma \neq 0$. Using Remark 12.12 we can see that u is a solution of IVP (12.32), (12.33) with $\gamma \neq 0$ if and only if u is a solution of IVP (12.19_λ), (12.20) with $\lambda = \mu$, $\alpha = |\gamma|$ or with $\lambda = \nu$, $\alpha = -|\gamma|$ on any interval (t_0, T) where u is positive or negative, respectively. In particular, we have the uniqueness of the solution of IVP (12.32), (12.33) (see Remarks 11.2) and therefore nontrivial solutions can exist for $\gamma \neq 0$ only. Any nontrivial solution can be multiplied by a positive constant such that $u'(0) = 1$ or $u'(0) = -1$ and therefore we can consider the cases $\gamma = 1$, $\gamma = -1$ only. Recall that the solution u of IVP (12.32), (12.33) is periodic with the period

$$\left[\left(\frac{\lambda_1}{\mu} \right)^{\frac{1}{p}} + \left(\frac{\lambda_1}{\nu} \right)^{\frac{1}{p}} \right] \pi$$

(cf. Remarks 11.2). The solution $\Phi_{+1}^{\mu,\nu}$ of IVP (12.32), (12.33) with $\gamma = 1$ has nodes $t_{j+}^{\mu,\nu}$ given by

$$t_{j+}^{\mu,\nu} = \left[\frac{j-1}{2} \left(\frac{\lambda_1}{\mu} \right)^{\frac{1}{p}} + \frac{j+1}{2} \left(\frac{\lambda_1}{\nu} \right)^{\frac{1}{p}} \right] \pi , \quad j = 1,3,5,\dots ,$$

$$t_{j+}^{\mu,\nu} = \frac{j}{2} \left[\left(\frac{\lambda_1}{\mu} \right)^{\frac{1}{p}} + \left(\frac{\lambda_1}{\nu} \right)^{\frac{1}{p}} \right] \pi , \quad j = 0,2,4,\dots .$$

The nodes $t_{j-}^{\mu,\nu}$ of the solution $\Phi_{-1}^{\mu,\nu}$ of IVP (12.32), (12.33) with $\gamma = -1$ are given by analogous formulas but the roles of μ, ν on the right-hand side are interchanged.

Let us denote by A_{-1}^{i} the component of A_{-1} containing (λ_i, λ_i), $i = 1,2,\dots$. Then it is easy to see that $t_{i+}^{\mu,\nu} = \pi$ or $t_{i-}^{\mu,\nu} = \pi$ for $(\mu,\nu) \in A_{-1}^{i}$. If $(\mu,\nu) \in A_{1}^{i}$ then $t_{i+}^{\mu,\nu} < \pi$, $t_{i-}^{\mu,\nu} < \pi$, $t_{(i+1)+}^{\mu,\nu} > \pi$, $t_{(i+1)-}^{\mu,\nu} > \pi$.

Let us suppose that the assertion of Theorem 12.11 is not true and denote by w a nontrivial solution of BVP (12.17), (12.18). Let v_i and v_{i+1} be the solutions of IVP (12.32), (12.33) with $\mu = \mu_i$, $\nu = \nu_i$ and $\mu = \mu_{i+1}$, $\nu = \nu_{i+1}$, respectively, and with $\gamma = \operatorname{sign} w'(0)$ (we have $w'(0) \neq 0$ in virtue of the uniqueness). Denote by t_j^{i} and t_j^{i+1} $(j = 0,1,2,\dots)$ the j-th (from the left) node of v_i and v_{i+1}, respectively. The function w

is a solution of IVP (12.21), (12.22) with $\chi = \chi_+$ or $\chi = \chi_-$ on any interval where $w > 0$ or $w < 0$, respectively. By Comparison Lemma 12.13 we have

$$t_j^{i+1} \leqq t_j^w \leqq t_j^i < \pi \quad (j = 1,2,\dots,i) , \tag{12.34}$$

where t_j^w is the j-th (from the left) node of w. More precisely, (12.34) follows directly from Lemma 12.13 for $j = 1$. Further, we can use Lemma 12.13 at $t_0 = t_j^w$ successively with $j = 1,2,\dots,i-1$ for the comparison of the (j+1)-st nodes of $u_i(t) = v_i(t - t_j^w + t_j^i)$, w, $u_{i+1} = v_{i+1}(t - t_j^w + t_j^{i+1})$. Now, using Comparison Lemma 12.13 once more, we obtain that w has no node in $(t_i^w, \pi]$ because $t_{i+1}^{i+1} > \pi$. Hence $w(\pi) \neq 0$, which is a contradiction. □

Before proving the main existence results, i.e. Theorems 12.3 and 12.5, we will formulate and prove two auxiliary assertions. Note that the meaning of J, S, G and f^* is the same as in Section 10.

<u>12.16. Lemma.</u> *Let the assumptions of Theorem* 12.3 *be fulfilled. Set*

$$\mathcal{H}(\tau,u) = J(u) - \tau G(u) - \tau f^* - (1 - \tau)\lambda S(u)$$

for $\tau \in [0,1]$, $u \in X = W_0^{1,p}(0,\pi)$, *where* $\lambda < \lambda_1$ *and* $\lambda \in (\lambda_i, \lambda_{i+1})$ *in the case* (12.3) *and* (12.4$_i$), *respectively. Then there exists* $r > 0$ *such that*

$$\mathcal{H}(\tau,u) \neq 0 \tag{12.35}$$

holds for all $\tau \in [0,1]$, $u \in X$ *with* $\|u\|_X \geqq r$.

<u>*Proof*</u> of this assertion can be obtained from that of Lemma 12.17 by setting $\mu_0 = \nu_0 = \lambda$, writing χ, $\tilde{\chi}$ instead of $\chi_\pm$, $\tilde{\chi}_\pm$, and using Theorem 12.10 instead of Theorem 12.11 (see below). □

<u>12.17. Lemma.</u> *Let the assumptions of Theorem* 12.5 *be fulfilled. Put*

$$\mathcal{H}'(\tau,u) = J(u) - \tau G(u) - \tau f^* - (1 - \tau)\mu_0 S(u^+) + (1 - \tau)\nu_0 S(u^-)$$

for $\tau \in [0,1]$, $u \in X$, *where* $\mu_i \leqq \mu_0 \leqq \mu_{i+1}$, $\nu_i \leqq \nu_0 \leqq \nu_{i+1}$ *are arbitrary but fixed. Then there exists* $r > 0$ *such that*

$$\mathcal{H}'(\tau,u) \neq 0 \tag{12.36}$$

holds for all $\tau \in [0,1]$, $u \in X$ *with* $\|u\|_X \geq r$.

Proof. Suppose the assertion is not true. Then there exist u_n , τ_n ($n = 1,2,\dots$) such that

$$\|u_n\|_X \to +\infty , \quad \tau_n \in [0,1] , \quad \tau_n \to \tau , \quad v_n = \frac{u_n}{\|u_n\|_X} \rightharpoonup v$$

and $\mathcal{H}(\tau_n, u_n) = 0$, i.e. also

$$J(v_n) - \tau_n \frac{G(u_n)}{\|u_n\|_X^{p-1}} - \tau_n \frac{f^*}{\|u_n\|_X^{p-1}} - (1 - \tau_n)\mu_0 S(v_n^+) + $$
$$+ (1 - \tau_n)\nu_0 S(v_n^-) = 0 . \tag{12.37}$$

We will show that these facts imply that

$$v_n \to v \quad \text{in } X , \tag{12.38}$$

$$\frac{G(u_n)}{\|u_n\|_X^{p-1}} \to h^* \quad \text{in } X^* \quad \text{for some } h^* \in X^* , \tag{12.39}$$

$$\frac{g(\cdot, u_n(\cdot))}{\|u_n\|_X^{p-1}} \rightharpoonup \tilde{\chi}_+ |v|^{p-2} v^+ - \tilde{\chi}_- |v|^{p-2} v^- \quad \text{in } L^q(0,\pi) , \tag{12.40}$$

(at least for a subsequence) with some $\tilde{\chi}_+$, $\tilde{\chi}_-$ satisfying (12.16_i).

It follows from (12.37) that

$$\left(J(v_n) - J(v_m), v_n - v_m\right)_X = \left(\tau_n \frac{G(u_n)}{\|u_n\|_X^{p-1}} - \tau_m \frac{G(u_m)}{\|u_m\|_X^{p-1}} + \tau_n \frac{f^*}{\|u_n\|_X^{p-1}} - \right.$$
$$- \tau_m \frac{f^*}{\|u_m\|_X^{p-1}} + (1 - \tau_n)\mu_0 S(v_n^+) - (1 - \tau_m)\mu_0 S(v_m^+) -$$
$$\left. - (1 - \tau_n)\nu_0 S(v_n^-) + (1 - \tau_m)\nu_0 S(v_m^-), v_n - v_m\right)_X . \tag{12.41}$$

We can suppose $v_n \to v$ in $C([0,\pi])$ in virtue of the compact imbedding $X \subsetneq\subsetneq C([0,\pi])$. Using (10.12) we conclude that the right-hand side in (12.41) tends to zero as $n, m \to +\infty$ and therefore $\{v_n\}$ is strongly convergent in X by (10.8), i.e. (12.38) holds. We have $\tau > 0$ because in the opposite case we would obtain from (12.37) by the limiting process that v is a nontrivial solution of BVP (11.6), (11.7) with $\mu = \mu_0$, $\nu = \nu_0$ and this would contradict $(\mu_0, \nu_0) \in A_0$. Now, (12.39) follows from (12.37), (12.38) because all the other terms in (12.37) are convergent. Further, it follows from (10.12), (12.38) and the imbedding $X \subsetneq\subsetneq C([0,\pi])$ that

$$\left\{ \frac{g(\cdot, u_n(\cdot))}{\|u_n\|_X^{p-1}} \right\}$$

is bounded in $L^q(0,\pi)$, i.e. we can suppose

$$\frac{g(\cdot, u_n(\cdot))}{\|u_n\|_X^{p-1}} \rightharpoonup h \quad \text{in} \quad L^q(0,\pi) \tag{12.42}$$

for some $h \in L^q(0,\pi)$. We obtain from (10.12) that $h(t) = 0$ a.e. in $M_0 = \{t \in (0,\pi);\ v(t) = 0\}$ and therefore we can write
$h(t) = \tilde{\chi}(t)|v(t)|^{p-2} v(t)$ and put

$$\tilde{\chi}_+(t) = \tilde{\chi}(t) \quad \text{on} \quad M_+ = \{t \in (0,\pi);\ v(t) \geqq 0\} ,$$

$$\tilde{\chi}_-(t) = \tilde{\chi}(t) \quad \text{on} \quad M_- = \{t \in (0,\pi);\ v(t) \leqq 0\} .$$

The convergence $v_n \to v$ in $C([0,\pi])$ and (12.6_i), (12.7_i) directly imply that $\tilde{\chi}_+$ and $\tilde{\chi}_-$ satisfy (12.16_i). This together with (12.42) yields (12.40).

Now, using (12.38), (12.39), (12.40) we obtain from (12.37) by the limiting process that v is a nontrivial solution of BVP (12.17), (12.18) with $\chi_+(t) = \tau\tilde{\chi}_+(t) + (1 - \tau)\mu_0$, $\chi_-(t) = \tau\tilde{\chi}_-(t) + (1 - \tau)\nu_0$ satisfying (12.16_i). This contradicts Theorem 12.11. □

<u>12.18. Proof of Theorem 12.3.</u> Using the regularity argument mentioned in Section 10 it is sufficient to prove the existence of a solution of the equation

$$J(u) + G(u) = f^*$$

which is equivalent to

$$w + G(J^{-1}(w)) = f . \tag{12.43}$$

Lemma 12.16 together with the properties of J ensures the existence of r such that (12.35) holds and

$$\tilde{\mathcal{H}}(\tau, w) \neq 0 \tag{12.44}$$

for all $\tau \in [0,1]$, $w \in X^*$, $\|w\| = R$ with R sufficiently large, where

$$\tilde{\mathcal{H}}(\tau,w) = w - \tau G\big(J^{-1}(w)\big) - (1-\tau)\lambda S\big(J^{-1}(w)\big) - \tau f^*$$

(we have used in fact that J is a (p-1)-homeomorphism of X onto X^*).
We have

$$\deg\left[I - \lambda S(J^{-1});\ B_R,\ 0\right] \neq 0$$

by the Borsuk theorem because $S(J^{-1})$ is odd. Using (12.44) and the homotopy invariance property of the Leray - Schauder degree we obtain

$$\deg\left[I - G(J^{-1}) - f^*;\ B_R,\ 0\right] \neq 0 \ .$$

This implies the existence of a solution of (12.43). □

<u>12.19. Proof of Theorem 12.5.</u> The proof is quite analogous to that of Theorem 12.3 but we use Lemma 12.17 instead of Lemma 12.16, the homotopy

$$\tilde{\mathcal{H}}'(\tau,w) = w - \tau G\big(J^{-1}(w)\big) - \tau f^* - (1-\tau)\mu_0 S\big(J^{-1}(w)^+\big) + \\ + (1-\tau)\nu_0 S\big(J^{-1}(w)^-\big)$$

instead of $\tilde{\mathcal{H}}$, and the fact that

$$\deg\left[I - \mu_0 S\big(J^{-1}(w)^+\big) + \nu_0 S\big(J^{-1}(w)^-\big);\ B_R,\ 0\right] \neq 0$$

instead of the Borsuk theorem. □

Before we prove existence results for quasihomogeneous operators, we need the following lemma.

<u>12.20. Lemma.</u> *Let the assumptions of Theorem* 12.8 *be fulfilled. Define* $\mathcal{H}$, $\mathcal{H}'$ *as in Lemmas* 12.16 *and* 12.17 *but with* J *replaced by* T . *Then the assertions of Lemmas* 12.16 *and* 12.17 *remain true.*

<u>*Proof.*</u> We will consider the assumptions (12.10_i) only. The case (12.8), (12.9_i) can be obtained from the above by setting $\mu_0 = \nu_0 = \lambda$ and using Theorem 12.10 instead of Theorem 12.11. Suppose that the assertion (12.36) is not true. Then there exist u_n , τ_n such that $\|u_n\|_X \to +\infty$, $\tau_n \in [0,1]$, $\tau_n \to \tau$, $v_n = \dfrac{u_n}{\|u_n\|_X} \rightharpoonup v$ and

$$\frac{T(u_n)}{\|u_n\|_X^{p-1}} = \tau_n \frac{G(u_n)}{\|u_n\|_X^{p-1}} + \tau_n \frac{f^*}{\|u_n\|_X^{p-1}} + (1 - \tau_n)\mu_0 S(v_n^+) - $$

$$- (1 - \tau_n)\nu_0 S(v_n^-) \ . \qquad (12.45)$$

We have $|u_n(t)| \to +\infty$ and

$$\frac{g(t,u_n(t))}{\|u_n\|_X^{p-1}} = \frac{g(t,u_n(t))}{|u_n(t)|^{p-2}u_n(t)} \cdot |v_n(t)|^{p-2} v_n(t)$$

(if n is sufficiently large) for a.a. $t \in M = \{t \in (0,\pi);\ v(t) \neq 0\}$. Consequently,

$$\frac{g(t,u_n(t))}{\|u_n\|_X^{p-1}} \to \tilde{\chi}_+(t)|v(t)|^{p-2} v^+(t) - \tilde{\chi}_-(t)|v(t)|^{p-2} v^-(t) \qquad (12.46)$$

a.e. in M , where

$$\tilde{\chi}_\pm(t) = \lim_{s \to \pm\infty} \frac{g(t,s)}{|s|^{p-2}s} \ .$$

At the same time, it follows from (10.12) that

$$\frac{g(t,u_n(t))}{\|u_n\|_X^{p-1}} \to 0$$

a.e. in $M_0 = (0,\pi) \setminus M$ and therefore (12.46) holds a.e. in $(0,\pi)$. Using the Lebesgue theorem and (10.12) we obtain that the convergence in (12.46) takes place also in the L^1-norm. It follows that the right hand side in (12.45) converges in X^* to

$$\tau\tilde{\chi}_+|v|^{p-2} v^+ - \tau\tilde{\chi}_-|v|^{p-2} v^- + (1 - \tau)\mu_0|v|^{p-2} v^+ - (1 - \tau)\nu_0|v|^{p-2} v^- ,$$

and therefore

$$\frac{T(u_n)}{\|u_n\|_X^{p-1}} \to J(v) \ .$$

We have $v \neq 0$ because

$$\frac{T(u_n)}{\|u_n\|_X^{p-1}} \geq C$$

due to the assumption that T is a (p-1)-homeomorphism. Hence we have a nontrivial solution of BVP (12.17), (12.18) with

$$\chi_+(t) = \tau\tilde{\chi}_+(t) + (1-\tau)\mu_0 , \quad \chi_-(t) = \tau\tilde{\chi}_-(t) + (1-\tau)\nu_0$$

satisfying (12.16_i). This contradicts Theorem 12.11. □

12.21. Proof of Theorem 12.8 is quite analogous to that of Theorems 12.3, 12.5 but we use Lemma 12.20 instead of Lemmas 12.16, 12.17. □

12.22. Lemma. *Let the assumptions of Theorem* 12.9 *be fulfilled. Then the assertions of Lemmas* 12.16 *and* 12.17 *remain true where* $\mathcal{H}$, $\mathcal{H}'$ *are defined as above with* J *replaced by* T .

Proof. Arguing via contradiction we obtain again (12.45). The growth condition (10.12) now implies that

$$\frac{G(u_n)}{\|u_n\|_X^{p-1}}$$

is bounded in $L^{p'}(0,\pi)$. We obtain from here (using the compact imbedding $L^{p'}(0,\pi) \hookrightarrow\hookrightarrow X^*$) that

$$\frac{G(u_n)}{\|u_n\|_X^{p-1}} \to h^* \quad \text{in} \quad X^*$$

for some $h^* \in X^*$. Analogously as in the proof of Lemma 12.17 we obtain (12.40) (with $q = p'$) which implies that the right hand side in (12.45) converges in X^* again to

$$\tau\tilde{\chi}_+|v|^{p-2} v^+ - \tau\tilde{\chi}_-|v|^{p-2} v^- + (1-\tau)\mu_0|v|^{p-2} v^+ - (1-\tau)\nu_0|v|^{p-2} v^- .$$

To complete the proof we argue as in the proof of Lemma 12.20. □

12.23. Proof of Theorem 12.9 is quite analogous to that of Theorems 12.3, 12.5, just using Lemma 12.22 instead of Lemmas 12.16, 12.17. □

12.24. Example. It is possible to verify that the operator T defined by

$$\left(T(u),v\right)_X = \int_0^{\pi} \left(1 + |u'|^{p-2}\right) u' \, v' \, dt ,$$

$u, v \in X$, is an odd $(p-1)$-homeomorphism of X onto X^* which is $(p-1)$-quasihomogeneous with respect to J. Let a function $g : [0,\pi] \times \mathbb{R} \to \mathbb{R}$ be given by the relation

$$g(t,s) = \lambda(t)|s|^{p-2} \left[c_1 s^+ - c_2 s^- + 1\right] ,$$

where $c_1\lambda(t), c_2\lambda(t) \in \left[\lambda_i + \delta, \lambda_{i+1} - \delta\right]$ for a.a. $t \in (0,\pi)$ with a small $\delta > 0$. Then for arbitrary $f \in L^1(0,\pi)$ there exists at least one $u \in X$ such that

$$\int_0^{\pi} \left(1 + |u'|^{p-2}\right) u' \, v' \, dt = \int_0^{\pi} c_1\lambda(t)|u^+|^{p-2} \, u \, v \, dt -$$

$$- \int_0^{\pi} c_2\lambda(t)|u^-|^{p-2} \, u \, v \, dt + \int_0^{\pi} \lambda(t)|u|^{p-2} \, v \, dt + \int_0^{\pi} f \, v \, dt$$

holds for each $v \in X$.

12.25. Partial differential equations. We will discuss the solvability of BVP

$$- \operatorname{div}\left(|\nabla u|^{p-2} \nabla u\right) = g(x,u) + f(x) , \quad x \in \Omega , \tag{12.47}$$

$$u = 0 \quad \text{on} \quad \partial\Omega , \tag{12.48}$$

where $g : \Omega \times \mathbb{R} \to \mathbb{R}$ is a Carathéodory function satisfying (10.18), $f \in L^{\alpha'}(\Omega)$ (for α' see Subsection 10.10). As in Subsection 10.10 we suppose that $\Omega \subset \mathbb{R}^N$ is a bounded domain with a Lipschitzian boundary $\partial\Omega$. We can define operators $J, S, G : X \to X^*$, where $X = W_0^{1,p}(\Omega)$ and an element $f^* \in X^*$ in the same way as in Subsection 10.10.

A function $u \in X$ is said to be *a weak solution* of BVP (12.47), (12.48) if it satisfies

$$J(u) - G(u) = f^* . \tag{12.49}$$

12.26. Theorem. *Suppose that* g *satisfies* (10.18) *and one of the following estimates:*

$$\limsup_{s \to \pm\infty} \frac{g(x,s)}{|s|^{p-2}s} \leq \lambda_1 - \delta \tag{12.50}$$

for a.a. $x \in \Omega$;

$$\lambda - c_1(\lambda,\lambda) + \delta \leq \liminf_{s \to \pm\infty} \frac{g(x,s)}{|s|^{p-2}s} \leq \limsup_{s \to \pm\infty} \frac{g(x,s)}{|s|^{p-2}s} \leq$$

$$\leq \lambda + c_1(\lambda,\lambda) - \delta \tag{12.51}$$

for a.a. $x \in \Omega$,

with a λ *which is not an eigenvalue of* (10.3), $\delta > 0$, *where* $c_1(\lambda,\lambda) = \inf_{\|u\|_X = 1} \|J(u) - \lambda S(u)\|_{X^*}$ *(see Section* 10*). Then for any* $f \in L^{\alpha'}(\Omega)$ *there exists at least one weak solution of BVP* (12.47), (12.48).

<u>12.27. Theorem.</u> *Let* T *be an odd* $(p-1)$*-homeomorphism of* X *onto* X^* *which is* $(p-1)$*-quasihomogeneous with respect to* J . *Suppose that* g *satisfies* (10.18), (12.50) *or* (12.51). *Then for each* $f^* \in X^*$ *there exists at least one solution of*

$$T(u) - G(u) = f^* .$$

<u>12.28. Remark.</u> The case (12.50) in Theorems 12.26, 12.27 is precisely the same as in Theorems 12.3, 12.5, 12.9 because the necessary information about the homogeneous equation can be obtained using the variational characterization of the first eigenvalue (see (10.21)). In the case $p = 2$ the variational approach can be used even in the case $i \geq 1$ (see (12.4_i)) and therefore the following theorem holds.

<u>12.29. Theorem.</u> *If* $p = 2$ *then the assertion of Theorem* 12.3 *and the assertion of Theorem* 12.9 *remain true for BVP* (12.1), (12.2) *replaced by BVP* (12.47), (12.48) *(with* $f \in L^{\alpha'}(\Omega)$ *).*

In order to prove the existence results 12.26, 12.27 we need the following theorems.

<u>12.30. Theorem.</u> *Let* $\chi \in L^\infty(\Omega)$ *satisfy*

$$\chi(x) \leq \lambda_1 - \delta \quad \textit{a.e. in } \Omega ,$$

with a $\delta > 0$. *Then there is no nontrivial weak solution of BVP*

$$- \operatorname{div} \left(|\nabla u|^{p-2} \nabla u \right) = \chi |u|^{p-2} u \quad \textit{in} \quad \Omega ,$$
$$u = 0 \quad \textit{on} \quad \partial\Omega .$$

Proof of this assertion is the same as that of Theorem 12.10 (see case (12.12)). □

12.31. Theorem. *Let* $p = 2$. *Suppose that* $\chi \in L^{\infty}(\Omega)$ *satisfies one of the following estimates*

$$\chi(x) \leqq \lambda_1 - \delta \quad \textit{a.e. in} \quad \Omega ,$$

$$\lambda_i + \delta \leqq \chi(x) \leqq \lambda_{i+1} - \delta \quad \textit{a.e. in} \quad \Omega$$

with a $\delta > 0$, *where* λ_i *are the eigenvalues of* (10.3). *Then there is no nontrivial weak solution of BVP*

$$- \Delta u = \chi u \quad \textit{in} \quad \Omega ,$$
$$u = 0 \quad \textit{on} \quad \partial\Omega .$$

Proof of this theorem follows directly from the variational characterization of the eigenvalues of BVP

$$- \Delta u - \lambda u = 0 \quad \text{in} \quad \Omega ,$$
$$u = 0 \quad \text{on} \quad \partial\Omega$$

(see BOCCARDO, DRÁBEK, GIACHETTI and KUČERA [30]). □

12.32. Proof of Theorem 12.26. Set

$$\mathcal{H}(\tau,v) = J(u) - \tau G(u) - \tau f^* - (1 - \tau)\lambda S(u)$$

for $\tau \in [0,1]$, $u \in X$, where either $\lambda < \lambda_1$ (in the case (12.50)) or (12.51) is satisfied. We will prove that there exists $r > 0$ such that

$$\mathcal{H}(\tau,u) \neq 0 \tag{12.52}$$

for all $\tau \in [0,1]$, $u \in X$ with $\|u\|_X \geqq r$. The case (12.50) is the same as in Lemma 12.16 but we use Theorem 12.30 instead of Theorem 12.10. Consider the case (12.51) and suppose that the assertion (12.52) is not true. Then there exist τ_n , u_n such that

$$\tau_n \in [0,1] , \quad \tau_n \to \tau , \quad \|u_n\|_X \to \infty , \quad v_n = \frac{u_n}{\|u_n\|_X} \rightharpoonup v$$

and

$$J(v_n) - \tau_n \frac{G(u_n)}{\|u_n\|_X^{p-1}} - \tau_n \frac{f^*}{\|u_n\|_X^{p-1}} - (1 - \tau_n)\lambda S(v_n) = 0 .$$

Analogously as in the proof of Lemma 12.16 (but using (10.18) instead of (10.12)) we obtain from here and from (12.51):

$$v_n \rightarrow v \quad \text{in} \quad X ,$$

$$\frac{G(u_n)}{\|u_n\|_X^{p-1}} \rightarrow h^* \quad \text{in} \quad X^* \quad \text{for some} \quad h^* \in X^* ,$$

$$\frac{g(\cdot, u_n(\cdot))}{\|u_n\|_X^{p-1}} \rightharpoonup \chi|v|^{p-2} v \quad \text{in} \quad L^{\alpha'}(\Omega)$$

with $|\chi(t) - \lambda| \leq c_1(\lambda,\lambda) - \delta$ a.e. in Ω . This implies

$$\left\| \frac{G(u_n)}{\|u_n\|_X^{p-1}} - \lambda S(v_n) + \frac{f^*}{\|u_n\|_X^{p-1}} \right\|_{X^*} \longrightarrow$$

$$\longrightarrow \sup_{\|w\|_X \leq 1} \int_\Omega \big(\chi(t) - \lambda\big) |v(t)|^{p-2} v(t)\, w(t)\, dt \leq c_1(\lambda,\lambda) - \delta .$$

Hence we obtain

$$\mathcal{H}(\tau_n, u_n) \geq \|u_n\|_X^{p-1} \Bigg(\|J(v_n) - \lambda S(v_n)\|_{X^*} -$$

$$- \tau \left\| \frac{G(u_n)}{\|u_n\|_X^{p-1}} - \lambda S(v_n) + \frac{f^*}{\|u_n\|_X^{p-1}} \right\|_{X^*} \Bigg) > 0$$

for n sufficiently large, which is a contradiction. The proof of Theorem 12.26 now follows from (12.52) in the same way as that of Theorem 12.3 from Lemma 12.16. □

12.33. Proof of Theorem 12.27. Combining the considerations from Subsection 12.32 and Lemma 12.20 we easily see that the same procedure can be used to prove Theorem 12.27. □

12.34. Proof of Theorem 12.29. This proof is quite similar to that of Theorem 12.3 but an analogue of Lemma 12.16 based on Theorem 12.31 must be used. □

13. PERTURBATION OF HOMOGENEOUS PROBLEMS - RESONANCE CASE

13.1. We will consider the equation

$$\operatorname{div}\left(|\nabla u(x)|^{p-2}\nabla u(x)\right)+\lambda_1|u(x)|^{p-2}u(x)+g\left(x,u(x)\right)=f(x)\ ,\quad x\in\Omega\ , \tag{13.1}$$

either with the Neumann boundary condition

$$|\nabla u(x)|^{p-2}\nabla u\cdot\nu(x)=0\ ,\quad x\in\partial\Omega\ , \tag{13.2}$$

or with the Dirichlet boundary condition

$$u(x)=0\ ,\quad x\in\Omega\ , \tag{13.3}$$

where $\Omega\subset\mathbb{R}^N$ is a bounded domain with a smooth boundary $\partial\Omega$, $\nu(x)$ is the outer normal with respect to $\partial\Omega$ at $x\in\partial\Omega$, $p>1$ is a real number, $g:\Omega\times\mathbb{R}\to\mathbb{R}$ is a Carathéodory function and λ_1 is the first eigenvalue of the equation

$$\operatorname{div}\left(|\nabla u|^{p-2}\nabla u\right)+\lambda|u|^{p-2}u=0 \tag{13.4}$$

with the boundary condition either (13.2) or (13.3).

13.2. Kernel of the homogeneous part. *The first eigenvalue* $\lambda_1=0$ *of BVP* (13.4), (13.2) *is simple, isolated and the corresponding eigenfunction is constant in* Ω (see DRÁBEK [94] and Section 14). Concerning BVP (13.4), (13.3) the following analogue of the Krein - Rutman theorem is proved in ANANE [12]: *Let* $\partial\Omega$ *be of class* $C^{2,\beta}$. *Then there exists the first eigenvalue* λ_1 *of BVP* (13.4), (13.3), *which is simple and isolated. The corresponding eigenfunction* $u_1\in C^{1,\alpha}(\overline{\Omega})$ *can be chosen positive in* Ω *and such that* $\frac{\partial u_1}{\partial\nu}<0$ *on* $\partial\Omega$.

13.3. Operator representation. Let g satisfy the growth restriction (10.18) formulated in Subsection 10.10. We denote $X=W^{1,p}(\Omega)$ or $X=W_0^{1,p}(\Omega)$ if BVP (13.1), (13.2) or BVP (13.1), (13.3) is considered, respectively. Let us define operators $J,\ S,\ G:X\to X^*$ and an element $f^*\in X^*$ in the same way as in Subsection 10.10. Further, denote

$$J_d=J+dS$$

for any $d\in\mathbb{R}$. The operator J_d for any $d>0$ is *a homeomorphism* of X onto X^* . Indeed, it follows from the definitions of J and S that

$$(J_d(u),u)_X = C\|u\|_X^p \quad \text{for all} \quad u \in X \quad (\text{with some} \quad C > 0)\,, \tag{13.5}$$

$$\begin{aligned}(J_d(u) - J_d(v),\, u - v)_X &\geq \\ &\geq (\|u\|_{1,p}^{p-1} - \|v\|_{1,p}^{p-1})(\|u\|_{1,p} - \|v\|_{1,p}) + \\ &+ d(\|u\|_p^{p-1} - \|v\|_p^{p-1})(\|u\|_p - \|v\|_p) > 0\end{aligned} \tag{13.6}$$

for all $u, v \in X$, $u \neq v$. Hence J_d is monotone and coercive and it follows from the theory of monotone operators that J_d maps X onto X^* (see e.g. LIONS [203]). The inequality (13.6) ensures also the existence of J_d^{-1}. Suppose that J_d^{-1} is not continuous, i.e. there are $u_n, u_0 \in X$ such that $J_d(u_n) \to J_d(u_0)$, $\|u_n - u_0\|_X \geq \delta > 0$. Then $\{u_n\}$ is bounded by (13.5) and we can suppose $u_n \rightharpoonup \tilde{u}$ in X for some $\tilde{u} \in X$. Hence

$$\begin{aligned}&(J_d(u_n) - J_d(\tilde{u}),\, u_n - \tilde{u})_X = \\ &= (J_d(u_n) - J_d(u_0),\, u_n - \tilde{u})_X + (J_d(u_0) - J_d(\tilde{u}),\, u_n - \tilde{u})_X \to 0\,.\end{aligned}$$

It follows from (13.6) that $\|u_n\|_X \to \|\tilde{u}\|_X$ and therefore $u_n \to \tilde{u}$. Further, $J_d(u_n) \to J_d(\tilde{u}) = J_d(u_0)$. This means that $\tilde{u} = u_0$, which contradicts the assumption.

A function $u \in X$ is said to be *a weak solution* of BVP (13.1), (13.2) or BVP (13.1), (13.3) if $X = W^{1,p}(\Omega)$ or $X = W_0^{1,p}(\Omega)$, respectively, and

$$J(u) - \lambda_1 S(u) - G(u) + f^* = 0\,. \tag{13.7}$$

<u>13.4. One-sided growth restrictions on g.</u> Let us suppose that there are constants $r, R \in \mathbb{R}$, $r < 0 < R$, and functions $a, A \in L^{\alpha'}(\Omega)$ (for α' see Subsection 10.10) such that

$$g(x,s) \geq A(x) \tag{13.8}$$

for a.a. $x \in \Omega$ and for all $s \leq r$;

$$g(x,s) \leq a(x) \tag{13.9}$$

for a.a. $x \in \Omega$ and for all $s \geq R$ (cf. Subsection 1.14).

Let us denote

$$g_{-\infty}(x) = \liminf_{s \to -\infty} g(x,s) \ , \quad g^{+\infty}(x) = \limsup_{s \to +\infty} g(x,s) \ .$$

13.5. Theorem. *Suppose* (10.18), (13.8) *and* (13.9) *hold. Then BVP* (13.1), (13.2) *as well as BVP* (13.1), (13.3) *have at least one weak solution for any* $f \in L^{\alpha'}(\Omega)$ *satisfying the condition*

$$\int_\Omega g^{+\infty}(x)\, u_1(x)\, dx < \int_\Omega f(x)\, u_1(x)\, dx < \int_\Omega g_{-\infty}(x)\, u_1(x)\, dx \ , \qquad (13.10)$$

where u_1 *is the positive eigenfunction corresponding to the smallest eigenvalue of BVP* (13.4), (13.2) *or BVP* (13.4), (13.3), *respectively.*

This assertion is a consequence of the following more general theorem.

13.6. Theorem. *Suppose* (10.18), (13.8) *and* (13.9) *hold. Let* $T : X \to X^*$ *be an odd mapping which is* (p-1)-*quasihomogeneous with respect to* J , *such that* $T_d = T + dS$ *is a homeomorphism for any* $d > 0$, *and*

$$(T(u),u)_X \geqq (J(u),u)_X \qquad (13.11)$$

for all $u \in X$. *Then the operator equation*

$$T(u) - \lambda_1 S(u) - G(u) + f^* = 0 \qquad (13.12)$$

has at least one solution for any $f^* \in X$ *which is defined by means of* $f \in L^{\alpha'}(\Omega)$ *satisfying* (13.10).

Proof. Let us choose a fixed $d > 0$ and define a homotopy $\mathcal{H} : [0,1] \times X \to X$ by

$$\mathcal{H}(\tau,u) = u - T_d^{-1}\big((\lambda_1 + \tau d)S(u) + \tau(G(u) - f^*)\big) \ .$$

The equation $\mathcal{H}(1,u) = 0$ is equivalent to (13.12). Suppose that

$$\mathcal{H}(\tau,u) \neq 0 \qquad (13.13)$$

for all $\tau \in [0,1]$, $u \in X$, $\|u\|_X = R$ with some $R > 0$. The mapping $T_d^{-1}\big((\lambda_1 + \tau d)S + \tau(G - f^*)\big)$ is compact (due to the compactness of S and G). The operator $\mathcal{H}(0,u) = u - T_d^{-1}\big(\lambda_1 S(u)\big)$ is odd. Hence

$$\deg\,[\mathcal{H}(0,\cdot);\, B_R,\, 0] \neq 0$$

by the Borsuk theorem. Further, (13.13) implies

$$\deg\left[\mathcal{H}(1,\cdot);\ B_R,\ 0\right] = \deg\left[\mathcal{H}(0,\cdot);\ B_R,\ 0\right] \neq 0$$

by the homotopy invariance property of the degree. It follows that there exists a solution $u \in B_R$ of $\mathcal{H}(1,u) = 0$, i.e. u is the solution of (13.12). Hence it is sufficient to show that (13.13) holds for $R > 0$ large enough. Suppose, by way of contradiction, that there exist $\tau_n \in [0,1]$, $u_n \in X$ ($n = 1,2,\ldots$) such that $\|u_n\|_X \to \infty$ and $\mathcal{H}(\tau_n,u_n) = 0$, i.e.

$$T(u_n) - \lambda_1 S(u_n) + (1 - \tau_n)dS(u_n) - \tau_n\left(G(u_n) - f^*\right) = 0 . \qquad (13.14)$$

We can suppose that $\tau_n \to \tau \in [0,1]$, $v_n = \dfrac{u_n}{\|u_n\|_X} \rightharpoonup v$ in X , $v_n \to v$ in $L^p(\Omega)$ (due to the compactness of the imbedding $X \hookrightarrow\hookrightarrow L^p(\Omega)$) and $v_n(x) \to v(x)$ a.e. in Ω . Dividing (13.14) by $\|u_n\|_X^{p-1}$ we obtain

$$\|u_n\|_X^{1-p}\, T(u_n) - \lambda_1 S(v_n) + (1 - \tau_n)dS(v_n) -$$

$$- \tau_n\|u_n\|_X^{1-p}\left(G(u_n) - f^*\right) = 0 . \qquad (13.15)$$

It follows from (10.18) that the sequence $\left\{\|u_n\|_X^{1-p}\, g(\cdot,u_n(\cdot))\right\}$ is bounded in $L^{\alpha'}(\Omega)$, i.e. we can suppose that

$$\|u_n\|_X^{1-p}\, g(\cdot,u_n(\cdot)) \rightharpoonup \tilde{g} \quad \text{in} \quad L^{\alpha'}(\Omega) \qquad (13.16)$$

for some $\tilde{g} \in L^{\alpha'}(\Omega)$. The compactness of the imbedding $L^{\alpha'}(\Omega) \hookrightarrow\hookrightarrow X^*$ implies

$$\|u_n\|_X^{1-p}\, G(u_n) \to g^* \quad \text{in} \quad X^* ,$$

$$(g^*,w)_X = \int_\Omega \tilde{g}\, w\, dx \quad \text{for all} \quad w \in X . \qquad (13.17)$$

This together with the compactness of S and the equation (13.15) ensures that $\left\{\|u_n\|_X^{1-p}\, T(u_n)\right\}$ is convergent, that is

$$\|u_n\|_X^{1-p}\, T(u_n) \to J(v) \quad \text{in} \quad X^* \qquad (13.18)$$

because T is (p-1)-quasihomogeneous with respect to J . At the same time $\|u_n\|_X^{1-p}\, \|T_d(u_n)\|_{X^*} \geq C > 0$ due to (13.5) and the assumption $(T(u),u)_X \geq (J(u),u)_X$. Therefore

$$\|u_n\|_X^{1-p}\, T_d(u_n) \to J_d(v) \neq 0$$

because of the compactness of S . This means

$$v \neq 0 . \tag{13.19}$$

If follows from (10.18), (13.16) and from $v_n \to v$ in $L^p(\Omega)$ that $\tilde{g} = 0$ a.e. in $M_0 = \{x \in \Omega;\ v(x) = 0\}$. Hence we can write

$$\tilde{g}(x) = \chi(x)\ |v(x)|^{p-2}\ v(x) . \tag{13.20}$$

The function χ is uniquely defined a.e. in $\Omega \setminus M_0$ and we set $\chi \equiv 0$ in M_0 . Further, the conditions (10.18), (13.8), (13.9) yield

$$\chi(x) \leqq 0 \quad \text{a.e. in } \Omega \tag{13.21}$$

(for precise proof see Remark 13.7 below). Define a mapping $\tilde{S} : X \to X^*$ by

$$\left(\tilde{S}(u),w\right)_X = \int_\Omega \chi|u|^{p-2}\ u\ w\ dx \tag{13.22}$$

for all $u, w \in X$. Now, (13.15) together with (13.17), (13.18), (13.20), (13.22) imply

$$J(v) - \lambda_1 S(v) + (1 - \tau) dS(v) - \tau\tilde{S}(v) = 0 .$$

In particular, this means

$$\left(J(v) - \lambda_1 S(v),\ v\right)_X = -\ (1 - \tau) d\left(S(v),v\right)_X + \tau\left(\tilde{S}(v),v\right)_X . \tag{13.23}$$

The left hand side is nonnegative and equals zero only for $v = \xi u_1$ (see (10.21) and Subsection 13.2 for u_1), the right hand side is nonpositive by (13.21), (13.22). Hence both sides in (13.23) must be equal to zero, which means $\tau = 1$, $v = \xi u_1$ with some $\xi \neq 0$ because of (13.19). It follows from (13.15) that

$$\left(T(u_n) - \lambda_1 S(u_n),\ v_n\right)_X + (1 - \tau_n) d\left(S(u_n),\ v_n\right)_X =$$

$$= \tau_n \int_\Omega \left[g\left(x,u_n(x)\right) - f(x)\right]\ v_n(x)\ dx .$$

The left hand side is nonnegative (see (10.21) and the assumption $\left(T(u),u\right)_X \geqq \left(J(u),u\right)_X$) and therefore

$$\liminf_{n \to \infty} \int_\Omega g\left(x,u_n(x)\right)\ v_n(x)\ dx \geqq \int_\Omega f(x)\ v(x)\ dx .$$

Now, it is sufficient to use Lemma 13.8 below to obtain

$$\int_\Omega g^{+\infty}(x)\; u_1(x)\; dx \geqq \int_\Omega f(x)\; u_1(x)\; dx\;,$$

or

$$\int_\Omega g_{-\infty}(x)\; u_1(x)\; dx \leqq \int_\Omega f(x)\; u_1(x)\; dx$$

if $\xi > 0$ or $\xi < 0$, respectively, which contradicts the assumption (13.10). □

13.7. Remark. Let us present precise proof that (13.21) holds. Suppose by way of contradiction that there is $M \subset \Omega \setminus M_0$ such that $\text{meas}\, M > 0$, $\chi > 0$ in M. We can suppose $v > 0$ in M. (The case $v < 0$ can be treated analogously.) If χ_M is the characteristic function of M then (13.16), (13.20) imply

$$\lim_{n\to\infty} \int_\Omega \frac{g(x,u_n(x))}{\|u_n\|_X^{p-1}}\, \chi_M(x)\; dx = \int_\Omega \chi(x)\,|v(x)|^{p-2}\, v(x)\; \chi_M(x)\; dx > 0\,. \qquad (13.24)$$

It follows from (10.18), (13.8), (13.9) that

if $\quad |u_n(x)| \leqq \|u_n\|_X \quad$ *then* $\quad \dfrac{g(x,u_n(x))}{\|u_n\|_X^{p-1}} \leqq \dfrac{m(x) + c\|u_n\|_X^{p-1}}{\|u_n\|_X^{p-1}}\;,$

if $\quad u_n(x) > \|u_n\|_X \quad$ *then* $\quad \dfrac{g(x,u_n(x))}{\|u_n\|_X^{p-1}} \leqq \dfrac{a(x)}{\|u_n\|_X^{p-1}}\;,$

if $\quad u_n(x) < -\|u_n\|_X \quad$ *then*

$$\frac{g(x,u_n(x))}{\|u_n\|_X^{p-1}} = \frac{g(x,u_n(x))}{\|u_n\|^{p-2}u_n(x)}\big(v_n(x) - v(x)\big) + \frac{g(x,u_n(x))}{\|u_n\|^{p-2}u_n(x)}\, v(x) \leqq$$

$$\leqq \frac{m(x) + c|u_n(x)|^{p-1}}{\|u_n\|^{p-1}}\, |v_n(x) - v(x)| - \frac{A(x)}{\|u_n\|_X^{p-1}}\, v(x)$$

for n so large that $\|u_n\|_X > \max\{|r|, |R|\}$. Hence

$$\frac{g(x,u_n(x))}{\|u_n\|_X^{p-1}}\, \chi_M(x) \leqq \frac{m(x) + c|u_n(x)|^{p-1}}{\|u_n\|^{p-1}}\, |v_n(x) - v(x)|\chi_M(x) + h(x)$$

with

$$h(x) = \frac{1}{(\max\{|r|,|R|\})^{p-1}} [a(x) - A(x)v(x) + m(x)] \in L^1(\Omega) .$$

It follows from Fatou's lemma and (13.8), (13.9) that

$$\limsup_{n\to\infty} \int_\Omega \left[\frac{g(x,u_n(x))}{\|u_n\|_X^{p-1}} - \frac{m(x) + c|u_n(x)|^{p-1}}{\|u_n\|_X^{p-1}} |v_n(x) - v(x)| \right] \chi_M(x)\, dx \leq$$

$$\leq \int_\Omega \limsup_{n\to\infty} \frac{g(x,u_n(x))}{\|u_n\|_X^{p-1}} \chi_M(x)\, dx = 0 .$$

(We use the fact that the second term on the left is nonpositive and that $u_n(x) \longrightarrow +\infty$ a.e. in M .) Thus,

$$\liminf_{n\to\infty} \int_\Omega \frac{g(x,u_n(x))}{\|u_n\|_X^{p-1}} \chi_M(x)\, dx \leq$$

$$\leq \limsup_{n\to\infty} \int_\Omega \frac{m(x) + c|u_n(x)|^{p-1}}{\|u_n\|^{p-1}} |v_n(x) - v(x)|\, \chi_M(x)\, dx .$$

However, the integral on the right hand side tends to zero because $v_n \longrightarrow v$ in $L^p(\Omega)$ and this contradicts (13.24).

<u>13.8. Lemma.</u> *Let us suppose* (10.18), (13.8), (13.9) *and let* $u_n \in X$ *be such that* $\|u_n\|_X \longrightarrow +\infty$, $v_n = \frac{u_n}{\|u_n\|_X} \longrightarrow \xi u_1$ *both in* $L^p(\Omega)$ *and a.e. in* Ω , $\xi \neq 0$. *Then*

$$\liminf_{n\to\infty} \int_\Omega g(x,u_n(x))\, v_n(x)\, dx \leq \int_\Omega a(x)\, \xi\, u_1(x)\, dx \tag{13.25}$$

or

$$\liminf_{n\to\infty} \int_\Omega g(x,u_n(x))\, v_n(x)\, dx \leq \int_\Omega A(x)\, \xi\, u_1(x)\, dx \tag{13.26}$$

provided $\xi > 0$ *or* $\xi < 0$, *respectively.*

<u>*Proof.*</u> Introduce functions $\tilde{v}_n$ by

$\tilde{v}_n(x) = v_n(x)$ for $x \in \Omega$, $v_n(x) \in [-|\xi|u_1(x), |\xi|u_1(x)]$,

$\tilde{v}_n(x) = |\xi|u_1(x)$ for $x \in \Omega$, $v_n(x) > |\xi|u_1(x)$,

$$\tilde{v}_n(x) = -|\xi|u_1(x) \quad \text{for} \quad x \in \Omega , \quad v_n(x) < -|\xi|u_1(x) .$$

We have $\tilde{v}_n \longrightarrow \xi u_1$ in $L^p(\Omega)$ and a.e. in Ω . It follows from (10.18), (13.8), (13.9) (where we can suppose $a(x) \geqq 0$, $A(x) \leqq 0$ without loss of generality) that

$$\int_\Omega g(x,u_n(x))(v_n(x) - \tilde{v}_n(x))\, dx \leqq \int_{M_n} (m(x) + cr^{p-1})|v_n(x) - \tilde{v}_n(x)|\, dx +$$

$$+ \int_{M_n^+} a(x)(v_n(x) - \tilde{v}_n(x))\, dx + \int_{M_n^-} (-A(x))|v_n(x) - \tilde{v}_n(x)|\, dx \leqq$$

$$\leqq \int_\Omega (m(x) + cr^{p-1} + a(x) - A(x))|v_n(x) - \tilde{v}_n(x)|\, dx \longrightarrow 0 ,$$

where $M_n = \{x \in \Omega;\ |u_n(x)| \leqq r\}$, $M_n^+ = \{x \in \Omega;\ u_n(x) > r\}$, $M_n^- = \{x \in \Omega;\ u_n(x) < -r\}$. Hence

$$\liminf_{n\to\infty} \int_\Omega g(x,u_n(x))\, v_n(x)\, dx \leqq \limsup_{n\to\infty} \int_\Omega g(x,u_n(x))\, \tilde{v}_n(x)\, dx .$$

If we knew that

$$g(x,u_n(x))\, \tilde{v}_n(x) \leqq \tilde{h}(x) \tag{13.27}$$

for some $\tilde{h} \in L^1(\Omega)$ then Fatou's lemma would imply that

$$\limsup_{n\to\infty} \int_\Omega g(x,u_n(x))\, \tilde{v}_n(x)\, dx \leqq \int_\Omega \limsup_{n\to\infty} g(x,u_n(x))\, \tilde{v}_n(x)\, dx .$$

The assertion would follow because either $u_n(x) \longrightarrow +\infty$ or $u_n(x) \longrightarrow -\infty$ for a.a. $x \in \Omega$ and therefore the last integral equals the right hand side in (13.25) or in (13.26) provided $\xi > 0$ or $\xi < 0$, respectively. Hence it is sufficient to show (13.27). The definition of $\tilde{v}_n$ and (10.18), (13.8), (13.9) imply

$$g(x,u_n(x))\tilde{v}_n(x) \leqq a(x)|\xi|u_1(x) \quad \text{in } M_n^+ ,$$

$$g(x,u_n(x))\tilde{v}_n(x) \leqq -A(x)|\xi|u_1(x) \quad \text{in } M_n^- ,$$

$$g(x,u_n(x))\tilde{v}_n(x) \leqq (m(x) + cr^{p-1})|\xi|u_1(x) \quad \text{in } M_n ,$$

and (13.27) follows. □

13.9. Remarks. (i) Let us observe that the proof of Theorem 13.6 becomes very simple and short for the special case of Theorem 13.5 (i.e. if we replace T by J) and a bounded nonlinearity g . Indeed, we get $\tilde{g} \equiv 0$ and it follows directly from (13.15) by using the compactness argument and the properties of J that $v_n \to v$ in X and that (13.23) holds with $\tilde{S} = 0$. (The last part of the proof remains without changes.)

(ii) Consider BVP (13.1), (13.3) with g bounded (cf. (i)). We will use this particular situation to explain very briefly another approach which can be used for the proof of results of the type of Theorem 13.5. Consider the equation

$$\operatorname{div}\left(|\nabla u_\varepsilon(x)|^{p-2}\,\nabla u_\varepsilon(x)\right) + \lambda_1 \frac{|u_\varepsilon(x)|^{p-2}\,u_\varepsilon(x)}{1+\varepsilon^{p-1}|u_\varepsilon(x)|^{p-1}} + g\left(x,u(x)\right) = f(x)\ , \quad x \in \Omega\ , \tag{13.1$_\varepsilon$}$$

with the boundary condition (13.3). It follows from the theory of monotone operators (see e.g. LIONS [203]) that for any $\varepsilon > 0$ there exists a weak solution of this problem, i.e. $u_\varepsilon \in X = W_0^{1,p}(\Omega)$, satisfying

$$J(u_\varepsilon) - \lambda_1 S_\varepsilon(u_\varepsilon) - G(u_\varepsilon) + f^* = 0 \tag{13.12$_\varepsilon$}$$

where $S_\varepsilon : X \to X^*$ is defined by

$$\left(S_\varepsilon(u),v\right)_X = \int_\Omega \frac{|u|^{p-2}\,u\,v}{1+\varepsilon^{p-1}|u|^{p-1}}\,dx\ .$$

Multiplying (13.12$_\varepsilon$) by $\varepsilon^p u_\varepsilon$, we can derive that $\|\varepsilon u_\varepsilon\|_X$ is bounded. Hence we can suppose $\varepsilon_n u_{\varepsilon_n} \rightharpoonup v$ in X for some $v \in X$ and a sequence $\{\varepsilon_n\}$, $\varepsilon_n \to 0$. Multiplying (13.12$_\varepsilon$) by ε_n^{p-1} and using the compactness argument, we obtain $\varepsilon_n u_{\varepsilon_n} \to v$,

$$J(v) - \lambda_1 S_1(v) = 0\ ,$$

i.e. v is a weak solution of BVP

$$\operatorname{div}\left(|\nabla v|^{p-2}\,\nabla v\right) + \lambda_1 \frac{|v|^{p-2}\,v}{1+|v|^{p-1}} = 0 \quad \text{in } \Omega\ ,$$

$$v = 0 \quad \text{on } \partial\Omega\ .$$

This implies $v = 0$ because λ_1 is the smallest eigenvalue of BVP (13.4), (13.3). Hence $\varepsilon_n u_{\varepsilon_n} \to 0$. If we were able to exclude the case $\|u_{\varepsilon_n}\|_X \to +\infty$ then from (13.12$_\varepsilon$) by using the compactness argument again we would obtain $u_{\varepsilon_n} \to u$ for some $u \in X$, and u would be a solution of our problem. However, if $\|u_{\varepsilon_n}\|_X \to +\infty$ then we can suppose $v_n = \dfrac{u_{\varepsilon_n}}{\|u_{\varepsilon_n}\|_X} \rightharpoonup v$ for some $v \in X$. Dividing (13.12$_\varepsilon$) by $\|u_{\varepsilon_n}\|_X^{p-1}$, we get $v_n \to v$,

$$J(v) - \lambda_1 S(v) = 0 ,$$

i.e. $v = \pm u_1$. This leads to a contradiction with (13.10) similarly as in the last part of the proof of Theorem 13.5.

(iii) Let us remark that the result similar to our Theorem 13.5 is proved in ANANE and GOSSEZ [13] by using the variational approach.

<u>13.10. Examples.</u> (i) Let us consider BVP

$$\begin{aligned} \operatorname{div}\left(|\nabla u(x)|^{p-2}\nabla u(x)\right) + \lambda_1 |u(x)|^{p-2} u(x) - |u(x)|^{q-2} u(x) = \\ = f(x), \quad x \in \Omega, \end{aligned} \tag{13.28}$$

$$u(x) = 0, \qquad x \in \partial\Omega, \tag{13.29}$$

where $1 < q \leqq p$. The function $g(x,u) = -|u(x)|^{q-2} u(x)$ fulfils the assumptions (10.18), (13.8) and (13.9), $g^{+\infty}(x) \equiv -\infty$, $g_{-\infty}(x) \equiv +\infty$. It follows from Theorem 13.5 that BVP (13.28), (13.29) has at least one weak solution $u \in W_0^{1,p}(\Omega)$ for any right hand side $f \in L^{\alpha'}(\Omega)$ (for α' see Subsection 10.10).

(ii) It follows from Theorem 13.6 that BVP

$$\begin{aligned} \operatorname{div}\left[\left(a(x) + |\nabla u(x)|^{p-2}\right)\nabla u(x)\right] + \lambda_1 |u(x)|^{p-2} u(x) - \\ - |u(x)|^{q-2} u(x) = f(x), \quad x \in \Omega \end{aligned}$$

(with $p \geqq 2$ and a smooth function $a(x)$ such that $0 \leqq a(x) \leqq$ const. on Ω) has at least one weak solution for an arbitrary right hand side $f \in L^{\alpha'}(\Omega)$ (see BOCCARDO, DRÁBEK and KUČERA [31] for details).

13.11. Reverse one-sided growth restrictions on g. Let us denote

$$g^{-\infty}(x) = \limsup_{s\to-\infty} g(x,s) , \quad g_{+\infty}(x) = \liminf_{s\to+\infty} g(x,s)$$

and suppose that there are constants $r, R \in \mathbb{R}$, $r < 0 < R$, and functions $a, A \in L^{\alpha'}(\Omega)$ such that

$$g(x,s) \leqq a(x) \tag{13.30}$$

for a.a. $x \in \Omega$ and for all $s \leqq r$;

$$g(x,s) \geqq A(x) \tag{13.31}$$

for a.a. $x \in \Omega$ and for all $s \geqq R$ (cf. Subsection 1.14). Moreover, we assume that

$$\lim_{|s|\to\infty} \frac{g(x,s)}{|s|^{p-1}} = 0 \tag{13.32}$$

for a.a. $x \in \Omega$.

Now we formulate in a certain sense dual version of Theorems 13.5, 13.6 for the case of Neumann boundary conditions.

13.12. Theorem. *Let us suppose* (10.18), (13.30) - (13.32) *and* $p > N$. *Then BVP* (13.1), (13.2) *has at least one weak solution for any* $f \in L^{\alpha'}(\Omega)$ *satisfying the condition*

$$\int_\Omega g^{-\infty}(x)\, dx < \int_\Omega f(x)\, dx < \int_\Omega g_{+\infty}(x)\, dx . \tag{13.33}$$

13.13. Theorem. *Suppose* (10.18), (13.30) - (13.32), $p > N$, $X = W^{1,p}(\Omega)$. *Let* $T : X \to X^*$ *be an odd mapping which is* (p-1)-*quasihomogeneous with respect to* J, *such that* $T_d = T + dS$ *is a homeomorphism for any* $d > 0$ *and* $(T(u),u)_X \geqq (J(u),u)_X$, $(T(u),u_1)_X = 0$ *for all* $u \in X$. *Then* (13.12) *has at least one solution for any* $f^* \in X^*$ *which is defined by means of* $f \in L^{\alpha'}(\Omega)$ *satisfying* (13.33).

Proof of Theorem 13.13. First, choose $d > 0$ such that there is no eigenvalue of BVP (13.4), (13.2) in the interval $(0,d]$. Note that $\lambda_1 = 0$ and $u_1 \equiv$ const. in our case. Define a homotopy $\mathcal{H} : [0,1] \times X \to X$ by

$$\mathcal{H}(\tau,u) = u - T_d^{-1}\big((2-\tau)dS(u) + \tau(G(u) - f^*)\big) .$$

We can follow the proof of Theorem 13.6 till we obtain

$$T(u_n) - (1 - \tau_n)dS(u_n) - \tau_n\left(G(u_n) - f^*\right) = 0 , \tag{13.14'}$$

$$\|u_n\|_X^{1-p} T(u_n) - (1 - \tau_n)dS(v_n) - $$
$$- \tau_n\|u_n\|_X^{1-p} \cdot \left(G(u_n) - f^*\right) = 0 , \tag{13.15'}$$

where $v_n = \dfrac{u_n}{\|u_n\|_X} \rightharpoonup v$, $\tau_n \to \tau$. It follows again from (10.18) that we can suppose

$$\frac{g\left(\cdot,u_n(\cdot)\right)}{\|u_n\|_X^{p-1}} \rightharpoonup \tilde{g} \quad \text{in} \quad L^{\alpha'}(\Omega) .$$

However, (13.30) - (13.32) ensure that $\tilde{g} = 0$, i.e. $\chi \equiv 0$ in the course of the proof of Theorem 13.6 (to be precise, we can proceed analogously to Remark 13.7). Then using the facts that T_d is a homeomorphism, T is (p-1)-quasi-homogeneous with respect to J , (13.5) and the assumption $\left(T(u),u\right)_X \geq$ $\geq \left(J(u),u\right)_X$, we derive that $v \neq 0$ and

$$J(v) - (1 - \tau)dS(v) = 0$$

in the same way as in the proof of Theorem 13.6. But $(1 - \tau)d$ is not an eigenvalue for $\tau \in [0,1)$ by the choice of d . Therefore $\tau = 1$, $v = \xi$ for some $\xi \neq 0$. Suppose $\xi > 0$ (the case $\xi < 0$ can be treated similarly). It follows from (13.14') that

$$\left(T(u_n),\xi\right)_X - (1-\tau_n)d\left(S(u_n),\xi\right)_X = \tau_n \int_\Omega \left[g\left(x,u_n(x)\right) - f(x)\right] \xi \, dx . \tag{13.34}$$

Since $\left(T(u_n),\xi\right)_X = 0$ by the assumption and $d > 0$, the left hand side of (13.34) is nonpositive for n large enough. Hence

$$\liminf_{n \to \infty} \int_\Omega g\left(x,u_n(x)\right) dx \leq \int_\Omega f(x) \, dx . \tag{13.35}$$

Due to the compact imbedding $W^{1,p}(\Omega) \hookrightarrow\hookrightarrow C(\overline{\Omega})$ (note that $p > N$) we have $u_n(x) > r$ for all $x \in \Omega$ if n is large enough. Then (13.35), (13.30), (13.31) and Fatou's lemma imply

$$\int_\Omega g_{+\infty}(x) \, dx \leq \int_\Omega f(x) \, dx$$

which contradicts (13.33). $\square$

13.14. Remarks. (i) Let us remark that Theorem 13.12 is a consequence of Theorem 13.13 as is seen from the considerations in Subsection 13.3.

(ii) The assumption $p > N$ in Theorems 13.12, 13.13 ensures the compact imbedding $W^{1,p}(\Omega) \subsetneq \subsetneq C(\bar{\Omega})$. In the case $1 < p \leq N$ we need some additional assumptions on g . Namely, suppose that

$$|g(x,s)| \leq h(x) \tag{13.36}$$

for all $s \in \mathbb{R}$, a.a. $x \in \Omega$ with some $h \in L^{\alpha'}(\Omega)$.

13.15. Theorem. *Suppose* (13.36). *Then BVP* (13.1), (13.2) *has at least one weak solution for any* $f \in L^{\alpha'}(\Omega)$ *satisfying* (13.33).

This assertion is a special version of the following theorem the proof of which is a simple modification of Theorem 13.13.

13.16. Theorem. *Suppose* (13.36), $X = W^{1,p}(\Omega)$. *Let* $T : X \to X^*$ *be an odd mapping which is* (p-1)*-quasihomogeneous with respect to* J , *such that* $T_d = T + dS$ *is a homeomorphism of* X *onto* X^* *for any* $d > 0$ *and* $(T(u),u)_X \geq (J(u),u)_X$, $(T(u),u_1)_X = 0$ *for all* $u \in X$. *Then* (13.12) *has at least one solution for any* $f^* \in X^*$ *which is defined by means of* $f \in L^{\alpha'}(\Omega)$ *satisfying* (13.33).

13.17. Example. Consider BVP

$$\operatorname{div}\left[\left(a(x) + |\nabla u(x)|^{p-2}\right)\nabla u(x)\right] + \operatorname{arctg} u(x) = f(x) , \quad x \in \Omega , \tag{13.37}$$

$$\left(a(x) + |\nabla u(x)|^{p-2}\right)\nabla u(x)\, \nu(x) = 0 , \quad x \in \partial\Omega , \tag{13.38}$$

where a is a smooth function on Ω , $0 \leq a(x) \leq \text{const.}$ It follows from Theorem 13.16 that BVP (13.37), (13.38) has a weak solution for any $f \in L^{\alpha'}(\Omega)$ satisfying

$$-\ (\text{meas } \Omega)\ \frac{\pi}{2} < \int_\Omega f(x)\, dx < (\text{meas } \Omega)\ \frac{\pi}{2} .$$

13.18. Nonlinearity with rapid growth. We will consider the equation

$$\operatorname{div}\left(|\nabla u(x)|^{p-2}\nabla u(x)\right) + \lambda_1 |u(x)|^{p-2} u(x) - $$
$$- |u(x)|^{q-2} u(x) + g\left(x,u(x)\right) = f(x) , \quad x \in \Omega , \tag{13.39}$$

with the boundary conditions (13.2) and (13.3), where $q > p$, $f \in L^{q'}(\Omega)$ ($\frac{1}{q} + \frac{1}{q'} = 1$), and g satisfies

$$|g(x,s)| \leq m(x) + c|s|^{p-1} , \tag{13.40}$$

$m \in L^{q'}(\Omega)$, $c > 0$. Set

$$X = W^{1,p}(\Omega) \cap L^q(\Omega) \quad \text{or} \quad X = W_0^{1,p}(\Omega) \cap L^q(\Omega) \tag{13.41}$$

if the boundary conditions (13.2) or (13.3) are considered, respectively. The space X defined by (13.41) with the norm

$$\|u\|_X = \left(\|u\|_{1,p}^p + \|u\|_q^p\right)^{\frac{1}{p}}$$

is a locally uniformly convex Banach space. The mappings $J, S, G : X \to X^*$ and an element $f^* \in X^*$ are again well-defined. Moreover, introduce mappings $Q, J_Q : X \to X^*$ by

$$\left(Q(u),v\right)_X = \int_\Omega |u(x)|^{q-2} u(x)\, v(x)\, dx , \tag{13.42}$$

$$J_Q = J + Q .$$

The *weak solution* of BVP (13.39), (13.2) or (13.39), (13.3) is defined as $u \in X$ satisfying

$$J(u) - \lambda_1 S(u) + Q(u) - G(u) + f^* = 0 . \tag{13.43}$$

The mapping J_Q is a homeomorphism of X onto X^*. This can be shown analogously as for J_d in Subsection 13.3 but by using the estimates

$$\frac{\left(J_Q(u),u\right)_X}{\|u\|_X} = \frac{\|u\|_{1,p}^p + \|u\|_q^q}{\left(\|u\|_{1,p}^p + \|u\|_q^p\right)^{1/p}} \geq \frac{\max\left(\|u\|_{1,p}^p, \|u\|_q^q\right)}{\left[2\max\left(\|u\|_{1,p}^p, \|u\|_q^p\right)\right]^{1/p}} \longrightarrow \infty$$

$$\text{for } \|u\|_X \to \infty ,$$

$$\left(J_Q(u) - J_Q(v),\ u - v\right)_X \geq \left(\|u\|_{1,p}^{p-1} - \|v\|_{1,p}^{p-1}\right)\left(\|u\|_{1,p} - \|v\|_{1,p}\right) +$$

$$+ \left(\|u\|_q^{q-1} - \|v\|_q^{q-1}\right)\left(\|u\|_q - \|v\|_q\right) > 0$$

for all $u, v \in X$, $u \neq v$, instead of (13.5), (13.6).

Note that the mappings S, G are compact again but Q is not compact for q so large that $W^{1,p}(\Omega)$ is not compactly imbedded into $L^q(\Omega)$.

Let us formulate, at first, the following assertion concerning the solvability of BVPs (13.39), (13.2) and (13.39), (13.3).

<u>13.19. Theorem.</u> *Let us suppose* (13.40), $q > p$. *Then each of BVPs* (13.39), (13.2) *and* (13.39), (13.3) *has at least one weak solution for any* $f \in L^{q'}(\Omega)$.

<u>13.20. Remark.</u> Theorem 13.19 is a special case of a more general Theorem 13.21 below. In the sequel, we will replace the terms $\operatorname{div}\left(|\nabla u|^{p-2}\nabla u\right)$ and $|u|^{q-2}u$ by a quasihomogeneous operator and by a Carathéodory function $b_q : \Omega \times \mathbf{R} \to \mathbf{R}$ satisfying

$$b_q(x,s) \leq m_q(x) + c|s|^{q-1} \tag{13.44}$$

with some $m_q \in L^{q'}(\Omega)$, $c \geq 0$,

$$b_q(x,s)\cdot s \geq c_0|s|^q \tag{13.45}$$

with some $c_0 > 0$.

More precisely, let us introduce an operator $B : X \to X^*$ by

$$\left(B(u),v\right)_X = \int_\Omega b_q\left(x,u(x)\right)\, v(x)\, dx \tag{13.46}$$

for all $u, v \in X$ and consider the equation

$$T(u) - \lambda_1 S(u) + B(u) - G(u) + f^* = 0\ . \tag{13.47}$$

<u>13.21. Theorem.</u> *Let us suppose* (13.40), $q > p$, (13.44), (13.45). *Let* $T : X \to X^*$ *be* (p-1)-*quasihomogeneous with respect to* J, *such that* $T_B = T + B$ *is a homeomorphism of* X *onto* X^* *and* $\left(T(u),u\right)_X \geq \left(J(u),u\right)_X$ *for all* $u \in X$. *Then* (13.47) *has at least one solution for any* $f^* \in X^*$

defined by means of $f \in L^{q'}(\Omega)$.

Proof. Let us define a mapping $\mathcal{H} : [0,1] \times X \to X$ by

$$\mathcal{H}(\tau,u) = u - T_B^{-1}\big(\tau(\lambda_1 S(u) + G(u) - f^*)\big) .$$

Similarly as in the proof of Theorem 13.6, it is sufficient to show that (13.13) holds with R large enough. (Note that $\mathcal{H}(1,u) = 0$ is equivalent to (13.47) and $\deg\,[\mathcal{H}(0,\cdot);\, B_R,\, 0] = \deg\,[I;\, B_R,\, 0] = 1$.) Suppose by way of contradiction that there exist $\tau_n \in [0,1]$, $u_n \in X$ $(n = 1,2,\dots)$ such that $\|u_n\|_X \to +\infty$ and

$$T(u_n) + B(u_n) - \tau_n\big(\lambda_1 S(u_n) + G(u_n) - f^*\big) = 0 . \tag{13.48}$$

In particular,

$$\big(B(u_n),u_n\big)_X = -\big(T(u_n) - \tau_n\lambda_1 S(u_n),\, u_n\big)_X - \tau_n\big(G(u_n) - f^*,\, u_n\big)_X .$$

The first term on the right hand side is nonpositive by the assumptions $\big(T(u),u\big)_X \geq \big(J(u),u\big)_X$ and (10.21). Hence (13.40) and the imbedding $L^q(\Omega) \subsetneq L^p(\Omega)$ imply that

$$c_0\|u_n\|_q^q \leq \|m\|_{q'}\, \|u_n\|_q + c\|u_n\|_q^p + \|f\|_{q'}\, \|u_n\|_q .$$

This yields that

$$\{\, u_n \,\} \quad \text{is bounded in} \quad L^q(\Omega) . \tag{13.49}$$

Consequently, (13.44) gives

$$\left[\int_\Omega \left|\frac{b_q\big(x,u_n(x)\big)}{\|u_n\|_X^{p-1}}\right|^{\frac{q}{q-1}} dx\right]^{\frac{q-1}{q}} \leq \left[\int_\Omega \left(\frac{m_q(x) + c\,|u_n(x)|^{q-1}}{\|u_n\|_X^{p-1}}\right)^{\frac{q}{q-1}} dx\right]^{\frac{q-1}{q}} \leq$$

$$\leq \|u_n\|_X^{1-p}\big(\|m_q\|_{q'} + \|u_n\|_q^{q-1}\big) \longrightarrow 0 ,$$

which means

$$\frac{B(u_n)}{\|u_n\|_X^{p-1}} \longrightarrow 0 \quad \text{in} \quad X^* \tag{13.50}$$

due to the imbedding $L^{q'}(\Omega) \subsetneq X^*$. Analogously we obtain (by using (13.40) and the imbedding $L^q(\Omega) \subsetneq L^p(\Omega)$)

$$\frac{G(u_n)}{\|u_n\|_X^{p-1}} \longrightarrow 0 \quad \text{in} \quad X^* . \tag{13.51}$$

We can suppose $\tau_n \to \tau$, $v_n = \dfrac{u_n}{\|u_n\|_X} \rightharpoonup v$ in X. Dividing (13.48) by $\|u_n\|_X^{p-1}$ and using (13.50), (13.51) and the compactness of S we get that

$$\left\{ \frac{T(u_n)}{\|u_n\|_X^{p-1}} \right\} \text{ is convergent.}$$

Hence

$$\frac{T(u_n)}{\|u_n\|_X^{p-1}} \longrightarrow J(v)$$

by the assumption that T is (p-1)-quasihomogeneous with respect to J. The limiting process in (13.48) yields

$$J(v) - \tau\lambda_1 S(v) = 0 . \tag{13.52}$$

Further,

$$(J(v),v)_X = \lim_{n\to\infty} \frac{(T(u_n),u_n)_X}{\|u_n\|_X^p} \geqq \lim_{n\to\infty} \frac{(J(u_n),u_n)_X}{\|u_n\|_X^p} =$$

$$= \lim_{n\to\infty} \frac{\|u_n\|_{1,p}^p}{\|u_n\|_{1,p}^p + \|u_n\|_q^p} = 1 .$$

Hence $v \neq 0$ and it follows from (13.52) that $\tau = 1$, $v = \xi u_1$ with $\xi \neq 0$. The compactness of the imbedding $X \hookrightarrow\hookrightarrow L^p(\Omega)$ ensures

$$\|v_n\|_p \to \xi\|u_1\|_p ,$$

and we have $\|u_n\|_X \to \infty$. Simultaneously,

$$\|u_n\|_X \cdot \|v_n\|_p = \|u_n\|_p \leq c_1\|u_n\|_q ,$$

which contradicts (13.49). □

13.22. Example. Consider the equation

$$\operatorname{div}\left[\left(a(x) + |\nabla u(x)|^{p-2}\right)\nabla u(x)\right] + \lambda_1 |u(x)|^{p-2} u(x) -$$
$$- \left(b(x) + |u(x)|^{q-2}\right)u(x) + g\left(x,u(x)\right) = f(x) , \quad x \in \Omega$$

with the boundary condition (13.3), where a, b are smooth functions on Ω, $0 \leqq a(x) \leqq c$, $0 \leqq b(x) \leqq c$, $q > p$, and g satisfies (13.40). The weak solution of this BVP is a solution of (13.47) with T, B defined by

$$(T(u),v)_X = \int_\Omega \left(a(x) + |\nabla u(x)|^{p-2}\right) \nabla u(x)\, \nabla v(x)\, dx ,$$

$$(B(u),v)_X = \int_\Omega \left(b(x) + |u(x)|^{q-2}\right) u(x)\, v(x)\, dx$$

for all $u, v \in X$, $X = W_0^{1,p}(\Omega) \cap L^q(\Omega)$. Suppose that $p \geqq 2$. Then it is easy to see that T is $(p-1)$-quasihomogeneous with respect to J. Further,

$$\left(T_B(u) - T_B(v),\, u - v\right)_X \geqq \left(J_Q(u) - J_Q(v),\, u - v\right)_X$$

and therefore we can show by considerations analogous to those from Subsection 13.3 that T_B is a homeomorphism of X onto X^* (cf. Subsection 13.18). Consequently, our problem has for any $f \in L^{q'}(\Omega)$ at least one weak solution by Theorem 13.21. Analogous considerations can be carried out for the boundary condition (13.38) from Example 13.17. (Then $\lambda_1 = 0$, $X = W^{1,p}(\Omega) \cap L^q(\Omega)$.)

13.22. Remark. Let us remark that analogously as in the case of Theorem 13.5 we can also use a different approach to the proof of Theorem 13.19 (cf. Remark 13.9 (ii)). We refer the reader to BOCCARDO, DRÁBEK and KUČERA [31] for details.

CHAPTER 5
Bifurcations of strongly nonlinear problems

14. GLOBAL BIFURCATION RESULTS FOR p-LAPLACIAN

14.1. Second order ordinary differential equations. Let us consider BVP

$$-\left(a(t)\,|u'(t)|^{p-2}\,u'(t)\right)' - \lambda c(t)\,|u'(t)|^{p-2}\,u'(t) = g\left(t,u(t),\lambda\right), \quad t \in [0,\pi], \tag{14.1}$$

$$u(0) = u(\pi) = 0. \tag{14.2}$$

We will suppose $p \geqq 2$, $a \in C^1([0,\pi])$, $a(t) > 0$ in $[0,\pi]$, $c \in C([0,\pi])$, $c(t) > 0$ in $[0,\pi]$. Let $g = g(t,s,\lambda)$ be a Carathéodory function, i.e. $g(\cdot,s,\lambda)$ is measurable for all $(s,\lambda) \in \mathbb{R}^2$ and $g(t,\cdot,\cdot)$ is continuous for a.a. $t \in (0,\pi)$. Moreover, let $g(t,0,\lambda) \equiv 0$ and

$$\lim_{s\to 0} \frac{g(t,s,\lambda)}{|s|^{p-1}} = 0 \tag{14.3}$$

uniformly for a.a. $t \in (0,\pi)$ and for λ from bounded intervals in $\mathbb{R}$.

Assume that there exist $m(t) \in L^1(0,\pi)$ and positive continuous function $\tilde{g} : \mathbb{R}^2 \to \mathbb{R}$ such that

$$|g(t,s,\lambda)| \leqq m(t)\left(1 + \tilde{g}(|s|,\lambda)\right)$$

holds for a.a. $t \in [0,\pi]$ and for all $(s,\lambda) \in \mathbb{R}^2$.

14.2. Operator representation. Set $X = W_0^{1,p}(0,\pi)$ and define operators $J,\ S : X \to X^*$, $G : \mathbb{R} \times X \to X^*$ by

$$\left(J(u),v\right)_X = \int_0^\pi a(t)\ |u'(t)|^{p-2}\ u'(t)\ v'(t)\ dt,$$

$$\left(S(u),v\right)_X = \int_0^\pi c(t)\ |u(t)|^{p-2}\ u(t)\ v(t)\ dt,$$

$$\left(G(\lambda,u),v\right)_X = \int_0^\pi g\left(t,u(t),\lambda\right) v(t)\, dt$$

for any $u, v \in X$. For the properties of J and S see Lemma 10.3, the operator G is compact.

A function $u \in X$ is said to be *a weak solution* of BVP (14.1), (14.2) if it satisfies the operator equation

$$J(u) = \lambda S(u) + G(\lambda,u) . \tag{14.4}$$

Let us remark that if a and c satisfy the assumptions formulated in Subsection 14.1 then any weak solution of BVP (14.1), (14.2) satisfies $u' \in C([0,\pi])$, $a(t)|u'(t)|^{p-2} u'(t)$ is absolutely continuous, the boundary condition (14.2) holds and the equation (14.1) is satisfied a.e. in $(0,\pi)$, i.e. u is *a solution* of BVP (14.1), (14.2) in the sense of Carathéodory (cf. DRÁBEK [84] and Section 10).

14.3. Eigenvalue and its multiplicity. We will say that λ is *an eigenvalue* of BVP

$$- \left(a(t)|u'(t)|^{p-2} u'(t)\right)' - \lambda c(t)|u(t)|^{p-2} u(t) = 0 , \ t \in [0,\pi] , \tag{14.5}$$

$$u(0) = u(\pi) = 0 \tag{14.6}$$

if the operator equation

$$J(u) - \lambda S(u) = 0$$

has a solution $u \in X$, $u \neq 0$. Such an element u is called *an eigenfunction* corresponding to λ. The eigenvalue λ is said to have finite *multiplicity* equal to n if there are exactly n pairs $\{(u_i,-u_i)\}_{i=1}^n$ of isolated normed eigenfunctions corresponding to λ. Let us recall that it is proved in NEČAS [231] that the eigenvalues of BVP (14.5), (14.6) form a countable discrete set $\{\lambda_i\}_{i=1}^\infty$, $0 < \lambda_1 < \lambda_2 < \dots$, $\lim\limits_{n\to\infty} \lambda_n = \infty$. Moreover, each eigenvalue λ_i, $i = 1,2,\dots$, of BVP (14.5), (14.6) has a finite multiplicity in the sense mentioned above (cf. Remark 10.5).

14.4. Continuum of nontrivial solutions. Let $E = \mathbb{R} \times X$ be equipped with the norm

$$\|(\lambda,u)\|_E = \left(|\lambda|^2 + \|u\|_X^2\right)^{\frac{1}{2}}, \quad (\lambda,u) \in E . \tag{14.7}$$

We say that

$$C = \{(\lambda,u) \in E; \quad \lambda \text{ and } u \text{ solve (14.4)}, \quad u \neq 0\}$$

is a *continuum of nontrivial solutions* of BVP (14.1), (14.2) if it is a connected set in E (with respect to the topology induced by the norm (14.7)).

14.5. The linearized eigenvalue problem. Let us denote by u any normed eigenfunction of BVP (14.5), (14.6). It is proved in NEČAS [231] that for $\rho(x) = |u'(x)|^{p-2}$ the set

$$W_0^{1,2}(\rho) = \left\{h;\ h(0) = h(\pi) = 0 \text{ and } \int_0^\pi (h')^2\ \rho\ dx = \|h\|^2_{1,2,\rho} < \infty\right\}$$

is a Hilbert space imbedded algebraically and topologically into $W^{1,q}(0,\pi)$ provided

$$1 \leqq q < \frac{2(p-1)}{2p-3} .$$

Moreover, the system of functions $\{v_n(t)\}_{n=1}^\infty = \{\sin nt\}_{n=1}^\infty$ is dense in $W_0^{1,2}(\rho)$. Note that $X \subset W_0^{1,2}(\rho)$ and that $\{v_n\}_{n=1}^\infty$ is dense also in X. Let $J'(u)$, $S'(u)$ be the Fréchet derivatives of J and S, respectively, at the point $u \in X$, i.e.

$$\left(J'(u)h,k\right)_{W_0^{1,2}(\rho)} = (p-1)\int_0^\pi a(t)\ |u'(t)|^{p-2}\ h'(t)\ k'(t)\ dt ,$$

$$\left(S'(u)h,k\right)_{W_0^{1,2}(\rho)} = (p-1)\int_0^\pi c(t)\ |u(t)|^{p-2}\ h(t)\ k(t)\ dt$$

for any $h, k \in W_0^{1,2}(\rho)$. Then it is also proved in NEČAS [231] that *the linearized eigenvalue problem*

$$J'(u)h - \mu S'(u)h = 0 \tag{14.8}$$

has only *simple eigenvalues* μ (i.e. with multiplicity one).

For a fixed eigenfunction u of BVP (14.5), (14.6) we will denote the space $W_0^{1,2}(\rho)$ simply by H .

<u>14.6. The degree of generalized monotone mappings.</u> Consider an operator $A : X \to X^*$ defined on a real separable reflexive Banach space X . The operator A is said *to satisfy the condition* $\alpha(X)$ if for an arbitrary sequence $u_n \in X$ the relations $u_n \rightharpoonup u_0$ in X and

$$\limsup_{n \to \infty} \left(A(u_n),\, u_n - u_0\right)_X \leq 0 \tag{14.9}$$

imply the strong convergence $u_n \to u_0$ in X .

An operator A is called *demicontinuous* if any sequence $u_n \in X$ strongly convergent to $u_0 \in X$ in X satisfies the relation $A(u_n) \rightharpoonup A(u_0)$ in X^*.

Let D be an arbitrary bounded open set in the space X with a boundary ∂D , let $\{v_i\}_{i=1}^{\infty}$ be an arbitrary complete subset of the space X , and let us assume that for every n the elements $v_1,\dots,v_n$ are linearly independent. By V_n let us denote the linear hull of the elements $v_1,\dots,v_n$. Let $A(u) \neq 0$ for any $u \in \partial D$. Set

$$A_n(u) = \sum_{i=1}^{n} \left(A(u), v_i\right)_X v_i \ .$$

It is possible to define the degree of the mapping A at 0 with respect to $D \subset X$ as the Brouwer degree of $A_n : V_n \to V_n$ at 0 with respect to $D \cap V_n$ for sufficiently large n . More precisely,

$$\text{Deg}\left[A;\, D,\, 0\right] = \lim_{n \to \infty} \deg_B \left[A_n;\, D \cap V_n,\, 0\right] \ . \tag{14.10}$$

It is shown in SKRYPNIK [276] that $\deg_B \left[A_n;\, D \cap V_n,\, 0\right]$ is constant for $n \geq n_0$ for some $n_0 \in \mathbb{N}$ and that the value of the limit in (14.10) is independent of the choice of the system of functions $\{v_i\}$ (cf. also BROWDER and PETRYSHYN [34]). Hence the degree *Deg* is well defined and has the properties similar to those of the Leray - Schauder degree.

A point $u_0 \in X$ will be called *a critical point* of A if $A(u_0) = 0$. We say that u_0 is *an isolated critical point* of A if there exists $\varepsilon > 0$ such that in $B_\varepsilon(u_0)$ the mapping A is equal to 0 only at u_0 . Then the limit

$$\text{Ind}\,(A, u_0) = \lim_{\varepsilon \to 0} \text{Deg}\left[A;\, B_\varepsilon(u_0),\, 0\right]$$

exist and is called *the index of the isolated critical point* u_0 of the mapping A.

Let us suppose that $\Psi : X \to \mathbb{R}$ is a continuously differentiable functional (in the Fréchet sense), and $\Psi'(u) = A(u)$, $u \in X$, where A is as above.

The following assertion is the finite-dimensional version of the result in AMANN [7]. It is proved in SKRYPNIK [276].

<u>14.7. Lemma.</u> *Let* u_0 *be a local minimum of* Ψ *and, at the same time, an isolated critical point of* A. *Then* $\mathrm{Ind}\,(A,u_0) = 1$.

<u>14.8. Remark.</u> Let $J : X \to X^*$ be defined as in Subsection 14.2 and let $K : X \to X^*$ be a compact operator. Then $A = J + K$ is continuous and satisfies the condition $\alpha(X)$. Indeed, the continuity of A is an easy consequence of the fact that J satisfies (J1) - (J3) from Subsection 10.1 (see Lemma 10.3), and K is compact. In order to verify the condition $\alpha(X)$, let us suppose that $u_n \rightharpoonup u_0$ in X and (14.9) is valid. We have

$$\left(A(u_n),\, u_n - u_0\right)_X = \left(J(u_n),\, u_n - u_0\right)_X + \left(K(u_n),\, u_n - u_0\right)_X .$$

The last term on the right hand side tends to zero due to the compactness of K. Hence (14.9) and the weak convergence $u_n \rightharpoonup u_0$ in X imply

$$\limsup_{n\to\infty} \left(J(u_n) - J(u_0),\, u_n - u_0\right)_X \leq 0 .$$

This inequality together with (10.8) implies that

$$\limsup_{n\to\infty} \|u_n - u_0\|_X = 0 ,$$

i.e. $u_n \to u_0$ in X.

<u>14.9. Theorem.</u> *Let* λ_n *be an eigenvalue of BVP* (14.5), (14.6). *Then there exists a continuum* C *of nontrivial solutions of BVP* (14.1), (14.2) *such that* $(\lambda_n,0)$ *belongs to the closure* $\overline{C}$, C *is either unbounded in* E *or there is an eigenvalue* $\lambda_m \neq \lambda_n$ *such that* $(\lambda_m,0) \in \overline{C}$.

<u>*Proof*</u> of this theorem will be carried out in several steps.

Step 1. Let $\delta > 0$ be such that

$$2\delta < \min\{\lambda_{n+1} - \lambda_n, \lambda_n - \lambda_{n-1}\} ,$$

where λ_{n-1} and λ_{n+1} are the eigenvalues of BVP (14.5), (14.6) preceding and following λ_n, respectively. We prove that

$$\operatorname{Deg}[J - (\lambda_n - \delta)S; B_r, 0] \neq \operatorname{Deg}[J - (\lambda_n + \delta)S; B_r, 0] \tag{14.11}$$

for any $r > 0$ and for $\delta > 0$ small enough. Let us define a twice continuously differentiable function $\psi : \mathbb{R} \to \mathbb{R}$ in the following way:

$$\psi(t) = 0 \qquad \text{for } t \leqq R ,$$
$$\psi(t) = (\lambda_n - \lambda_1 + 2\delta)(t - 2R) \qquad \text{for } t \geqq 3R ,$$

ψ positive and strictly convex in $(R,3R)$, where $R > 0$ is a fixed real number. Define a functional $F_\lambda : X \to \mathbb{R}$ by

$$F_\lambda(u) = \frac{1}{p}(J(u),u)_X - \frac{1}{p}\lambda(S(u),u)_X + \psi\left(\frac{1}{p}(S(u),u)_X\right).$$

Then F_λ is twice continuously differentiable and the critical points of F'_λ correspond to the solutions of the equation

$$J(u) - \left[\lambda - \psi'\left(\frac{1}{p}(S(u),u)_X\right)\right]S(u) = 0 . \tag{14.12}$$

Let us suppose that $u_0 \in X$ is a critical point of F'_λ, $\lambda \in [\lambda_n - \delta, \lambda_n + \delta] \setminus \{\lambda_n\}$. Then either $u_0 = 0$ or $u_0 \neq 0$. In the case $u_0 \neq 0$ it follows from (14.12) that

$$\lambda - \psi'\left[\frac{1}{p}(S(u_0),u_0)_X\right] = \lambda_k$$

for some eigenvalue $\lambda_k < \lambda$ and $u_0 = \ell u_k$ for some $\ell = \ell(\lambda) \in \mathbb{R}$ (u_k is a normalized eigenfunction corresponding to λ_k). Simultaneously, due to the definition of ψ, for any normed eigenfunction u_k corresponding to $\lambda_k < \lambda$ we find precisely one $\ell_k = \ell_k(\lambda) > 0$ such that $u_0 = \ell_k u_k$ is a critical point of F'_λ. Hence F'_λ has a finite number of isolated critical points of type 0, $\ell_k u_k$, $-\ell_k u_k$, where u_k is the eigenfunction corresponding to $\lambda_k < \lambda$. If $\kappa > 0$ is large enough, we can suppose (due to the definition of ψ) that all these critical points lie in B_κ and that

$$(F'_\lambda(u),u)_X > 0 \tag{14.13}$$

for any $u \in \partial B_\kappa$, $\lambda \in [\lambda_n - \delta, \lambda_n + \delta] \setminus \{\lambda_n\}$. Then it follows from (14.13) and from the properties of the degree (see SKRYPNIK [276]) that

$$\text{Deg}\,\left[F'_\lambda;\ B_\kappa,\ 0\right] = 1\ . \tag{14.14}$$

Let $u_k^\lambda = \ell_k u_k$ (with $\ell_k \in \mathbb{R}$ defined above) be any nonzero critical point of F'_λ. We claim that for $k < n$ and for $\delta > 0$ small enough we have

$$\text{Ind}\,\left(F'_{\lambda_n-\delta},\ u_k^{\lambda_n-\delta}\right) = \text{Ind}\,\left(F'_{\lambda_n+\delta},\ u_k^{\lambda_n+\delta}\right) = \pm\,1\ .$$

We also claim that

$$\text{Ind}\,\left(F'_{\lambda_n+\delta},\ u_n^{\lambda_n+\delta}\right) = \pm\,1\ .$$

Suppose for a moment that the claims are true. Then for $\lambda = \lambda_n - \delta$ we have

$$\text{Ind}\,\left(F'_{\lambda_n-\delta}\ ,\ 0\right) = 1 - s\ , \tag{14.15}$$

where s is the sum of indices of all critical points of $F'_{\lambda_n-\delta}$ different from 0 (see the additivity property of the degree in SKRYPNIK [276] and (14.14)). For $\lambda = \lambda_n + \delta$ we have

$$\text{Ind}\,\left(F'_{\lambda_n+\delta}\ ,\ 0\right) = 1 - (s + \bar{s})\ , \tag{14.16}$$

where $\bar{s}$ is the sum of indices of the critical points $u_n^{\lambda_n+\delta}$. Since the multiplicity of λ_n is odd, we have $\bar{s} \neq 0$. Hence in virtue of (14.15), (14.16) we have

$$\text{Ind}\,\left(F'_{\lambda_n-\delta}\ ,\ 0\right) \neq \text{Ind}\,\left(F'_{\lambda_n+\delta}\ ,\ 0\right)\ .$$

Because J, S are homogeneous and $F'_\lambda(u) = J(u) - \lambda S(u)$ for $u \in B_R$, we have (14.11) with an arbitrary $r > 0$ and $\delta > 0$ small enough.

Step 2. We prove the claims. Let u_k be the eigenfunction corresponding to λ_k. We take the basis $\{v_i\}_{i=1}^\infty$ in X and in H, where H corresponds to u_k (see Subsection 14.5). By the definition of the degree the index of u_k^λ is equal to

$$\deg_B\,\left[\Phi_{\lambda,q}\ ;\ B_\varepsilon(u_k^\lambda) \cap V_q\ ,\ 0\right]\ ,$$

where

$$\Phi_{\lambda,q}(u) = \sum_{i=1}^{q} \left(F'_\lambda(u),\ v_i\right)_X v_i\ ,$$

$q \geqq q(\lambda)$ and $\varepsilon > 0$ is small enough. We have

$$\left(F''_\lambda(u_k^\lambda)w,\ v\right)_H = \left(J'(u_k^\lambda)w,\ v\right)_H -$$
$$- \left[\lambda - \psi'\left(\frac{1}{p}\left(S(u_k^\lambda),\ u_k^\lambda\right)_X\right)\right]\left(S'(u_k^\lambda)w,\ v\right)_H +$$
$$+ \psi''\left(\frac{1}{p}\left(S(u_k^\lambda),\ u_k^\lambda\right)_X\right)\left(S(u_k^\lambda),\ w\right)_X\left(S(u_k^\lambda),\ v\right)_X$$

for any $w, v \in H$. Note that

$$\lambda - \psi'\left(\frac{1}{p}\left(S(u_k^\lambda),\ u_k^\lambda\right)_X\right) = \lambda_k \ .$$

Let us suppose that there is $w_0 \in H$, $w_0 \neq 0$, such that $\left(F''(u_k^\lambda)w_0,\ v\right)_H = 0$ for all $v \in H$. Then for $v = u_k^\lambda$ we get

$$\left(J'(u_k^\lambda)w_0,\ u_k^\lambda\right)_H - \lambda_k\left(S'(u_k^\lambda)w_0,\ u_k^\lambda\right)_H +$$
$$+ \psi''\left(\frac{1}{p}\left(S(u_k^\lambda),\ u_k^\lambda\right)_X\right)\left(S(u_k^\lambda),\ w_0\right)_X\left(S(u_k^\lambda),\ u_k^\lambda\right)_X = 0 \ . \qquad (14.17)$$

Because

$$\left(J'(u_k^\lambda)w_0\ ,\ u_k^\lambda\right)_H = (p-1)\left(J(u_k^\lambda),\ w_0\right)_X \ ,$$
$$\left(S'(u_k^\lambda)w_0\ ,\ u_k^\lambda\right)_H = (p-1)\left(S(u_k^\lambda),\ w_0\right)_X$$

and $\left(S(u_k^\lambda),\ u_k^\lambda\right)_X \neq 0$, it follows from (14.17) that $\left(S(u_k^\lambda),\ w_0\right)_X = 0$. However, in this case

$$\left(J'(u_k^\lambda)w_0,\ v\right)_H - \lambda_k\left(S'(u_k^\lambda)w_0,\ v\right)_H = 0$$

for any $v \in H$, and since λ_k is a simple eigenvalue of the linear problem (14.8) (with $u = u_k^\lambda$), we would have $w_0 = u_k^\lambda$ which contradicts $\left(S(u_k^\lambda),\ w_0\right)_X = 0$. Hence

$$F''_\lambda(u_k^\lambda)\ w \neq 0 \qquad (14.18)$$

for any $w \in H$, $w \neq 0$ and for $\lambda \in [\lambda_n - \delta,\ \lambda_n + \delta]$ if $k < n$, $\lambda = \lambda_n + \delta$ if $k = n$.

We will show that there exists $q_0 = q_0(\delta)$ such that

$$\Phi'_{\lambda,q}(u_k^\lambda)\ w \neq 0 \qquad (14.19)$$

for all $\lambda \in [\lambda_n - \delta,\ \lambda_n + \delta]$ if $k < n$, $\lambda = \lambda_n + \delta$ if $k = n$, and for any $w \in V_q$, $w \neq 0$, $q \geq q_0$. Let $k < n$. Suppose that (14.19) is not true, i.e. there exist $q \to \infty$, $\lambda(q) \in [\lambda_n - \delta, \lambda_n + \delta]$, $w_q \in V_q$, $w_q \neq 0$ such that

$$\Phi'_{\lambda(q),q}\left(u_k^{\lambda(q)}\right)w_q = 0 \ . \tag{14.20}$$

We can suppose that $\lambda(q) \to \lambda$, $\|w_q\|_H = 1$ and $w_q \rightharpoonup w_0$ in H for some $w_0 \in H$. Choose $\tilde{w}_q \in V_q$ such that $\tilde{w}_q \to w_0$ in H as $q \to \infty$. Then (14.20) implies

$$\left(F''_{\lambda(q)}\left(u_k^{\lambda(q)}\right)w_q, \ w_q - w_0\right)_H = \left(F''_{\lambda(q)}\left(u_k^{\lambda(q)}\right)w_q, \ \tilde{w}_q - w_0\right)_H \ .$$

Since the right hand side tends to zero and

$$\left(F''_{\lambda(q)}\left(u_k^{\lambda(q)}\right)w_0, \ w_q - w_0\right)_H \to 0$$

(notice that $u_k^{\lambda(q)} = \ell_k(q)u_k$ with some $\ell_k(q)$ from a compact interval not containing 0), we get

$$\left(F''_{\lambda(q)}\left(u_k^{\lambda(q)}\right)(w_q - w_0), \ w_q - w_0\right)_H \to 0 \tag{14.21}$$

for $q \to \infty$. It follows from (14.21), from the definition of the norm in H and from the compactness of $S'(u_k^\lambda) : H \to H$ that

$$w_q \to w_0 \quad \text{in } H \ .$$

Since $\lambda(q) \to \lambda$ implies $u_k^{\lambda(q)} \to u_k^\lambda$ in X , we obtain

$$\left(F''_\lambda(u_k^\lambda)w_0, \ v\right)_H = 0$$

for any $v \in H$ with $\|w_0\|_H = 1$. However, this is a contradiction with (14.18). Analogously we prove (14.19) also for $k = n$.

Since

$$\Phi'_{\lambda,q}(u_k^\lambda)w = \sum_{i=1}^{q}\Big[\left(J'(u_k^\lambda)w, \ v_i\right)_H - \lambda\left(S'(u_k^\lambda)w, \ v_i\right)_H + \\ + \psi''\left(\frac{1}{p}\left(S(u_k^\lambda), \ u_k^\lambda\right)_X\right)\left(S(u_k^\lambda), \ w\right)_X\left(S(u_k^\lambda), \ v_i\right)_X\Big] \ v_i \ ,$$

$w \in V_q$, and u_k^λ depends continuously on λ , we see that $\det \Phi'_{\lambda,q}(u_k^\lambda)$ is a continuous function of λ and

$$\det \Phi'_{\lambda,q}(u_k^\lambda) \neq 0$$

by virtue of (14.19) for all $\lambda \in [\lambda_n - \delta, \lambda_n + \delta]$ if $k < n$, $q \geqq q_0$. Hence for $k < n$, $\lambda \in [\lambda_n - \delta, \lambda_n + \delta]$ the Brouwer degree $\deg_B [\Phi_{\lambda,q} ; B_\varepsilon(u_k^\lambda) \cap V_q , 0]$ is a constant function of λ either equal to $+1$ for all $q \geqq q_0$ or equal to -1 for all $q \geqq q_0$. We obtain directly from (14.19) that

$$\deg_B [\Phi_{\lambda_n+\delta,q} ; B_\varepsilon(u_n^\lambda) \cap V_q , 0] = \pm 1$$

independently of $q \geqq q_0$. If we take $q(\lambda) = q_0$ in the definition of $\Phi_{\lambda,q}$ the claims are proved.

Step 3. Set

$$P(\lambda,u) = J(u) - \lambda S(u) - G(\lambda,u) .$$

Then it follows immediately from (14.3) that

$$\lim_{\|u\|_X \to 0} \frac{G(\lambda,u)}{\|u\|_X^{p-1}} = 0 ,$$

and the homotopy invariance property of the degree (see SKRYPNIK [276]) yields that

$$\text{Deg } [P(\lambda_n - \delta, \cdot); B_r, 0] \neq \text{Deg } [P(\lambda_n + \delta, \cdot); B_r, 0] \tag{14.22}$$

for $r > 0$ and for $\delta > 0$ small enough.

Step 4. Following step by step the proof of RABINOWITZ [260, Theorem 1.3], using (14.3) and (14.22), the existence of a continuum C of nontrivial solutions of BVP (14.1), (14.2) with the desired properties can be proved. This completes the proof of Theorem 14.9. □

14.10. Second order problem with constant coefficients. Let us consider the special case of BVP (14.1), (14.2) with $a(t) \equiv c(t) \equiv 1$ in $[0,\pi]$. Then the eigenvalues of BVP (14.5), (14.6) are simple and any eigenfunction corresponding to the n-th eigenvalue λ_n has precisely $n - 1$ simple nodes (i.e. $u'(t_0) \neq 0$ for $u(t_0) = 0$) in $(0,\pi)$ (see Theorem 11.3). If $g = g(t,s,\lambda)$ is a continuous function then one can prove that $|u'|^{p-2} u' \in C^1([0,\pi])$ for any solution u of BVP (14.1), (14.2) (see Theorem 10.4). Using the assumption (14.3) if follows directly from the equation (14.1) that any nontrivial solution of BVP (14.1), (14.2) has only simple nodes in $[0,\pi]$ (at 0 and at π it means that $u'_+(0) \neq 0$ and $u'_-(\pi) \neq 0$, respectively). We also have the following information about the structure of C.

14.11. Lemma. *The convergence* $(\lambda_n, u_n) \to (\lambda, u)$ *in* E, $(\lambda_n, u_n), (\lambda, u) \in C$, *yields* $u_n \to u$ *in* $C^1([0,\pi])$.

Proof. We have

$$-\left(|u_n'|^{p-2} u_n'\right)' = \lambda_n |u_n|^{p-2} u_n + g(t, u_n, \lambda_n), \tag{14.23}$$

$$-\left(|u'|^{p-2} u'\right) = \lambda |u|^{p-2} u + g(t, u, \lambda) \tag{14.24}$$

and $u_n \to u$ in $C([0,\pi])$ due to the continuous imbedding $X \hookrightarrow C([0,\pi])$. From (14.23), (14.24) we get that

$$|u'(t)|^{p-2} u'(t) - |u_n'(t)|^{p-2} u_n'(t) =$$

$$= k + \int_0^t \Big[\lambda_n |u_n(\tau)|^{p-2} u_n(\tau) - \lambda |u(\tau)|^{p-2} u(\tau) +$$

$$+ g\big(\tau, u_n(\tau), \lambda_n\big) - g\big(\tau, u(\tau), \lambda\big)\Big]\, d\tau,$$

i.e.

$$|u_n'(t)|^{p-2} u_n'(t) \to k + |u'(t)|^{p-2} u'(t) \quad \text{in} \quad C([0,\pi]).$$

But $u_n \to u$ in X implies $u_n \to u$ uniformly in $[0,\pi]$. Hence $k = 0$. Since the function $s \mapsto |s|^{\frac{1}{p-1}} \operatorname{sign} s$ is $\frac{1}{p-1}$-Hölder continuous we have $u_n' \to u'$ in $C([0,\pi])$ which concludes the proof. □

14.12. Remark. In other words, Lemma 14.11 states that the topology on C induced by the norm in E is equivalent to the topology on C induced by the norm

$$\|(\lambda, u)\|_1 = \left(|\lambda|^2 + \|u\|^2_{C^1([0,\pi])}\right)^{\frac{1}{2}}.$$

14.13. Results of CRANDAL and RABINOWITZ type. Let us suppose that λ_n is the n-th eigenvalue of BVP (14.5), (14.6) and u_n is the corresponding normalized eigenfunction satisfying $u_n'(0) > 0$. Using the same arguemnt as in RABINOWITZ [260] it is possible to show that there are two maximal connected subsets of C (C being from Theorem 14.9) bifurcating from $(\lambda_n,0)$ in the directions u_n and $-u_n$. More precisely, let $\tau \in (0,1)$ and

$$K_\tau^+ = \{(\lambda,u) \in E;\ (\phi^*,u)_X > \tau\|u\|_X\},$$

$$K_\tau^- = \{(\lambda,u) \in E;\ (\phi^*,u)_X < -\tau\|u\|_X\},$$

where $\phi^* \in X^*$ is a fixed element such that

$$(\phi^*,u_n)_X = 1.$$

Then there are maximal connected sets C_n^+, C_n^- such that $C_n^+ \cup C_n^- = C$, C_n^+, C_n^- contain in their closure the point $(\lambda_n,0)$, and

$$C_n^+ \cap B_s(\lambda_n,0) \subset K_\tau^+, \qquad C_n^- \cap B_s(\lambda_n,0) \subset K_\tau^-$$

with some $s = s(\tau) > 0$ small enough (here $B_s(\lambda_n,0)$ is the ball in E with radius $s > 0$ centred at the point $(\lambda_n,0)$).

It follows immediately from Lemma 14.11 that $C_n^+ \cap C_n^- = \emptyset$. Moreover, if $m \neq n$ then $C_m^+ \cap C_n^+ = \emptyset$, $C_m^- \cap C_n^- = \emptyset$ due to the nodal properties of the eigenfunctions.

<u>14.14. Theorem.</u> *Let* λ_n *be an eigenvalue of BVP* (14.5), (14.6) *with* $a(t) \equiv c(t) \equiv 1$. *Let a function* $g = g(t,s,\lambda)$ *be continuous and satisfy* (14.3). *Then there are two unbounded continua of nontrivial solutions* C_n^+ *and* C_n^- *bifurcating from* $(\lambda_n,0)$ *with the property that if* $(\lambda,u) \in C_n^\pm$ *then* u *has* $n-1$ *simple nodes in* $(0,\pi)$ *and* $\operatorname{sign} u'(0) = \pm 1$.

<u>*Proof.*</u> It follows from the above considerations that the continuum C_n bifurcating from $(\lambda_n,0)$ which can be decomposed into $C_n^+ \cup C_n^-$ does not satisfy the latter possibility given in Theorem 14.9. According to Lemma 14.11 both C_n^+ and C_n^- preserve the nodal properties of u_n and $-u_n$, respectively. Hence neither C_n^+ nor C_n^- contains points of the form (λ,u), $(\lambda,-u)$. Then, following the proof of Theorem 1.27 in RABINOWITZ [260] we get that both C_n^+ and C_n^- are unbounded. $\square$

14.15. Fourth order problem. Let us consider BVP

$$\left(a(t)|u''(t)|^{p-2}u''(t)\right)'' - \lambda c(t)|u(t)|^{p-2}u(t) = g\left(t,u(t),u'(t),\lambda\right), \quad t \in [0,\pi], \tag{14.25}$$

$$u(0) = u'(0) = u(\pi) = u'(\pi) = 0 \tag{14.26}$$

with a and c satisfying the assumptions from Subsection 14.1. We suppose that $g = g(t,s,r,\lambda)$ is a Carathéodory function, i.e. $g(\cdot,s,r,\lambda)$ is measurable for all $(s,r,\lambda) \in \mathbb{R}^3$ and $g(t,\cdot,\cdot,\cdot)$ is continuous for a.a. $t \in (0,\pi)$. We also assume that $g(t,0,0,\lambda) = 0$ and

$$\lim_{(s,r)\to(0,0)} \frac{g(t,s,r,\lambda)}{\left(s^2+r^2\right)^{\frac{p-1}{2}}} = 0$$

uniformly for a.a. $t \in (0,\pi)$ and λ from bounded intervals. Moreover, let $m(t) \in L^1(0,\pi)$ and let $\tilde{g} : \mathbb{R}^3 \to \mathbb{R}$ be a positive and continuous function such that

$$|g(t,s,r,\lambda)| \leq m(t)\left(1 + \tilde{g}(|s|,|r|,\lambda)\right)$$

holds for a.a. $t \in [0,\pi]$ and for all $(s,r,\lambda) \in \mathbb{R}^3$. Set $X = W_0^{2,p}(0,\pi)$ and define operators $J, S : X \to X^*$ and $G : \mathbb{R} \times X \to X^*$ as follows:

$$\left(J(u),v\right)_X = \int_0^\pi a(t)|u''(t)|^{p-2}u''(t)\,v''(t)\,dt,$$

$$\left(S(u),v\right)_X = \int_0^\pi c(t)|u(t)|^{p-2}u(t)\,v(t)\,dt,$$

$$\left(G(\lambda,u),v\right)_X = \int_0^\pi g\left(t,u(t),u'(t),\lambda\right)v(t)\,dt$$

for any $u, v \in X$.

The operators J, S and G have the same properties as those defined in Subsection 14.2.

Let us recall that the eigenvalues of BVP

$$\left(a(t)|u''(t)|^{p-2}u''(t)\right)'' - \lambda c(t)|u(t)|^{p-2}u(t) = 0, \quad t \in [0,\pi], \tag{14.27}$$

$$u(0) = u'(0) = u(\pi) = u'(\pi) = 0 \tag{14.28}$$

form a countable discrete set $\{\lambda_i\}_{i=1}^{\infty}$, $0 < \lambda_1 < \lambda_2 < \dots$, $\lim_{n\to\infty} \lambda_n = \infty$. Moreover, each eigenvalue λ_0 of BVP (14.27), (14.28) admits only a finite number of isolated normed eigenfunctions (see KRATOCHVÍL and NEČAS [180], cf. Subsection 10.9).

Let u be any normalized eigenfunction of BVP (14.27), (14.28). Then the set

$$W_0^{2,2}(\rho) =$$

$$= \left\{h;\ h \text{ satisfies boundary condition (14.28)},\ \int_0^{\pi} (h'')^2 \rho\, dx = \|h\|_{2,2,\rho}^2 < \infty\right\},$$

where $\rho(t) = |u''(t)|^{p-2}$, is a Hilbert space imbedded algebraically and topologically into $W^{2,q}(\Omega)$ provided

$$1 \leqq q < \frac{2(p-1)}{2p-3} .$$

Moreover, the linear eigenvalue problem

$$\int_0^{\pi} a(t)|u''(t)|^{p-2} h''(t)\, k''(t)\, dt - \mu \int_0^{\pi} c(t)|u(t)|^{p-2} h(t)\, k(t)\, dt = 0$$

for any $k \in W_0^{2,2}(\rho)$ has only simple eigenvalues (see KRATOCHVÍL and NEČAS [180]).

Fix the eigenfunction u and denote $W_0^{2,2}(\rho)$ simply by H . For the sequence $\{v_i\}_{i=1}^{\infty}$ take the eigenfunctions of the eigenvalue problem

$$u'''' - \lambda u = 0 \quad \text{in} \quad (0,\pi) ,$$

$$u(0) = u'(0) = u(\pi) = u'(\pi) = 0 .$$

Then $\{v_i\}_{i=1}^{\infty}$ is dense both in X and in H . By *a weak solution* of BVP (14.25), (14.26) we will mean a function $u \in X$ satisfying (14.4) (with J , S and G defined above in this subsection). Similarly as in Subsection 14.4 we define a continuum C of nontrivial weak solutions of BVP (14.25), (14.26). Using essentially the same approach as in the proof of Theorem 14.9 we get the following assertion.

14.16. Theorem. *Let* λ_n *be an eigenvalue of the homogeneous BVP* (14.27), (14.28) *of odd multiplicity. Then there exists a continuum* C *of nontrivial weak solutions of BVP* (14.25), (14.26) *such that* $(\lambda_n, 0)$ *belongs to the closure* $\overline{C}$, C *is either unbounded in* E *or there is an eigenvalue* $\lambda_m \neq \lambda_n$ *such that* $(\lambda_m, 0) \in \overline{C}$.

<u>14.17. Partial differential equations.</u> We will consider the bifurcation problem

$$- \operatorname{div} \left(|\nabla u|^{p-2} \nabla u\right) = \lambda |u|^{p-2} u + g\left(x, u(x), \lambda\right) , \quad x \in \Omega , \tag{14.29}$$

$$u(x) = 0 , \quad x \in \partial\Omega , \tag{14.30}$$

where $\Omega \subset \mathbf{R}^N$ is a bounded domain with a sufficiently smooth boundary $\partial\Omega$, and $p > 1$. Suppose that a Carathéodory function $g = g(x,s,\lambda)$ satisfies (14.3) with $[0,\pi]$ replaced by $\Omega \subset \mathbf{R}^N$. Let α and α' be as in Subsection 10.10. Assume that there are a function $m(x) \in L^{\alpha'}(\Omega)$ and a constant $c > 0$ such that

$$|g(x,s)| \leqq m(x) + c|s|^{\alpha-1}$$

for a.a. $x \in \Omega$ and for all $s \in \mathbf{R}$. Set $X = W_0^{1,p}(\Omega)$ and define $J, S : X \to X^*$ and $G : \mathbf{R} \times X \to X^*$ as follows

$$\left(J(u), v\right)_X = \int_\Omega |\nabla u|^{p-2} \nabla u \, \nabla v \, dx ,$$

$$\left(S(u), v\right)_X = \int_\Omega |u|^{p-2} u \, v \, dx ,$$

$$\left(G(\lambda, u), v\right)_X = \int_\Omega g\left(x, u(x), \lambda\right) v(x) \, dx$$

for any $u, v \in X$. The operators J , S and G have the same properties as those defined in Subsection 14.2 for $p \geqq 2$ and $N = 1$. In the case $1 < p < 2$ the operator J is not strongly monotone in the sense of (10.8). Hence we must verify the condition $\alpha(X)$ for $A = J + K$, where $K : X \to X^*$ is a compact operator, using a slightly different approach than in Remark 14.8. Continuity of A is again a consequence of the fact that J satisfies (J1) - (J3) from Subsection 10.1 and K is compact. Let $u_n \rightharpoonup u_0$ in X and let (14.9) be valid. Similarly as in Remark 14.8 we get

$$\limsup_{n \to \infty} \left(J(u_n) - J(u_0), u_n - u_0\right)_X \leqq 0 . \tag{14.31}$$

It follows from the definition of J that

$$\left(J(u_n) - J(u_0), u_n - u_0\right)_X \geq$$

$$\geq \left(\|u_n\|_X^{p-1} - \|u_0\|_X^{p-1}\right)\cdot\left(\|u_n\|_X - \|u_0\|_X\right) \tag{14.32}$$

for any $n = 1,2,\ldots$ (cf. Subsection 13.3). However, (14.31), (14.32) imply that $\|u_n\|_X \to \|u_0\|_X$ which together with the weak convergence $u_n \rightharpoonup u$ in X yield $u_n \to u_0$ in X.

A function $u \in X$ is called *a weak solution* of BVP (14.29), (14.30) or BVP

$$-\operatorname{div}\left(|\nabla u|^{p-2}\nabla u\right) = \lambda|u|^{p-2}u \quad \text{in } \Omega, \tag{14.33}$$

$$u = 0 \quad \text{on } \partial\Omega \tag{14.34}$$

if it satisfies

$$J(u) = \lambda S(u) + G(\lambda,u) \tag{14.35}$$

or

$$J(u) = \lambda S(u), \tag{14.36}$$

respectively.

Let us recall the result of ANANE [12] concerning the first eigenvalue λ_1 of BVP (14.33), (14.34) formulated in Subsection 13.2.

<u>14.18. Theorem.</u> *Let the boundary* $\partial\Omega$ *be of class* $C^{2,\beta}$, *let* λ_1 *be the first eigenvalue of BVP* (14.33), (14.34). *Then there exists a continuum* C *of nontrivial weak solutions of BVP* (14.29), (14.30) *such that* $(\lambda_1,0)$ *belongs to the closure* $\overline{C}$, C *is either unbounded in* E *or there is an eigenvalue* λ_0 *of BVP* (14.33), (14.34) *such that* $\lambda_0 \neq \lambda_1$ *and* $(\lambda_0,0) \in E$.

Proof. We prove that

$$\operatorname{Deg}\left[J - (\lambda_1 - \delta)S; B_r, 0\right] \neq \operatorname{Deg}\left[J - (\lambda_1 + \delta)S; B_r, 0\right] \tag{14.37}$$

for $r > 0$ and for $\delta > 0$ small enough.

Similarly as in the proof of Theorem 14.9 we define a function $\psi : \mathbb{R} \to \mathbb{R}$ by

$$\psi(t) = 0 \quad \text{for } t \leq R,$$

$$\psi(t) = 2\delta(t - 2R) \quad \text{for } t \geq 3R,$$

ψ positive and strictly convex in $(R,3R)$, where $R > 0$ is a fixed number and $\delta > 0$ is chosen in such a way that $(\lambda_1, \lambda_1 + \delta]$ does not contain any eigenvalue of BVP (14.33), (14.34). Following the notation from the proof of Theorem 14.9, we obtain that F_λ is at least once continuously differentiable (note that $p > 1$) and that the critical points of F'_λ correspond to the solutions of the equation (14.12). We also obtain that for $\lambda = \lambda_1 - \delta$ the point $0 \in X$ is the only critical point of F'_λ while for $\lambda = \lambda_1 + \delta$ there are precisely three isolated critical points of F'_λ : $0, u_1, -u_1$, where $u_1 > 0$ is an eigenfunction of BVP (14.33), (14.34) corresponding to λ_1 (see Subsection 13.2). Since 0 is the minimum of $F_{\lambda_1-\delta}$, due to Lemma 14.7 we have

$$\operatorname{Ind}\left(F'_{\lambda_1-\delta}, 0\right) = 1 . \tag{14.38}$$

Due to the homogeneity of J and S it follows from (14.38) that

$$\operatorname{Deg}\left[J - (\lambda_1 - \delta)S; B_r, 0\right] = 1 \tag{14.39}$$

for an arbitrary $r > 0$. The points u_1 and $-u_1$ are minima of $F_{\lambda_1+\delta}$ and hence by Lemma 14.7

$$\operatorname{Ind}\left(F'_{\lambda_1+\delta}, u_1\right) = \operatorname{Ind}\left(F'_{\lambda_1+\delta}, -u_1\right) = 1 . \tag{14.40}$$

Simultaneously,

$$\operatorname{Deg}\left[F'_{\lambda_1+\delta}; B_\kappa, 0\right] = 1 \tag{14.41}$$

for $\kappa > 0$ large enough due to the definition of ψ. It follows from (14.40), (14.41) and the additivity property of the degree (see SKRYPNIK [276]) that

$$\operatorname{Deg}\left[J - (\lambda_1 + \delta)S; B_r, 0\right] = -1 \tag{14.42}$$

with an arbitrary $r > 0$. The relation (14.37) follows from (14.39) and (14.42). To complete the proof we proceed in the same way as in Steps 3 and 4 of the proof of Theorem 14.9. □

<u>14.19. Remark.</u> Note that the simplicity of λ_1 was not essential in the proof of Theorem 14.18. In order to establish (14.37) (and hence to prove Theorem 14.18) it is sufficient to know that the set of the normalized eigenfunctions corresponding to λ_1 is finite.

The simplicity of λ_1 allows us to strengthen the assertion of Theorem 14.18 in the following sense.

14.20. Theorem. *Let the assumptions of Theorem 14.18 be fulfilled. Moreover, suppose that there exists* $\delta > 0$ *such that*

$$J(u) \neq \lambda_1 S(u) + G(\lambda_1, u) \tag{14.43}$$

for $0 < \|u\|_X \leqq \delta$. *Then there are maximal connected subsets* C^+ , C^- *of* C *containing* $(\lambda_1, 0) \in E$ *in their closures,* $C^\pm \cap B_s(\lambda_1, 0) \subset K^\pm_\tau$ *(for* $K^\pm_\tau$ *and* $B_s(\lambda_1, 0)$ *see Subsection 14.13), and such that either*

(i) *both* C^+ , C^- *are unbounded in* E , *or*

(ii) *both* C^+ , C^- *contain in their closures a point different from* $(\lambda_1, 0) \in E$.

The proof of this assertion may proceed step by step as the proof of Theorem 2 in DANCER [70]. In fact, due to our hypothesis (14.43), we need only Lemmas 1 and 2 from [70], where the linearity of the principal part of the equation is not essential.

14.21. Neumann boundary data. Let us consider BVP

$$-\operatorname{div}\left(|\nabla u|^{p-2}\nabla u\right) = \lambda |u|^{p-2} u + g\left(x, u(x), \lambda\right) \quad \text{in } \Omega , \tag{14.44}$$

$$N(u) \equiv |\nabla u|^{p-2} \nabla u \cdot \nu = 0 \quad \text{on } \partial\Omega . \tag{14.45}$$

Setting $X = W^{1,p}(\Omega)$ and defining the operators J , S and G as in Subsection 14.17 we define a weak solution of BVP (14.44), (14.45) as a function $u \in X$ satisfying (14.35). The following analogue of the result of ANANE [12] holds.

14.22. Lemma. *The first eigenvalue* $\lambda_1 = 0$ *of the homogeneous BVP*

$$-\operatorname{div}\left(|\nabla u|^{p-2}\nabla u\right) = \lambda |u|^{p-2} u \quad \textit{in } \Omega , \tag{14.46}$$

$$N(u) = 0 \qquad \textit{on } \partial\Omega \tag{14.47}$$

is simple and isolated. There exists precisely one normalized positive eigenfunction $u_1 \equiv \dfrac{1}{(\text{meas } \Omega)^{1/p}}$ *corresponding to* $\lambda_1 = 0$.

Proof. The simplicity of λ_1 follows from the identity

$$0 = \lambda_1 = \min_{u \in X,\, u \neq 0} \frac{\int_\Omega |\nabla u|^p \, dx}{\int_\Omega |u|^p \, dx} .$$

Let us suppose that there are $\lambda_n \to 0$ (the eigenvalues of BVP (14.46), (14.47)) with the corresponding normalized eigenfunctions u_n. Then due to the compactness of S we can suppose that $u_n \to u$ in X and $\big(J(u),u\big)_X = 0$. Since $\|u\|_X = 1$, we should have

$$\text{either} \quad u \equiv \frac{1}{(\text{meas } \Omega)^{1/p}} \quad \text{or} \quad u \equiv - \frac{1}{(\text{meas } \Omega)^{1/p}} .$$

Simultaneously, taking $v \equiv 1$ in

$$\int_\Omega |\nabla u_n|^{p-2} \nabla u_n \nabla v \, dx = \int_\Omega |u_n|^{p-2} u_n v \, dx ,$$

we get

$$\int_\Omega |u_n|^{p-2} u_n \, dx = 0 ,$$

which is a contradiction. □

If we use Lemma 14.22 instead of the result of ANANE [12], we can prove analogous assertions as Theorems 14.18, 14.20 concerning the global bifurcation for the Neumann BVP (14.44), (14.45) with $\lambda_1 = 0$.

14.23. Remarks. (i) Let X be a separable reflexive Banach space, let $J : X \to X^*$ satisfy (J1) - (J3) and let $K : X \to X^*$ be compact. It is possible to show that if $J(u) + K(u) \neq 0$ for any $u \in \partial D$, the following equality holds:

$$\text{Deg}\,[J + K; D, 0] = \deg\,[I + J^{-1} \circ K ; D, 0] .$$

It is however, more convenient to use in this section the properties of the degree Deg than the properties of the Leray - Schauder degree. One of the reasons is the fact that J^{-1} is not continuously differentiable for $1 < p < +\infty$.

(ii) Since zero is a degenerate critical point of $J + S$ we cannot use a standard method for the evaluation of its index (see SKRYPNIK [276]). We overcome this difficulty by defining a functional F_λ and investigating its critical points.

(iii) If a weak solution u of BVP (14.29), (14.30) satisfies apriori $u \in L^\infty(\Omega)$ then it follows from the result of TOLKSDORF [285] that the derivatives of u are already Hölder continuous. In particular, if g is bounded, we obtain the regularity in this sense in the case $p > N$ due to Sobolev's imbedding theorem.

(iv) The results of this section generalize and amend the results concerning the local bifurcation from Ljusternik - Schnirelmann eigenvalues (see e.g. FUČÍK, NEČAS, SOUČEK and SOUČEK [129]). Our assertions generalize also some bifurcation results for nonlinear problems with linear principal part (see e.g. H. KIELHOFER [177]).

15. LOCAL BIFURCATION OF GENERALIZED SPECTRUM

15.1. In this section we will study the global structure of the set $A_{-1}(r)$ of all pairs $(\mu,\nu) \in \mathbb{R}^2$ for which the nonlinear BVP

$$- \left(a(t,u)u'\right)' - \mu c(t,u)u^+ + \nu c(t,u)u^- = 0 \quad \text{in} \quad [0,\pi] \,, \tag{15.1}$$

$$u(0) = u(\pi) = 0 \tag{15.2}$$

has a solution u with the norm in $C^1([0,\pi])$ equal to $r > 0$. First, we will give a characterization of the set A_{-1} for the weakly nonlinear BVP

$$- \left(a(t)u'\right)' - \mu c(t)u^+ + \nu c(t)u^- = 0 \quad \text{in} \quad [0,\pi] \,, \tag{15.3}$$

$$u(0) = u(\pi) = 0 \,. \tag{15.4}$$

Note that in this case the set A_{-1} does not depend on $r > 0$ because the problem is homogeneous. Let us also remark that in the case of constant coefficients the set A_{-1} of generalized eigenvalues can be described explicitly (see FUČÍK [126], DANCER [71,72] and Section 1 of this book). Further, by using the characterization of A_{-1} for BVP (15.3), (15.4) with $a(t)$, $c(t)$ replaced by $a_w(t) = a\left(t,w(t)\right)$, $c_w(t) = c\left(t,w(t)\right)$ and applying a fixed point method we will obtain information about the character of $A_{-1}(r)$ for any $r > 0$. In particular, $A_{-1}(r)$ in a certain sense tends to $A_{-1}(0)$ for $r \to 0$ (the set A_{-1} corresponding to BVP (15.3), (15.4) with $a(t) = a(t,0)$, $c(t) = c(t,0)$). Any $(\mu,\nu) \in A_{-1}(0)$ is *a bifurcation point* of BVP (15.1), (15.2) (with respect to the line of trivial solutions - see Theorem 15.18).

15.2. Let us consider BVP (15.3), (15.4). We suppose that $a \in C^1([0,\pi])$, $c \in C([0,\pi])$, $c(t) > 0$, $m \leqq a(t) \leqq M$ for any $t \in [0,\pi]$, where $0 < m < M$. For any $k = 1,2,\ldots$, write

$$Z_k = \{u \in C^1([0,\pi]);\ u \text{ has precisely } k-1 \text{ simple nodes in } (0,\pi)\},$$

$$Z_k^+ = \{u \in Z_k;\ u'(0) > 0\},\quad Z_k^- = \{u \in Z_k;\ u'(0) < 0\}.$$

(Recall that by a simple node we mean t such that $u(t) = 0$, $u'(t) \neq 0$.)

15.3. Remark. Let us consider the eigenvalue problem

$$-\left(a(t)u'\right)' - \lambda c(t)u = 0 \quad \text{in } [0,\pi], \tag{15.5}$$

$$u(0) = u(\pi) = 0. \tag{15.6}$$

Recall that all eigenvalues of BVP (15.5), (15.6) are simple and form a sequence $\{\lambda_n\}_{n=1}^{\infty}$, $0 < \lambda_1 < \lambda_2 < \ldots$, $\lim_{n\to\infty} \lambda_n = \infty$. Further, $v_n \in Z_n$ for the eigenfunctions v_n corresponding to λ_n. Hence the eigenfunctions corresponding to the first eigenvalue λ_1 do not change sign in $[0,\pi]$; for $n = 2k$ the eigenfunction v_n corresponding to λ_n consists of k positive and k negative semiwaves; for $n = 2k+1$ there is an eigenfunction $v_n \in Z_k^+$ consisting of $k+1$ positive and k negative semiwaves.

15.4. Remark. Consider IVP

$$-\left(a(t)u'\right)' - \mu c(t)u^+ + \nu c(t)u^- = 0 \quad \text{in } [0,\infty], \tag{15.7}$$

$$u(0) = 0, \quad u'(0) = 1. \tag{15.8}$$

If α, β are two successive nodes of a solution of IVP (15.7), (15.8) then in interval $[\alpha,\beta]$ the equation (15.7) reads either

$$-\left(a(t)u'\right)' - \mu c(t)u^+ = 0, \tag{15.9}$$

or

$$-\left(a(t)u'\right)' + \nu c(t)u^- = 0, \tag{15.10}$$

where $u^+ = u$ or $u^- = -u$, respectively. The following assertions provide information about how the distance between the nodes of a solution of IVP (15.7), (15.8) depends on μ, ν.

15.5. Lemma. *For* $\mu > 0$, $\nu > 0$ *set*

$$d^+(\mu) = \sup\{|\alpha - \beta|;\ \alpha, \beta \text{ are successive nodes of } u,\ u \text{ satisfies (15.9) in } [\alpha,\beta]\},$$

$$d^-(\nu) = \sup\{|\alpha - \beta|;\ \alpha, \beta \text{ are successive nodes of } u,\ u \text{ satisfies (15.10) in } [\alpha,\beta]\}.$$

Then $d^+(\mu) \to 0$ *or* $d^-(\nu) \to 0$ *if and only if* $\mu \to +\infty$ *or* $\nu \to -\infty$, *respectively.*

15.6. Remark. In Lemma 15.5 let us write $d^+_{a,c}(\mu)$ and $d^-_{a,c}(\nu)$ instead of $d^+(\mu)$ and $d^-(\nu)$, respectively, in order to emphasize the dependence on the coefficients in (15.9) and (15.10). Then the convergence $d^+_{a,c}(\mu) \to 0$ for $\mu \to +\infty$ and $d^-_{a,c}(\nu) \to 0$ for $\nu \to +\infty$ is uniform with respect to a, c satisfying $m \leqq a(t) \leqq M$, $c(t) \geqq c_0$ (with $0 < m < M$, $c_0 > 0$ fixed).

15.7. Lemma. (i) *Let us suppose that* u_i *satisfy*

$$-\left(a(t)u_i'\right)' - \mu_i c(t)u_i^+ = 0,$$

$u_i(t) > 0$ *on* $(\alpha,\beta) \subset (0,\pi)$, $i = 1,2$, $u_1(\alpha) = u_1(\beta) = 0$, $u_2(\alpha) + u_2(\beta) > 0$. *Then* $\mu_2 < \mu_1$.

(ii) *Let* u_i *satisfy*

$$-\left(a(t)u_i'\right)' + \nu_i c(t)u_i^- = 0,$$

$u_i(t) < 0$ *on* $(\alpha,\beta) \subset (0,\pi)$, $i = 1,2$, $u_1(\alpha) = u_1(\beta) = 0$, $u_2(\alpha) + u_2(\beta) < 0$. *Then* $\nu_2 < \nu_1$.

The proofs of Lemmas 15.5, 15,7 and Remark 15.6 follow directly from the Sturm comparison theorem (see e.g. KAMKE [168]).

15.8. Lemma. *Let us suppose that*

$$-\left(a(t)u_i'\right)' - \mu_i c(t)u_i^+ + \nu_i c(t)u_i^- = 0 \quad \text{in} \quad [0,\pi], \tag{15.11}$$

$$u_i(0) = u_i(\pi) = 0 \,, \tag{15.12}$$

$i = 1,2$. *If* $\operatorname{sign} u_1'(0) = \operatorname{sign} u_2'(0) \neq 0$ *and* $\mu_1 \leqq \mu_2$, $\nu_1 \leqq \nu_2$ *with at least one strict inequality sign then* u_1 *and* u_2 *cannot have the same non-zero number of nodes in* $(0,\pi)$.

Proof. Let us suppose that $u_1, u_2 \in Z_n^+$ for some $n = 2,3,\dots$, and $\mu_1 \leqq \mu_2$, $\nu_1 \leqq \nu_2$ with at least one strict inequality sign. Elementary considerations yield the existence of an interval $(\alpha,\beta) \subset (0,\pi)$ such that $u_1(\alpha) = u_1(\beta) = 0$, $|u_2(\alpha)| + |u_2(\beta)| > 0$ and $u_1(t)\cdot u_2(t) > 0$ in (α,β) . However, this contradicts Lemma 15.7. □

15.9. Lemma. *Let* $u \in Z_n$ *be the solution of BVP* (15.3), (15.4).

(i) *If* $n = 2k$, $k = 1,2,\dots$, *then* $\mu > \lambda_k$, $\nu > \lambda_k$;

(ii) *if* $n = 2k + 1$, $k = 1,2,\dots$, *then either* $\mu > \lambda_{k+1}$, $\nu > \lambda_k$ *(provided* $u'(0) > 0$ *) or* $\mu > \lambda_k$, $\nu > \lambda_{k+1}$ *(provided* $u'(0) < 0$ *).*

Proof. Let $n = 2k + 1$, $u'(0) > 0$. Elementary considerations, together with Remark 15.3, imply that there exist intervals (α_k,β_k) , $(\alpha_{k+1},\beta_{k+1})$ and eigenfunctions v_k , v_{k+1} of BVP (15.5), (15.6) corresponding to λ_k , λ_{k+1} , respectively, such that $u(\alpha_k) = u(\beta_k) = 0$, $v_k(\alpha_k) + v_k(\beta_k) < 0$, $u(t) < 0$, $v_k(t) < 0$ for $t \in (\alpha_k,\beta_k)$, and $u(\alpha_{k+1}) = u(\beta_{k+1}) = 0$, $v_{k+1}(\alpha_{k+1}) + v_{k+1}(\beta_{k+1}) > 0$, $u(t) > 0$, $v_{k+1}(t) > 0$ for $t \in (\alpha_{k+1},\beta_{k+1})$. The assertion follows from Lemma 15.7. The other cases can be treated similarly. □

Let us introduce sets

$$A_{-1} = \{(\mu,\nu) \in \mathbf{R}^2;\ \text{BVP (15.3), (15.4) has a nontrivial solution}\},$$

$$A_{-1}^+ = \{(\mu,\nu) \in \mathbf{R}^2;\ \text{BVP (15.3), (15.4) has a solution in } Z_n^+\},$$

$$A_{-1}^- = \{(\mu,\nu) \in \mathbf{R}^2;\ \text{BVP (15.3), (15.4) has a solution in } Z_n^-\},$$

$n = 1,2,\dots$.

15.10. Theorem. *The following assertion holds*

$$A_{-1} = \bigcup_{n=1}^{\infty} [A_n^+ \cup A_n^-] \,,$$

$$A_1^+ = \{(\mu,\nu) \in \mathbb{R}^2;\quad \mu = \lambda_1 ,\quad \nu \textit{ is arbitrary}\},$$

$$A_n^+ = \{(\mu,\nu) \in \mathbb{R}^2;\quad \nu = f_n(\mu)\},\quad n = 2,3,\dots ,$$

$$A_n^- = \{(\mu,\nu) \in \mathbb{R}^2;\quad (\nu,\mu) \in A_n^+\},\quad n = 1,2,3,\dots ,$$

where f_n *are continuous decreasing functions such that:*

(i) *if* $n = 2k$, $k = 1,2,\dots$, *then* f_n *is defined on* $(\lambda_k,+\infty)$, $\lim_{\mu\to\lambda_n^+} f_n(\mu) = +\infty$, $\lim_{\mu\to\infty} f_n(\mu) = \lambda_k$ *and* $f_n(\lambda_n) = \lambda_n$;

(ii) *if* $n = 2k + 1$, $k = 1,2,\dots$, *then* f_n *is defined on* $(\lambda_{k+1},+\infty)$, $\lim_{\mu\to\lambda_{k+1}^+} f_n(\mu) = +\infty$, $\lim_{\mu\to+\infty} f_n(\mu) = \lambda_k$ *and* $f_n(\lambda_n) = \lambda_n$.

Proof. The first equality follows from the fact that any nontrivial solution of BVP (15.3), (15.4) has a finite number of simple nodes, and from the uniqueness of solutions to the IVP for ordinary differential equations of the second order. The second equality is evident because u is a positive or a negative solution of BVP (15.3), (15.4) if and only if it is the eigenfunction of BVP (15.5), (15.6) corresponding to the first eigenvalue. Further, let $n = 2k + 1$ for some $k = 1,2,\dots$. Let $\mu \in (\lambda_{k+1},\infty)$ be arbitrary but fixed. Denote by $u_{\mu,\nu}$ the solution of IVP (15.7), (15.8) and by $t_n^{\mu,\nu}$ the n-th node of $u_{\mu,\nu}$ in $(0,+\infty)$. Lemmas 15.5, 15.7, together with Remark 15.3, imply that $t_n^{\mu,\nu} < \pi$ if ν is large enough. On the other hand, $t_n^{\mu,\nu} > \pi$ for ν small enough by the Sturm comparison theorem (see e.g. KAMKE [168]). Hence, due to the continuous dependence of $u_{\mu,\nu}$ on the parameters μ , ν , there exists at least one $\nu > 0$ such that $t_n^{\mu,\nu} = \pi$. For this ν , $u_{\mu,\nu}$ is the solution of BVP (15.3), (15.4), $u_{\mu,\nu} \in Z_n^+$. Lemma 15.9 (ii) implies that $\nu \in (\lambda_k,+\infty)$ and Lemma 15.8 ensures the uniqueness of ν . Hence for any $\mu \in (\lambda_{k+1},+\infty)$ we can set $f_n(\mu) = \nu$, where ν is such that BVP (15.3), (15.4) has a solution $u_{\mu,\nu} \in Z_n^+$. In the same way as above, we can prove that for any $\nu \in (\lambda_k,+\infty)$ there exists exactly one $\mu \in (\lambda_{k+1},+\infty)$ such that BVP (15.3), (15.4) has a nontrivial solution $u_{\mu,\nu} \in Z_n^+$. Hence f_n maps $(\lambda_{k+1},+\infty)$ onto $(\lambda_k,+\infty)$, and it is decreasing by Lemma 15.8. It follows that f_n is also continuous and $\lim_{\mu\to\lambda_{k+1}^+} f_n(\mu) = +\infty$, $\lim_{\mu\to+\infty} f_n(\mu) = \lambda_k$. Due to Lemma 15.7, BVP (15.3), (15.4) has no solution $u \in Z_n^+$ if $\mu \leq \lambda_{k+1}$, which proves the assertion concerning A_n^+ with $n = 2k + 1$. Analogously for

A_n^- . The proof for $n = 2k$, $k = 1,2,\dots$, can be done in a similar way. $\square$

15.11. Strongly nonlinear BVP. Let us suppose that $a(t,s) \in C^1([0,\pi] \times \mathbb{R})$, $c(t,s) \in C([0,\pi] \times \mathbb{R})$, $m \leq a(t,s) \leq M$, $c(t,s) > 0$ for all $(t,s) \in [0,\pi] \times \mathbb{R}$ with some $M > m > 0$. Set $C^1 = C^1([0,\pi])$, $C_0^2 = \{u \in C^2([0,\pi]);\ u(0) = u(\pi) = 0\}$ and denote by $\|\cdot\|_{C^i}$ the usual norm in $C^i([0,\pi])$, $i = 1,2$. If $w \in C^1$ then $a_w(t) = a(t,w(t))$, $c_w(t) = c(t,w(t))$ satisfy all the assumptions imposed on a and c in Subsection 15.2. Further, $c_w(t) \geq \gamma(r)$ for any $t \in [0,\pi]$ and $w \in C^1$, $\|w\|_{C^1} \leq r$ with some $\gamma(r) > 0$ depending only on $r > 0$.

15.12. Remark. Let us denote by $\lambda_n(w)$ the n-th eigenvalue of BVP (15.5), (15.6) where a and c are replaced by a_w and c_w . Set

$$\lambda_n^M(r) = \inf\{\lambda_n(w);\ \|w\|_{C^1} \leq r\}, \qquad \lambda_n^m(r) = \sup\{\lambda_n(w);\ \|w\|_{C^1} \leq r\}.$$

It follows from the continuous dependence of the eigenvalues of BVP (15.5), (15.6) on the coefficients that $\lim_{r\to 0^+} \lambda_n^M(r) = \lim_{r\to 0^+} \lambda_n^m(r) = \lambda_n(0)$. The variational characterization of $\lambda_n(w)$ ensures that $\lambda_n^M \leq \lambda_n^M(r)$, $\lambda_n^m \leq \lambda_n^m(r)$ for all $r > 0$ with some $\lambda_n^m \geq \lambda_n^M > 0$.

15.13. Remark. Let $A_n^{\pm}(w)$, $n = 1,2,\dots$, be the sets from Theorem 15.10 for BVP (15.5), (15.6) with a_w , c_w instead of a , c . If $n = 2k$, $w \in C^1$, $\|w\|_{C^1} \leq r$ and $\mu \in (\lambda_k^m(r), +\infty)$ then there are unique ν_+ and ν_- such that $(\mu,\nu_+) \in A_n^+(w)$ and $(\mu,\nu_-) \in A_n^-(w)$, respectively. If $n = 2k+1$, $w \in C^1$, $\|w\|_{C^1} \leq r$ and $\mu \in (\lambda_k^m(r), +\infty)$ or $\mu \in (\lambda_{k+1}^m(r), +\infty)$ then there are unique ν_+ and ν_- such that $(\mu,\nu_+) \in A_n^+(w)$ and $(\mu,\nu_-) \in A_n^-(w)$, respectively (see Theorem 15.10). In any case, the set

$$\{\nu \in \mathbb{R};\ (\mu,\nu) \in A_n^+(w) \text{ for some } w \in C^1,\ \|w\|_{C^1} = r\}$$

is bounded for any $r > 0$ and μ fixed from the corresponding interval just described. Analogously for $A_n^-(w)$. The last assertion follows from Lemma 15.5 and Remark 15.6.

15.14. Lemma. *Let* $z_n \in C_0^2$ *satisfy*

$$- \left(a(t,w_n)z_n'\right)' = f_n ,$$

and let $z \in C_0^2$ *be a solution of*

$$- \left(a(t,w)z'\right)' = f .$$

Suppose that $w_n \to w$ *in* C^1 *and* $f_n \to f$ *in* $C([0,\pi])$. *Then* $z_n \to z$ *in* C_0^2 .

Proof. Set

$$L_n(v) = - \left(a(t,w_n)v'\right)' , \quad L(v) = - \left(a(x,w)v'\right)' .$$

Since $w_n \to w$ in C^1 , we have $L_n(v) \to L(v)$ in $C([0,\pi])$ for any $v \in C_0^2$. Hence

$$\|z_n - z\|_{C^2} = \|L_n^{-1}(f_n) - L^{-1}(f)\|_{C^2} \leq$$

$$\leq \|L_n^{-1}(f_n) - L_n^{-1}(f)\|_{C^2} + \|L_n^{-1}(L_n - L)L^{-1}(f)\|_{C^2} \leq$$

$$\leq c\left(\|f_n - f\|_{C([0,\pi])} + \|(L_n - L)\left(L^{-1}(f)\right)\|_{C([0,\pi])}\right)$$

with $c > 0$ independent of n . (The boundedness of L_n^{-1} follows by elementary considerations.) □

15.15. Theorem. *Let* $r > 0$ *be arbitrary but fixed.*

(i) *If* $n = 2k$, $k = 1,2,\ldots$, *then for any* $\mu \in \left(\lambda_k^m(r), +\infty\right)$ *we can find* $\nu \in \left(\lambda_k^M(r), + \infty\right)$ *such that BVP* (15.1), (15.2) *has a solution* $u \in Z_n^+$, $\|u\|_{C^1} = r$. *The same holds for* Z_n^- .

(ii) *If* $n = 2k + 1$, $k = 1,2,\ldots$, *then for any* $\mu \in \left(\lambda_{k+1}^m(r), +\infty\right)$ *we can find* $\nu \in \left(\lambda_k^M(r), + \infty\right)$ *such that BVP* (15.1), (15.2) *has a solution* $u \in Z_n^+$, $\|u\|_{C^1} = r$, *and for any* $\mu \in \left(\lambda_n^m(r), + \infty\right)$ *we can find* $\nu \in \left(\lambda_{k+1}^M, + \infty\right)$ *such that BVP* (15.1), (15.2) *has a solution* $u \in Z_n^-$, $\|u\|_{C^1} = r$.

(iii) *If* $n = 1$ *then there exists* $\mu_r \in [\lambda_1^M(r), \lambda_1^m(r)]$ *such that there is* $u \in Z_1^+$ *satisfying BVP* (15.1), (15.2) *with* $\mu = \mu_r$ *and any* $\nu \in \mathbb{R}$, $\|u\|_{C^1} = r$, *and there exists* $\nu_r \in [\lambda_1^M(r), \lambda_1^m(r)]$ *such that there is* $u \in Z_1^-$ *satisfying BVP* (15.1), (15.2) *with any* μ *and* $\nu = \nu_r$, $\|u\|_{C^1} = r$.

Proof. Suppose that $n = 2k$ for some $k = 1,2,\dots$, and that $\mu \in (\lambda_k^m(r), +\infty)$. For some $w \in C^1$, $\|w\|_{C^1} \leq r$, there is a unique $\nu_w \in (\lambda_n(r), +\infty)$ such that $(\mu,\nu_w) \in A_n^+(w)$ (see Theorem 15.10). Denote by B_r the ball in C^1 and define a mapping $S : \overline{B}_r \to \overline{B}_r$ which associates with any fixed $w \in \overline{B}_r$ the function v satisfying

$$-\left(a(t,w)w'\right)' - \mu c(t,w)v^+ + \nu_w c(t,w)v^- = 0 \quad \text{in} \quad [0,\pi] , \tag{15.13}$$

$$v(0) = v(\pi) = 0 , \quad v \in Z_n^+ , \quad \|v\|_{C^1} = r . \tag{15.14}$$

Theorem 15.10, the positive homogeneity of (15.13) (with respect to v) and the uniqueness theorem for the second order ordinary differential equations imply that S is well-defined. Let us prove that S is a continuous mapping from C^1 into C_0^2 . Suppose that $w_n \to w$ in C^1 and set $v_n = S(w_n)$, $v = S(w)$, $\nu_n = \nu_{w_n}$. The Arzelà - Ascoli theorem and Remark 15.13 imply that there are subsequences (denoted again by $\{v_n\}$, $\{\nu_n\}$) such that $v_n \to \hat{v}$ in $C([0,\pi])$, $\nu_n \to \hat{\nu} \in [\lambda_k^M(r), +\infty)$. Hence $\mu c(t,w_n)v_n^+ - \nu_n c(t,w_n)v_n^- \to \mu c(t,w)\hat{v}^+ - \hat{\nu} c(t,w)\hat{v}^-$ in $C([0,\pi])$. It follows from Lemma 15.14 that $v_n \to \hat{v}$ in C^2 , that is, $\hat{v}$ satisfies (15.13). Further, $\hat{v} \in Z_n^+$ because $v_n \in Z_n^+$. (In the opposite case $\hat{v}$ would have a double node which is impossible due to the uniqueness of solution of the IVP.) Theorem 14.10 ensures that there are unique ν_w and v satisfying BVP (15.13), (15.14). This implies $\nu = \hat{\nu}$, $v_n \to \hat{v} = v$ for the whole sequence $\{v_n\}$ and the continuity of $S : \overline{B}_r \to C_0^2$ is proved. Now, we can apply the Schauder fixed point theorem in B_r . Hence, for any $\mu \in (\lambda_k^m(r), +\infty)$ we get $\nu \in (\lambda_k^M(r), +\infty)$, $u \in Z_n^+$ satisfying BVP (15.1), (15.2) and $\|u\|_{C^1} = r$.

The proof of (ii) can proceed in the same way. If $n = 1$ then for $r > 0$ fixed we define a mapping $S : \overline{B}_r \to \overline{B}_r$ which associates with any fixed $w \in \overline{B}_r$ the solution of

$$- \left(a(t,w)v'\right)' - \lambda_1(w)\, c(t,w)\, v = 0 \quad \text{in} \quad [0,\pi] \,, \tag{15.15}$$

$$v(0) = v(\pi) = 0 \,, \quad v > 0 \quad \text{in} \quad (0,\pi) \,, \quad \|v\|_{C^1} = r \,. \tag{15.16}$$

In the same way as above we prove the continuity of S from C^1 into C_0^2. The fixed point u of S is a positive solution of BVP (15.1), (15.2) with $\mu = \lambda_1(\mu)$ satisfying $\|u\|_{C^1} = r$. If we replace μ by ν and $v > 0$ by $v < 0$ we get the second part of the assertion (iii). □

15.16. Theorem. *Let* $(\mu_0, \nu_0) \in A_n^+(0)$ *be fixed. Then for any* $r > 0$ *sufficiently small there exist* u_r, ν_r *such that* u_r *is a solution of BVP* (15.1), (15.2) *with* $\mu = \mu_0$, $\nu = \nu_r$, $u_r \in Z_n^+$, $\|u_r\|_{C^1} = r$. *Moreover,*

$$\nu_r \to \nu_0 \,, \quad \frac{u_r}{\|u_r\|_{C^1}} \to u \quad (\textit{if} \ \ r \to 0_+ \,),$$

where $u \in Z_n^+$ *is a solution of BVP* (15.3), (15.4) *with* $a(t) = a(t,0)$, $c(t) = c(t,0)$, $\mu = \mu_0$, $\nu = \nu_0$, *and* $\|u\|_{C^1} = 1$.

The same assertion holds for $A_n^-(0)$ *(with* Z_n^+ *replaced by* Z_n^- *).*

Proof. If $r > 0$ is sufficiently small, then $\mu_0 > \lambda^m_{[\frac{n}{2}]}(r)$ (see Theorem 14.10 and Remark 15.12). Theorem 15.15 ensures the existence of u_r, ν_r with the above presented properties. Set $v_r = \dfrac{u_r}{\|u_r\|_{C^1}}$. Since $\|v_r\|_{C^1} = 1$ there is a sequence $\{r_k\}$, $r_k \to 0_+$ such that $v_{r_k} \to v$ in $C([0,\pi])$ for some v, and we can suppose $\nu_{r_k} \to \nu$ for some $\nu \in \mathbb{R}$ by Remark 15.13. We pass to the limit as $k \to \infty$ in

$$- \left(a(t,u_{r_k})v'_{r_k}\right)' - \mu_0 c(t,u_{r_k})v^+_{r_k} + \nu_{r_k} c(t,u_{r_k})v^-_{r_k} = 0 \,.$$

The last equation and Lemma 15.14 imply that $v_{r_k} \to v$ in C_0^2, and we obtain

$$- \left(a(t,0)v'\right)' - \mu_0 c(t,0)v^+ + \nu c(t,0)v^- = 0 \quad \text{in} \quad [0,\pi] \,, \tag{15.17}$$

$$v(0) = v(\pi) = 0 \,, \quad v \in Z_n^+ \,, \quad \|v\|_{C^1} = 1 \,. \tag{15.18}$$

Since v and ν satisfying BVP (15.17), (15.18) (with μ_0 given) are determined uniquely, we obtain $v_r \to v$ in C_0^2, $\nu_r \to \nu = \nu_0$ (see Theorem 15.10). □

15.17. Remark. Theorem 15.16 together with Theorem 15.10 ensure that any $(\mu_0,\nu_0) \in A_{-1}(0)$ is a *bifurcation point* of BVP (15.1), (15.2). Note that the following more detailed assertion can be proved analogously to Theorem 15.16.

15.18. Theorem. *Let* $(\mu_0,\nu_0) \in A_n^+(0)$, *let* Γ *be a curve in* $\mathbb{R}^2$ *containing* (μ_0,ν_0) *and transversal to* $A_0^+(0)$. *Then for any* $r > 0$ *small enough there exist* $(\mu_r,\nu_r) \in \Gamma$ *and a solution* $u_r \in Z_n^+$ *of BVP* (15.1), (15.2) *with* $\mu = \mu_r$, $\nu = \nu_r$, $\|u_r\|_{C^1} = r$. *Moreover,* $(\mu_r,\nu_r) \to (\mu_0,\nu_0)$, $\dfrac{u_r}{\|u_r\|_{C^1}} \to u$ *for* $r \to 0_+$ *where* $u \in Z_n^+$ *is a solution to BVP* (15.3), (15.4) *with* $a(t) = a(t,0)$, $c(t) = c(t,0)$, $\mu = \mu_0$, $\nu = \nu_0$ *and* $\|u\|_{C^1} = 1$.

Analogously for $A_n^-(0)$.

References

[1] R. A. ADAMS: *Sobolev Spaces*, Academic Press 1975.

[2] S. AGMON, A. DOUGLIS, L. NIRENBERG: Estimates near the boundary for solutions of elliptic partial differential equations satisfying general boundary conditions I, Comm. Pure Appl. Math. 12 (1959), 623 - 727.

[3] S. AHMAD: A resonance problem in which the nonlinearity may grow linearly, Proc. Amer. Math. Society 93 (1984), 381 - 384.

[4] S. AHMAD: Nonselfadjoint resonance problems with unbounded perturbations, Nonlinear Analysis T.M.A. 10 (1986), 147 - 156.

[5] S. AHMAD: Multiple nontrivial solutions of resonant and nonresonant asymptotically linear problems, Proc. Amer. Math. Society 96 (1986), 405 - 409.

[6] S. AHMAD, A. C. LAZER: Critical point theory and a theorem of Amaral and Pera, Boll. Un. Mat. Italiana 3-B (1984), 583 - 598.

[7] H. AMANN: A note on degree theory for gradient mappings, Proc. Amer. Math. Society 85 (1982), 591 - 595.

[8] H. AMANN, A. AMBROSETTI, G. MANCINI: Elliptic equations with non-invertible Fredholm linear part and bounded nonlinearities, Math. Z. 158 (1978), 179 - 194.

[9] A. AMBROSETTI, G. MANCINI: Theorems of existence and multiplicity for nonlinear elliptic problems with noninvertible linear part, Ann. Sc. Norm. Superiore 5 (1978), 15 - 28.

[10] A. AMBROSETTI, G. MANCINI: Existence and multiplicity results for non-linear elliptic problems with linear part at resonance. The case of the simple eigenvalue, J. Differential Equations 28 (1978), 220 - 245.

[11] A. AMBROSETTI, G. PRODI: On the inversion of some mappings with singularities between Banach spaces, Annali Mat. Pura Appl. 93 (1973), 321 - 347.

[12] A. ANANE: Simplicité et isolation de la premiére valeur propre du p-laplacien avec poids, C. R. Acad. Sci. Paris 305, Sér. 1 (1987), 725 - 728.

[13] A. ANANE, J. P. GOSSEZ: Strongly nonlinear elliptic problems near resonance: A variational approach, Comm. Part. Diff. Equations 15 (1990), 1141 - 1159.

[14] M. ARIAS: Existence results on the one-dimensional Dirichlet problem suggested by the piecewise linear case, Proc. Amer. Math. Society 97 (1986), 121 - 127.

[15] M. ARIAS: Nonselfadjoint boundary value problems at resonance with nonlinearities which may grow linearly, Nonlinear Analysis T.M.A. 15 (1990), 155 - 163.

[16] M. d'AUJOURD'HUI: Nonautonomous boundary value problems with jumping nonlinearities, Nonlinear Analysis T.M.A. 11 (1987), 969 - 977.

[17] M. d'AUJOURD'HUI: Problèmes aux limites elliptiques demilinéaires, Thése No.962 (1987), École Polytechnique Federale de Lausanne, pp. 127.

[18] M. d'AUJOURD'HUI: The stability of the resonance set for a problem with jumping nonlinearity, Proc. R. Soc. Edinb. A 107 (1987), 201 - 212.

[19] M. d'AUJOURD'HUI: On the number of solutions of some semilinear boundary value problems, in Proceedings of Equadiff 87.

[20] J. P. G. AZORERO, I. P. ALONSO: Existence and nonuniqueness for the p-laplacian: nonlinear eigenvalues, Comm. Part. Diff. Equations 12 (1987), 1389 - 1430.

[21] J. P. G. AZORERO, I. P. ALONSO: Comportement asymptotique des valeurs propres du p-laplacien , C. R. Acad. Sci. Paris 307, Sér. I (1988), 75 - 78.

[22] M. BADIALE, D. LUPO: Some remarks on a multiplicity result by Mawhin and Schmidt, preprint.

[23] A. BAHRI, H. BERESTYCKI: Points critiques de perturbations de funtionelles paires et applications, C. R. Acad. Sci. Paris, Sér. A-B (291), (1980), A 189 - A 192.

[24] A. BAHRI, H. BERESTYCKI: A perturbation method in critical point theory and applications, Trans. Amer. Math. Society 267 (1981), 1 - 32.

[25] G. BARLES: Remarks on uniqueness results of the first eigenvalue of the p-laplacian, Ann. Fac. Sci. Toulouse 9 (1988), 65 - 75.

[26] W. BARTH, R. S. MARTIN, J. H. WILKINSON: Calculation of the eigenvalues of a symmetric tridiagonal matrix by the method of bisection, Numer. Math. 9 (1967), 386 - 393.

[27] H. BERESTYCKI, D. G. de FIGUEIREDO: Double resonance in semilinear elliptic problems, Comm. Part. Diff. Equations 6 (1981), 91 - 120.

[28] L. BERS, F. JOHN, M. SCHECHTER: *Partial Differential Equations*, Interscience, New York, 1964.

[29] T. BHATTACHARYA: Radial symmetry of the first eigenfunction for the p-laplacian in the ball, Proc. Amer. Math. Society 104 (1988), 169 - 174.

[30] L. BOCCARDO, P. DRÁBEK, D. GIACHETTI, M. KUČERA: Generalization of Fredholm alternative for nonlinear differential operators, Nonlinear Analysis T.M.A. 10 (1986), 1083 - 1103.

[31] L. BOCCARDO, P. DRÁBEK, M. KUČERA: Landesman - Lazer conditions for strongly nonlinear boundary value problems, Comment. Math. Univ. Carolinae 30 (1989), 411 - 427.

[32] H. BRÉZIS: Semilinear equations in $\mathbb{R}^n$ without condition at infinity, Appl. Math. Optim. (in print).

[33] F. E. BROWDER: *Problèmes nonlinéaires*, Les presses de l'Université de Montreal, 1966.

[34] F. E. BROWDER, W. V. PETRYSHYN: Approximation methods and the generalized topological degree for nonlinear mappings in Banach spaces, J. Funct. Analysis 3 (1969), 217 - 245.

[35] L. BRÜLL, J. MAWHIN: Finiteness of the set of solutions of some boundary-value problems for ordinary differential equations, Archivum Math. 24 (1988), 163 - 172.

[36] A. CAÑADA: K-set contractions and nonlinear vector boundary value problems, J. Math. Anal. Appl. 117 (1986), 1 - 22.

[37] A. CAÑADA: Nonlinear boundary value problems for elliptic systems, Proc. Edinb. Math. Soc. 30 (1987), 257 - 272.

[38] A. CAÑADA: Nonselfadjoint semilinear elliptic boundary value problems, Annali Mat. Pura Appl. 148 (1987), 237 - 250.

[39] A. CAÑADA, P. MARTINES-AMORES: Solvability of some operator equations and periodic solutions of nonlinear functional differential equations, J. Differential Equations 48 (1983), 415 - 429.

[40] A. CAÑADA, P. MARTINES-AMORES: Periodic solutions of nonlinear vector ordinary differential equations of higher order at resonance, Nonlinear Analysis T.M.A. 7 (1983), 747 - 761.

[41] A. CAÑADA, R. ORTEGA: Existence theorems for equations in normed spaces and nonlinear boundary-value problems for nonlinear vector ordinary differential equations, Proc. R. Soc. Edinb. 98 A (1984), 1 - 11.

[42] A. CAPOZZI, D. LUPO, S. SOLIMINI: On the existence of a nontrivial solution to nonlinear problems at resonance, Nonlinear Analysis T.M.A. 13 (1989), 151 - 163.

[43] G. CARISTI: Monotone perturbations of linear operators having nullspace made of oscillatory functions, Nonlinear Analysis T.M.A. (1987), 851 - 860.

[44] G. CARISTI: On periodic solutions of systems of coupled pendulum-like equations, Int. J. Nonl. Mech. (in print).

[45] G. CARISTI: Periodic solutions of bounded perturbations of linear second order ordinary differential systems, Preprint no. 136, Univ. Trieste 1987, pp. 1 - 13.

[46] A. CASTRO: A two point boundary value problem with jumping nonlinearities, Proc. Amer. Math. Society 79 (1980), 207 - 211.

[47] A. CASTRO, A. KUREPA: Infinitely many radially symmetric solutions to a superlinear Dirichlet problem in a ball, Proc. Amer. Math. Society 101 (1987), 57 - 64.

[48] A. CASTRO, A. KUREPA: Radially symmetric solutions to a superlinear Dirichlet problem in a ball with jumping nonlinearities, Trans. Amer. Math. Society 315 (1989), 353 - 372.

[49] A. CASTRO, R. SHIVAJI: Multiple solutions for a Dirichlet problem with jumping nonlinearities, in: "Trends in Theory and Practice of Nonlinear Analysis" (V. Lakshmikantham Ed.), North Holland, Amsterodam, 1985.

[50] A. CASTRO, R. SHIVAJI: Multiple solution for a Dirichlet problem with jumping nonlinearities II, J. Math. Anal. Appl. 133 (1988), 509 - 528.

[51] L. CESARI, R. KANNAN: Qualitative study of a class of nonlinear boundary value problems at resonance, J. Differential Equations 56 (1985), 63 - 81.

[52] L. CESARI, R. KANNAN: Existence of solutions of a nonlinear differential equation, Proc. Amer. Math. Society 88 (1983), 605 - 613.

[53] J. CHABROWSKI: On the solvability of the Dirichlet problem for nonlinear elliptic equations, J. d'Analyse Math. 50 (1988), 65 - 78.

[54] J. CHABROWSKI: Remarks on multiplicity results for the Dirichlet problem for nonlinear elliptic equations, Rendiconti Circ. Mat. Palermo 37 (1988), 307 - 320.

[55] J. CHABROWSKI: Quasilinear ellipticity and the Dirichlet problem, Israel J. Math. 63 (1988), 353 - 379.

[56] K. C. CHANG: A variant mountain pass lemma, Sci. Sinica Sér. A (1983), 1241 - 1255.

[57] K. C. CHANG: Variational methods and sub and super-solutions, Sci. Sinica Sér. A (1983), 1256 - 1265.

[58] R. CHIAPPINELLI, J. MAWHIN, R. NUGARI: Generalized Ambrosetti-Prodi conditions for nonlinear two-point boundary value problems, J. Differential Equations 69 (1987), 422 - 434.

[59] R. CHIAPPINELLI, J. MAWHIN, R. NUGARI: Bifurcation from infinity and multiple solutions for some Dirichlet problems with unbounded nonlinearities, preprint.

[60] G. CITTI: Existence of infinitely many solutions for a quasilinear degenerate elliptic equation in $\mathbb{R}^n$, Nonlinear Analysis T.M.A. 12 (1988), 871 - 879.

[61] G. I. ČOBANOV: Semilinear elliptic equation with asymptotes.Some multiplicity and existence results, Math. Balcanica 1 (1987), 3 - 13.

[62] M. M. COCLITE: An existence result for variational problems and applications to some nonlinear hyperbolic and elliptic equations involving critical Sobolev exponent, Annali Mat. Pura Appl. 148 (1987), 207 - 226.

[63] M. M. COCLITE, G. PALMIERI: Multiplicity results for variational problems and applications, Boll. Un. Mat. Italiana 1-B (1987), 347 - 371.

[64] E. A. CODDINGTON, N. LEVINSON: *Theory of Ordinary Differential Equations*, McGraw-Hill, New York - Toronto - London 1955.

[65] J. V. A. CONCALVES: On bounded nonlinear perturbations of an elliptic equation at resonance, Nonlinear Analysis T.M.A. 9 (1985), 57 - 60.

[66] R. CONTI, R. IANNACCI, M. N. NKASHAMA: Periodic solutions of Liénard systems at resonance, Annali Mat. Pura Appl. 139 (1985), 313 - 328.

[67] D. G. COSTA, D. G. de FIGUEIREDO, J. V. A. CONCALVES: On the uniqueness of solution for a class of semilinear elliptic problems, J. Math. Anal. Appl. 123 (1987), 170 - 180.

[68] D. G. COSTA, A. S. OLIVEIRA: Existence of solution for a class of semilinear elliptic problems at double resonance, Boll. Soc. Bras. Mat. 19 (1988), 21 - 37.

[69] M. G. CRANDALL, P. H. RABINOWITZ: Bifurcation from simple eigenvalues, J. Functional Analysis 8 (1971), 321 - 340.

[70] E. N. DANCER: On the structure of the solutions of non-linear eigenvalue problems, Indiana Univ. Math. J. 23 (11) (1974), 1069 - 1076.

[71] E. N. DANCER: On a nonlinear elliptic boundary-value problem, Bull. Austral. Math. Soc. 12 (1975), 399 - 405.

[72] E. N. DANCER: Boundary value problems for weakly nonlinear ordinary differential equations, Bull. Austral. Math. Soc. 15 (1976), 321 - 328.

[73] E. N. DANCER: On the Dirichlet problem for weakly nonlinear elliptic partial differential equations, Proc. R. Soc. Edinb. 76 A (1977), 283 - 300.

[74] E. N. DANCER: On the use of asymptotics in nonlinear boundary value problems, Annali Mat. Pura Appl. 4 (1982), 167 - 185.

[75] E. N. DANCER: Counterexamples to some conjectures on the number of solutions on nonlinear equations, Math. Ann. 272 (1985), 421 - 440.

[76] E. N. DANCER: A counterexample to the Lazer-McKenna conjecture, Nonlinear Analysis T.M.A. 13 (1989), 19 - 21.

[77] E. N. DANCER: Multiple solutions of asymptotically homogeneous problems, Annali Mat. Pura Appl. 224 (1988), 63 - 78.

[78] K. DEIMLING: *Nonlinear Functional Analysis*, Springer-Verlag, Berlin - Heidelberg 1985.

[79] T. R. DING: Some fixed point theorems and periodically perturbed nondissipative systems, Chinese Ann. Math. 2 (1981), 281 - 300.

[80] T. R. DING: An infinite class of periodic solutions of periodically perturbed Duffing equations at resonance, Proc. Amer. Math. Society 86 (1982), 47 - 54.

[81] T. R. DING: Nonlinear oscillations at a point of resonance, Sci. Sinica Sér. A 25 (1982), 918 - 931.

[82] T. R. DING: Unbounded perturbations of forced harmonic oscillations at resonance, Proc. Amer. Math. Society 88 (1983), 59 - 66.

[83] P. DRÁBEK: Remarks on multiple periodic solutions of nonlinear ordinary differential equations, Comment. Math. Univ. Carolinae 21 (1980), 155 - 160.

[84] P. DRÁBEK: Ranges of a-homogeneous operators and their perturbations, Časopis pěst. mat. 105 (1980), 167 - 183.

[85] P. DRÁBEK: Solvability of the superlinear elliptic boundary value problem, Comment. Math. Univ. Carolinae 22 (1981), 27 - 35.

[86] P. DRÁBEK: Bounded nonlinear perturbations of second order linear elliptic problems, Comment. Math. Univ. Carolinae 22 (1981), 215 - 221.

[87] P. DRÁBEK: Solvability of nonlinear problems at resonance, Comment. Math. Univ. Carolinae 23 (1982), 359 - 367.

[88] P. DRÁBEK: Existence and multiplicity results for some weakly nonlinear elliptic problems at resonance, Časopis pěst. mat. 108 (1983), 272 - 284.

[89] P. DRÁBEK: Solvability of boundary value problems with homogeneous ordinary differential operators, Rendiconti Ist. Mat. Univ. Trieste 18 (1986), 105 - 124.

[90] P. DRÁBEK: On the resonance problem with nonlinearity which has arbitrary linear growth, J. Math. Anal. Appl. 127 (1987), 435 - 442.

[91] P. DRÁBEK: A resonance problem for nonlinear Duffing equation, Comment. Math. Univ. Carolinae 29 (1988), 205 - 215.

[92] P. DRÁBEK: Landesman-Lazer type condition and nonlinarities with linear growth, Czech. Math. J. 40 (1990), 70 - 86.

[93] P. DRÁBEK: Landesman-Lazer condition for nonlinear problems with jumping nonlinearities, J. Differential Equations 85 (1990), 186 - 199.

[94] P. DRÁBEK: On the global bifurcation for a class of degenerate equations, Annali Mat. Pura Appl. 155 (1991).

[95] P. DRÁBEK, S. INVERNIZZI: On the periodic BVP for the forced Duffing equations with jumping nonlinearity, Nonlinear Analysis T.M.A. 10 (1986), 643 - 650.

[96] P. DRÁBEK, S. INVERNIZZI: Periodic solutions for systems of forced coupled pendulum-like equations, J. Differential Equations 76 (1987), 390 - 402.

[97] P. DRÁBEK, M. KUČERA: Bifurcations of second order problems with jumping nonlinearities, Bull. Austr. Math. Society 37 (1988), 179 - 187.

[98] P. DRÁBEK, F. NICOLOSI: Semilinear boundary value problems at resonance with general nonlinearities, preprint 10/1990, VŠSE Plzeň.

[99] P. DRÁBEK, S. TERSIAN: Characterizations of the range of Neumann problem for semilinear elliptic equations, Nonlinear Analysis T.M.A. 11 (1987), 733 - 739.

[100] P. DRÁBEK, P. TOMICZEK: Remark on the structure of the range of second order nonlinear elliptic operator, Comment. Math. Univ. Carolinae 30 (1989), 455 - 464.

[101] N. DUNFORD, J. T. SCHWARTZ: *Linear Operators. Part I*, Interscience Publ., New York, 1958.

[102] H. EGNELL: Existence and nonexistence results for m-Laplace equations involving critical Sobolev exponents, preprint.

[103] H. ELOUARDI, F. de THÉLIN: Supersolutions and stabilization of the solution of a nonlinear parabolic system, Publ. Mat. Univ. Barcelona 33 (1989), 369 - 381.

[104] C. FABRY, A. FONDA: Periodic solutions of nonlinear differential equations with double resonance, Raport no.135, Sémin. Math. 1988, Louvain la Neuve, pp. 23.

[105] C. FABRY, J. MAWHIN, M. N. NKASHAMA: A multiplicity result for periodic solutions of forced nonlinear second order ordinary differential equations, Bull. London Math. Society 18 (1986), 173 - 180.

[106] M. C. L. FERNANDES, P. OMARI, F. ZANOLIN: On the solvability of a semilinear two-point BVP around the first eigenvalue, Differential and Integral Equations 2 (1989), 63 - 79.

[107] M. C. L. FERNANDES, F. ZANOLIN: Periodic solutions of a second order differential equation with one-sided growth restrictions on the restoring term, Arch. Math. 51 (1988), 151 - 163.

[108] M. FIEBIG-WITTMAACK: Multiplicity of solutions of a nonlinear boundary problem with homogeneous Neumann boundary conditions, Applicable Analysis 29 (1988), 253 - 268.

[109] D. G. de FIGUEIREDO: Semilinear elliptic equations at resonance: Higher eigenvalues and unbounded nonlinearities, in: "Recent Advances in Differential Equations" (R. Conti Ed.), pp. 89 - 99, Academic Press, London 1981.

[110] D. G. de FIGUEIREDO: On the superlinear Ambrosetti-Prodi problem, Nonlinear Analysis T.M.A. 8 (1984), 655 - 666.

[111] D. G. de FIGUEIREDO: On the existence of multiple ordered solutions of nonlinear eigenvalue problems, Nonlinear Analysis T.M.A. 11 (1987), 481 - 492.

[112] D. G. de FIGUEIREDO: On superlinear elliptic problems with nonlinearities interacting only with higher eigenvalues, Rocky Mountain J. Math. 18 (1988), 287 - 303.

[113] D. G. de FIGUEIREDO, J. P. GOSSEZ: Resonance below the first eigenvalue for a semilinear elliptic problem, Math. Ann. 281 (1988), 589 - 610.

[114] D. G. de FIGUEIREDO, W. M. NI: Perturbations of second order linear elliptic problems by nonlinearities without Landesman-Lazer condition, Nonlinear Analysis T.M.A. 5 (1981), 57 - 60.

[115] D. G. de FIGUEIREDO, S. SOLIMINI: A variational approach to superlinear elliptic problems, Comm. Partial Differential Equations 9 (1984), 669 - 717.

[116] A. FONDA: Variational problems at resonance without monotonicity, Bull. Cl. Sciences 5° série, Tome LXXIV (1988), 54 - 63.

[117] A. FONDA: Existence and multiplicity results for nonlinear boundary value problems by the use of topological and variational methods, PhD Thesis, Scuola Internat. Sup. di Studi Avanzati, Trieste 1988, pp. 168.

[118] A. FONDA, J. P. GOSSEZ: Semicoercive variational problems at resonance: an abstract approach, Differential and Integral Equations 3 (1990), 695 - 708.

[119] A. FONDA, P. HABETS: Periodic solutions of asymptotically positively homogeneous differential equations, J. Differential Equations 81 (1989), 68 - 97.

[120] A. FONDA, J. MAWHIN: Multiple periodic solutions of conservative systems with periodic nonlinearity, preprint.

[121] A. FONDA, J. MAWHIN: Quadratic forms, weighted eigenfunctions and boundary value problems for nonlinear second order ordinary differential equations, Proc. Royal Soc. Edinb. 112 (1989), 145 - 154.

[122] A. FONDA, F. ZANOLIN: On the use of time - maps for the solvability of nonlinear boundary value problems, preprint SISSA 121 M (1989).

[123] D. FORTUNATO, E. JANNELLI: Infinitely many solutions for some nonlinear elliptic problems in symmetrical domains, Proc. R. Soc. Edinb. 105 A (1987), 205 - 213.

[124] G. FOURNIER. J. MAWHIN: On periodic solutions of forced pendulum-like equations, preprint.

[125] S. FUČÍK: *Solvability of Nonlinear Equations and Boundary Value Problems*, D. Reidel Publ. Company, Holland 1980.

[126] S. FUČÍK: Boundary value problems with jumping nonlinearities, Časopis pěst. mat. 101 (1976), 69 - 87.

[127] S. FUČÍK, M. KUČERA, J. NEČAS: Ranges of nonlinear asymptotically linear operators, J. Differential Equations 17 (1975), 375 - 394.

[128] S. FUČÍK, A. KUFNER: *Nonlinear Differential Equations*, Elsevier, Holland 1980.

[129] S. FUČÍK, J. NEČAS, J. SOUČEK, V. SOUČEK: *Spectral Analysis of Nonlinear Operators*, Lecture Notes in Mathematics 346, Springer-Verlag 1973.

[130] T. GALLOUËT, O. KAVIAN: Résultats d'Existence et de Non-Existence pour certains Problèmes Demilinéaires a l'infini, Ann. Fac. Sc. de Toulouse (1981).

[131] T. GALLOUËT, O. KAVIAN: Resonance for jumping nonlinearities, Comm. Partial Differential Equations 7 (1982), 325 - 342.

[132] T. GALLOUËT, J. M. MOREL: The equation $-\Delta u + |u|^{\alpha-1} u = f$ for $0 \leqq \alpha \leqq 1$, Nonlinear Analysis T.M.A. 11 (1987), 893 - 912.

[133] F. GIANNONI, A. M. MICHELETTI: Some remarks about elliptic problems with jumping nonlinearity, Rendiconti di Matematica Appl., Sér. VII, Vol. 7 (1987), 145 - 157.

[134] F. GIANNONI A. M. MICHELETTI: On the number of solutions of some ordinary periodic boundary value problems by their geometrical properties, Preprint 1988/18, Univ. Pisa.

[135] F. GIANNONI, A. M. MICHELETTI: Some remarks about multiplicity results for some semilinear elliptic problems by singularities theory,

Rendiconti di Mat., Univ. Roma "La Sapienza", Vol. 8, Fas. 3 (1988), 367 - 384.

[136] M. GIAQUINTA, E. GIUSTI: On the regularity of the minima of variational integrals, Acta Math. 148 (1982), 31 - 46.

[137] D. GILBARG, N. S. TRUDINGER: *Elliptic Partial Differential Equations of Second Order*, Springer, New York, 1983.

[138] R. GLOWINSKI, A. MAROCCO: On the solutions of a class of nonlinear Dirichlet problems by a penalty-duality method and finite elements of order one, in "Optimization Techniques, IFIP Technical Conference", Lecture Notes in Computer Sciences 27, pp. 327 - 333, Springer Verlag, Berlin 1975.

[139] R. GLOWINSKI, A. MAROCCO: Sur l'approximation par éléments finis d'ordre 1, et la résolution par penalisation-dualité, d'une classe de problèmes de Dirichlet non linéaires, C. R. Acad. Sci. Paris Sér. A 278 (1984), 1649 - 1652.

[140] M. GUEDDA, L. VERON: Quasilinear elliptic equations involving critical Sobolev exponents, Nonlinear Analysis T.M.A. 13 (1989), 879 - 902.

[141] C. P. GUPTA: Perturbations of second order linear elliptic problems by unbounded nonlinearities, Nonlinear Analysis T.M.A. 6 (1982), 919 - 933.

[142] C. P. GUPTA: Solvability of a boundary value problem with the nonlinearity satisfying a sign condition, J. Math. Anal. Appl. 129 (1988), 482 - 492.

[143] C. P. GUPTA, J. J. NIETO, L. SANCHES: Periodic solutions of some Liénard and Duffing equations, J. Math. Anal. Appl. 140 (1989), 67 - 82.

[144] P. HABETS, M. N. NKASHAMA: On periodic solutions of nonlinear second order vector differential equations, Proc. R. Soc. Edinb. 104 A (1986), 107 - 125.

[145] P. HABETS, M. RAMOS, L. SANCHES: Jumping nonlinearity for 2nd order ODE with positive forcing, prepublicacões, Univ. de Lisboa 3/90 (1990).

[146] A. el HACHIMI, F. de THÉLIN: Supersolutions and stabilization of the solutions of the equation: $(\partial u/\partial t) - \mathrm{div}\,(|\Delta u|^{p-2}\,\Delta u) = f(x,u)$, Nonlinear Analysis T.M.A. 12 (1988), 1385 - 1398.

[147] J. K. HALE: *Ordinary Differential Equations*, Wiley - Interscience, New York, 1969.

[148] G. A. HARRIS: An extension of a theorem on semilinear elliptic problems, Nonlinear Analysis T.M.A. 14 (1990), 231 - 250.

[149] G. A. HARRIS: On multiple solutions of a nonlinear Neumann problem, preprint.

[150] G. A. HARRIS: The influence of boundary data on the number of solutions of boundary value problems with jumping nonlinearities, Trans. Amer. Math. Soc., to appear.

[151] G. A. HARRIS: A nonlinear Dirichlet problem with nonhomogeneous boundary data, Appl. Anal. 33 (1989), 169 - 182.

[152] D. C. HART, A. C. LAZER, P. J. McKENNA: Multiple solutions of two--point boundary value problems with jumping nonlinearities, J. Differential Equations 59 (1985), 266 - 281.

[153] J. HEINONEN, T. KILPELÄINEN, J. MALÝ: Connectedness in fine topologies, Universität Jyväskylä, preprint 97/1989.

[154] J. HEINONEN, T. KILPELÄINEN, O. MARTIO: Fine topology and quasilinear elliptic equations, Ann. Inst. Four. Univ. Grenoble 39 (1989), 293 - 318.

[155] G. HETZER: A note on a paper of Howard Shaw concerning a nonlinear elliptic boundary value problem, J. Differential Equations 32 (1979), 186 - 192.

[156] H. HIRANO: Multiple nontrivial solutions of semilinear elliptic equations, Proc. Amer. Math. Society 103 (1988), 468 - 472.

[157] H. HIRANO: Unbounded nonlinear perturbations of linear elliptic problems at resonance, J. Math. Analysis Appl. 132 (1988), 434 - 446.

[158] H. HIRANO: Existence of nontrivial solutions of semilinear elliptic equations, Nonlinear Analysis T.M.A. 13 (1989), 695 - 705.

[159] H. HOFER: Variational and topological methods in partially ordered Hilbert spaces, Math. Ann. 261 (1982), 493 - 514.

[160] Y. X. HUANG: On eigenvalue problems of the p-laplacian with Neumann boundary conditions, Proc. Amer. Mat. Society 109 (1990), 177 - 183.

[161] R. IANNACCI, M. N. NKASHAMA: Nonlinear boundary value problems at resonance, Nonlinear Analysis T.M.A. 11 (1987), 455 - 474.

[162] R. IANNACCI, M. N. NKASHAMA: Unbounded perturbations of forced second order ordinary differential equations at resonance, J. Differential Equations 69 (1987), 289 - 309.

[163] R. IANNACCI, M. N. NKASHAMA, P. OMARI, F. ZANOLIN: Periodic solutions of forced Liénard equations with jumping nonlinearities under non-uniform conditions, Proc. R. Soc. Edinb. 110 A (1988), 183 - 198.

[164] R. IANNACCI, M. N. NKASHAMA, J. R. WARD: Nonlinear second order elliptic partial differential equations at resonance, Trans. Amer.

Math. Society 311 (1989), 711 - 726.

[165] S. INVERNIZZI: A note on nonuniform nonresonance for jumping nonlinearities, Comment. Math. Univ. Carolinae 27 (1986), 285 - 291.

[166] S. INVERNIZZI: On the periodic BVP for the forced Duffing equation, Rendiconti Ist. Mat. Univ. Trieste 19 (1987), 64 - 75.

[167] L. JIAQUAN: A note on resonance problem,Boll. Un. Mat. Italiana 4-A (1990), 129 - 139.

[168] E. KAMKE: *Differential Gleichungen, Lözungs-methoden und Lözungen*, Leipzig 1959.

[169] R. KANNAN, V. LAKSHMIKANTHAM, J. J. NIETO: Sufficient conditions for existence of solutions of nonlinear boundary value problems at resonance, Nonlinear Analysis T.M.A. 7 (1983), 1013 - 1020.

[170] R. KANNAN, R. ORTEGA: Periodic solutions of pendulum-type equations, J. Differential Equations 59 (1985), 123 - 144.

[171] R. KANNAN, R. ORTEGA: An asymptotic result in forced oscillations of pendulum-type equations, Applicable Analysis 22 (1986), 45 - 53.

[172] R. KANNAN, R. ORTEGA: Superlinear elliptic boundary value problems, Czech. Math. J. 37 (1987), 386 - 399.

[173] R. KENT NAGLE, K. POTHOVEN, K. SINGKOFER: Nonlinear elliptic equations at resonance where the nonlinearity depends essentially on the derivatives, J. Differential Equations 38 (1980), 210 - 225.

[174] R. KENT NAGLE, K. SINGKOFER: Equations with unbounded nonlinearities, Nonlinear Analysis T.M.A. 4 (1980), 1189 - 1201.

[175] R. KENT NAGLE, K. SINGKOFER: Nonlinear ordinary differential equations at resonance with slowly varying nonlinearities, Applicable Analysis 11 (1980), 137 - 149.

[176] R. KENT NAGLE, K. SINGKOFER: Existence and multiplicity of solutions to nonlinear differential equations at resonance, J. Math. Anal. Appl. 94 (1983), 222 - 236.

[177] H. KIELHÖFER: A bifurcation theorem for potential operators, J. Functional Analysis 77 (1988), 1 - 8.

[178] T. KILPELÄINEN: Potential theory for supersolutions of degenerate elliptic equations, Indiana Univ. Math. J. 38 (1989), 253 - 275.

[179] T. KILPELÄINEN, J. MALÝ: On the nonlinear Dirichlet problem, Universität Jyväskylä, preprint 102/1989.

[180] A. KRATOCHVÍL, J. NEČAS: O diskretnosti spektra nělinějnoj zadači Šturma-Liouvillja četvertogo porjadka, Comment. Math. Univ. Carolinae 12 (1971), 639 - 653.

[181] M. G. KREIN, M. A. RUTMAN: Linějnyje operatory, ostavljajuščije invariantnym konus v prostranstve Banacha, Uspěchi Mat. Nauk, Tom 3 (23) (1948), 3 - 95.

[182] A. KUFNER, A. M. SÄNDIG: *Some Applications of Weighted Sobolev Spaces*, Teubner, Leipzig 1987.

[183] A. KUFNER, O. JOHN, S. FUČÍK: *Function Spaces*, Academia, Praha 1977.

[184] O. LADYZHENSKAYA, N. URALTSEVA: *Linear and Quasilinear Elliptic Equations*, Moscow, 1964 (Russian), English translation: New York, Academic Press 1968.

[185] E. M. LANDESMAN, A. C. LAZER: Nonlinear perturbations of linear elliptic boundary value problems at resonance, J. Math. Mech. 19 (1970), 609 - 623.

[186] A. C. LAZER, D. E. LEACH: Bounded perturbations of forced harmonic oscillators at resonance, Annali Mat. Pura Appl. 82 (1969), 49 - 68.

[187] A. C. LAZER, P. J. McKENNA: On the number of solutions of a nonlinear Dirichlet problem, J. Math. Anal. Appl. 84 (1981), 282 - 294.

[188] A. C. LAZER, P. J. McKENNA: On limitations to the solution set of some nonlinear problems, in: "Dynamical Systems II", pp. 247 - 253, Academic Press, New York - London 1982.

[189] A. C. LAZER, P. J. McKENNA: On a conjecture on the number of solutions of a nonlinear Dirichlet problem with jumping nonlinearity, in: "Trends in Theory and Practice of Nonlinear Differential Equations (Arlington, Texas 1982)", pp. 301 - 313, Lecture Notes in Pure and Appl. Math. 90, Dekker, New York 1984.

[190] A. C. LAZER, P. J. McKENNA: On a conjecture related to the number of solutions of a nonlinear Dirichlet problem, Proc. R. Soc. Edinb., Sec. A 95 (1983), 275 - 283.

[191] A. C. LAZER, P. J. McKENNA: Recent multiplicity results for nonlinear boundary value problems, in: "Differential Equations (Birmingham, Alabama 1983)", pp. 391 - 396, North Holland, Amsterdam - New York 1984.

[192] A. C. LAZER, P. J. McKENNA: Multiplicity results for a class of semilinear elliptic and parabolic boundary value problems, J. Math. Anal. Appl. 107 (1985), 371 - 395.

[193] A. C. LAZER, P. J. McKENNA: Multiplicity results for a semilinear boundary value problem with the nonlinearity crossing higher eigenvalues, Nonlinear Analysis T.M.A. 9 (1985), 335 - 350.

[194] A. C. LAZER, P. J. McKENNA: Critical point theory and boundary value problems with nonlinearities crossing multiple eigenvalues, Comm. Part. Diff. Equations 10 (1985), 107 - 150.

[195] A. C. LAZER, P. J. McKENNA: Multiplicity results for a semilinear boundary value problem with the nonlinearity crossing several eigenvalues, J. Reine Angew. Math. 368 (1986), 184 - 200.

[196] A. C. LAZER, P. J. McKENNA: A semi-Fredholm principle for periodically forced systems with homogeneous nonlinearities, Proc. Amer. Math. Society 106 (1989), 119 - 125.

[197] M. LEVI, F. C. HOPPENSTEAD, M. L. MIRANKER: Dynamics of the Josephson junction, Quart. Appl. Math. 36 (1978/79), 167 - 198.

[198] L. LIBOURTY: Traité de Glaceologie, Masson and Lie, Paris (I) 1964 et (II) 1965.

[199] G. M. LIEBERMAN: Boundary regularity for solutions of degenerate elliptic equations, Nonlinear Analysis T.M.A. 12 (1988), 1203 - 1219.

[200] P. LINDQVIST: Stability for the solution of $\operatorname{div}(|\nabla u|^{p-2} \nabla u) = f$ with varying p, J. Math. Anal. Appl. 127 (1987), 93 - 102.

[201] P. LINDQVIST: Regularity for the gradient of the solution to a nonlinear obstacle problem with degenerate ellipticity, Nonlinear Analysis T.M.A. 12 (1988), 1245 - 1255.

[202] P. LINDQVIST: On the equation $\operatorname{div}(|\nabla u|^{p-2} \nabla u) + \lambda |u|^{p-2} u = 0$, Proc. Amer. Math. Society 109 (1990), 157 - 164.

[203] J. L. LIONS: *Quelques méthodes de résolution de problèmes aux limites nonlinéaires*, Dunod Gauthier-Villars, Paris 1969.

[204] D. LUPO, S. SOLIMINI: A note on a resonance problem, preprint.

[205] D. LUPO, S. SOLIMINI, P. N. SRIKANTH: Multiplicity results for an O.D.E. problem with even nonlinearity, Nonlinear Analysis T.M.A. 12 (1988), 657 - 674.

[206] J. J. MANFREDI: p-harmonic functions in the plane, Proc Amer. Math. Soc. 103 (1988), 473 - 480.

[207] J. A. MARLIN: Periodic motions of coupled simple pedulums with periodic disturbances, Internat. J. Nonlinear Mech. 3 (1968), 439 - 447.

[208] J. MAWHIN: Une généralization de théoremes de J. A. Marlin, Internat. J. Nonlinear Mech. 5 (1970), 335 - 339.

[209] J. MAWHIN: Compacité, monotonie et convexité dans l'étude des problèmes aux limites semi-linéaires, "Sémin. d'Analyse Moderne" No. 19, Université de Sherbrooke 1981.

[210] J. MAWHIN: Periodic oscillations of forced pendulum-like equations, in: "Ordinary and Partial Differential Equations", Lecture Notes in Math., No. 964, pp. 458 - 476, Springer Verlag 1982.

[211] J. MAWHIN: Boundary value problems with nonlinearities having infinite jumps, Comment. Math. Univ. Carolinae 25 (1984), 401 - 414.

[212] J. MAWHIN: Forced second order conservative systems with periodic nonlinearity, Ann. Inst. H. Poincaré 6 (1989), 415 - 434.

[213] J. MAWHIN: Recent results on periodic solutions of the forced pendulum equation, Rend. Ist. Mat. Univ. Trieste 19 (1987), 119 - 129.

[214] J. MAWHIN, K. SCHMIDT: Landesman-Lazer type problems at an eigenvalue of odd multiplicity, Results in Math. 14 (1988), 138 - 146.

[215] J. MAWHIN, J. R. WARD: Periodic solutions of some forced Liénard differential equations at resonance, Arch. Math. 41 (1983), 337 - 351.

[216] J. MAWHIN, J. R. WARD: Nonresonance and existence for nonlinear elliptic boundary value problems, Nonlinear Analysis T.M.A. 5 (1981), 677 - 684.

[217] J. MAWHIN, M. WILLEM: Variational methods and boundary value problems for vector second order differential equations and applications to the pendulum equation, in "Nonlin. Anal. Optim.", ed. C. Vinti, Lecture Notes in Math. no. 1107, 1984.

[218] J. MAWHIN, M. WILLEM:Multiple solutions of the periodic boundary value problem for some forced pendulum-type equations, J. Differential Equations 52 (1984), 264 - 287.

[219] P. J. McKENNA, J. RAUCH: Strongly nonlinear perturbations of non-negative boundary value problems with kernel, J. Differential Equations 28 (1977), 253 - 265.

[220] P. J. McKENNA, R. REDLINGER, W. WALTER: Multiplicity results for asymptotically homogeneous semilinear boundary value problems, Ann. Mat. Pura Appl. 143 (1986), 247 - 258.

[221] G. METZEN: Existence of periodic solutions of second order differential equations with delay, Proc. Amer. Math. Society 103 (1988), 765 - 772.

[222] G. METZEN: A semilinear problem with jumping nonlinearities in unbounded domains, Nonlinear Analysis T.M.A. 12 (1988), 1221 - 1230.

[223] G. METZEN: Semilinear fourth order boundary value problems, Bull. Austral. Math. Society, Vol. 42 (1990), 101 - 114.

[224] A. M. MICHELETTI: On number of solutions of some nonlinear elliptic equations, Bollettino Un. Mat. Italiana 2-B (1988), 509 - 527.

[225] A. M. MICHELETTI: A remark on the resonance set for a semilinear elliptic equation, Preprint 1989/5, Universitá di Pisa, 1989, pp. 10.

[226] P. S. MILOJEVIČ: Solvability of some semilinear equations with strong nonlinearities and applications to elliptic problems, Applicable Analysis 25 (1987), 181 - 196.

[227] P. S. MILOJEVIČ: Solvability of semilinear equations with strong nonlinearities and applications to elliptic boundary value problems, Comment. Math. Univ. Carolinae 28 (1987), 735 - 750.

[228] C. MORREY: *Multiple Integrals in the Calculus of Variations*, Springer Verlag, Berlin - Heidelberg - New York 1966.

[229] E. NABANA, F. de THÉLIN: Unicité de la solution radiale positive de l'équation quasilinéaire: $\Delta_p u + f(u,|x|) = 0$, C.R. Acad. Sci. Paris 307 (1988), 763 - 766.

[230] J. NEČAS: Sur l'alternative de Fredholm pour les operateurs nonlinéaires avec applications aux problèmes aux limites, Ann. Scuola Norm. Sup. Pisa 23 (1969), 331 - 345.

[231] J. NEČAS: O diskretnosti spektra nělinějnoj zadači Šturma-Liouvillja vtorogo porjadka, Dokl. Akad. Nauk SSSR 201 (1971), 1045 - 1048.

[232] J. J. NIETO: Aronszajn's theorem for some nonlinear Dirichlet problems with unbounded nonlinearities, Proc. Edinb. Math. Society 31 (1988), 345 - 351.

[233] J. J. NIETO: Remarks on some nonlinear Dirichlet problems with unbounded nonlinearities, Comment. Math. Univ. Carolinae 31 (1990), 511 - 515.

[234] J. J. NIETO, L. SANCHES: Periodic boundary value problem for some Duffing equations, Differential and Integral Equations 1 (1988), 399 - 408.

[235] F. I. NJOKU, F. ZANOLIN: On the solvability of a nonlinear two point BVP between the first two eigenvalues, Differential and Integral Equations 3 (1990), 571 - 588.

[236] M. N. NKASHAMA: Solutions périodiques des systémes non conservatifs périodiquement perturbés, Bull. Soc. Math. France 113 (1985), 387 - 402.

[237] M. N. NKASHAMA: Peridically perturbed nonconservative systems of Liénard type, Proc. Amer. Math. Society 111 (1991), 677 - 682.

[238] M. N. NKASHAMA, J. SANTANILLA: Existence of multiple solutions for some nonlinear boundary value problems, J. Differential Equations 84 (1990), 148 - 164.

[239] NGUYEN PHUONG CÁC: On an elliptic boundary value problem at double resonance, J. Math. Anal. Appl. 132 (1988), 473 - 483.

[240] NGUYEN PHUONG CÁC: On nontrivial solutions of an asymptotically linear Dirichlet problem, J. Differential Equations 75 (1988), 103 - 117.

[241] NGUYEN PHUONG CÁC: On the number of solutions of an elliptic boundary value problem with jumping nonlinearity, Nonlinear Analysis T.M.A. 13 (1989), 341 - 353.

[242] NGUYEN PHUONG CÁC: On nontrivial solutions of a Dirichlet problem whose jumping nonlinearity crosses a multiple eigenvalue, J. Differential Equations 80 (1989), 379 - 404.

[243] P. OMARI, G. VILLARI, F. ZANOLIN: Periodic solutions of the Liénard equation with one-sided growth restriction, J. Differential Equations 67 (1987), 278 - 293.

[244] P. OMARI, F. ZANOLIN: Existence results for forced nonlinear periodic BVPs at resonance, Annali Mat. Pura Appl. 141 (1985), 127 - 157.

[245] P. OMARI, F. ZANOLIN: Some remarks about the paper "Periodic solutions of the Liénard equation with one sided growth restrictions" (unpublished internal report), Trieste 1986.

[246] P. OMARI, F. ZANOLIN: On the existence of periodic solutions of forced Liénard differential equations, Nonlinear Analysis T.M.A. 11 (1987), 275 - 284.

[247] P. OMARI, F. ZANOLIN: A note on nonlinear oscillations at resonance, Acta Math. Sinica, Vol. 3 (1987), 351 - 361.

[248] P. OMARI, F. ZANOLIN: Nonlinear oscillations at resonance, in: Proceedings of 11th Inter. Conf. on Nonlinear Oscillations", Budapest 1987, pp. 463 - 466.

[249] R. ORTEGA: A counterexample for the damped pendulum equation, Bull. Cl. Sciences 5° série, Tome LXXIII (1987), 405 - 409.

[250] R. ORTEGA: Stability and index of periodic solutions of an equation of Duffing type, Boll. Un. Mat. Italiana 3-B (1989), 533 - 546.

[251] R. ORTEGA: Stability of a periodic problem of Ambrosetti-Prodi type, Differential and Integral Equations 3 (1990), 275 - 284.

[252] M. ÔTANI: Existence and nonexistence of nontrivial solutions of some nonlinear degenerate elliptic equations, J. Functional Analysis 76 (1988), 140 - 159.

[253] M. ÔTANI, T. TESHIMA: On the first eigenvalue of some quasilinear elliptic equations, Proc. Japan Acad. 64, Sér. A (1988), 8 - 10.

[254] M. C. PÉLLISIER, L. REYMOND: Étude d'un modéle mathématique d'écoulement de glacier, C. R. Acad. Sci. Paris, Sér. A 279 (1979), 531 - 534.

[255] W. V. PETRYSHYN, Z. S. YU: Boundary value problems at resonanace for certain semilinear ordinary differential equations, J. Math. Anal. Appl. 98 (1984), 72 - 91.

[256] W. V. PETRYSHYN, Z. S. YU: On the solvability of an equation describing the periodic motions of a satellite in its elliptic orbit, Nonlinear Analysis T.M.A. 9 (1985), 969 - 975.

[257] M. del PINO, M. ELGUETA, R. MANASEVICH: A homotopic deformation along p of a Leray-Schauder degree result and existence for

$$(|u'|^{p-2} u')' + f(t,u) = 0 , \quad u(0) = u(T) = 0 , \quad p > 1 ,$$

J. Differential Equations 80 (1989), 1 - 13.

[258] M. del PINO, R. MANASEVICH: Oscillation and nonoscillation for

$$(|u'|^{p-2} u')' + a(t)|u|^{p-2} u = 0 , \quad p > 1 ,$$

Houston J. Math. 14 (1988), 173 - 177.

[259] S. I. POCHOŽAJEV: O razrešimosti nělinějnych uravněnij s něčotnymi operatorami, Funkc. Anal. Priloženija 1 (1967), 66 - 72.

[260] P. H. RABINOWITZ: Some global results for nonlinear eigenvalue problems, J. Functional Analysis 7 (1971), 487 - 513.

[261] M. RAMASWAMY: On the global set of solutions of a nonlinear ODE: Theoretical and numerical description, J. Differential Equations 65 (1987), 1 - 48.

[262] M. RAMOS, L. SANCHES: Multiple periodic solutions for some nonlinear ordinary differential equations of higher order, Differential and Integral Equations 2 (1989), 81 - 90.

[263] B. RUF: On nonlinear elliptic problems with jumping nonlinearities, Ann. Mat. Pura Appl. 128 (1980), 133 - 151.

[264] B. RUF: Multiplicity results for superlinear elliptic equations, in: "Nonlinear Funct. Anal. Appl. (Maratea, 1985)", pp. 353 - 367, Reidel, Dordrecht - Boston, Mass. 1986.

[265] B. RUF: Remarks and generalizations related to a recent multiplicity result of A. Lazer and P. McKenna, Nonlinear Analysis T.M.A. 9 (1985), 1325 - 1330.

[266] B. RUF: A nonlinear Fredholm alternative for second order ordinary differential equations, Math. Nachr. 127 (1986), 299 - 308.

[267] B. RUF, S. SOLOMINI: On a class of superlinear Sturm-Liouville problems with arbitrarily many solutions, SIAM J. Math. Anal. 17 (1986), 761 - 771.

[268] B. RUF, P. N. SRIKANTH: Multiplicity results for superlinear elliptic problems with partial interference with the spectrum, J. Math. Anal. Appl. 118 (1986), 15 - 23.

[269] B. RUF, P. N. SRIKANTH: Multiplicity results for ODEs with nonlinearities crossing all but finite number of eigenvalues, Nonlinear Analysis T.M.A. 10 (1986), 157 - 163.

[270] L. SANCHES: Resonance problems with nonlinearity interfering with eigenvalues of higher order, Applicable Analysis 25 (1987), 275 - 286.

[271] J. SANTANILLA: Solvability of a nonlinear boundary value problem without Landesman-Lazer condition, Nonlinear Analysis T.M.A. 13 (1989), 683 - 693.

[272] M. SCHECHTER: Nonlinear elliptic boundary value problems at resonance, Nonlinear Analysis T.M.A. 14 (1990), 889 - 903.

[273] M. SCHECHTER, J. SHAPIRO, M. SNOW: Solutions of the nonlinear problem Au = N(u) in a Banach space, Trans. Amer. Math. Society 241 (1978), 69 - 78.

[274] K. SCHMIDT: Boundary value problems with jumping nonlinearities, Rocky Mountain J. Math. 16 (1986), 481 - 496.

[275] H. SHAW : Nonlinear elliptic boundary value problems at resonance, J. Differential Equations 26 (1977), 335 - 346.

[276] I. V. SKRYPNIK: *Nonlinear Elliptic Boundary Value Problems* (Russian) Naukovaja Dumka, Kyjev 1973, English translation: Teubner, Leipzig 1986.

[277] S. SOLIMINI: Existence of a third solution for a class of B.V.P. with jumping nonlinearities, Nonlinear Analysis T.M.A. 7 (1983), 917 - 927.

[278] S. SOLIMINI: Multiplicity results for a nonlinear Dirichlet problem, Proc. R. Soc. Edinb. 96 A (1984), 331 - 336.

[279] S. SOLIMINI: Some remarks on the number of solutions of some nonlinear elliptic problems, Ann. Inst. H. Poincaré 2 (1985), 143 - 156.

[280] S. SOLIMINI: On the solvability of some elliptic partial differential equations with the linear part at resonance, J. Math. Anal. Appl. 117 (1986), 138 - 152.

[281] SONG-SUN LIN: Some results for semilinear differential equations at resonance, J. Math. Anal. Appl. 93 (1983), 574 - 592.

[282] G. TARANTONELLO: On the number of solutions for the forced pendulum equation, J. Differential Equations 80 (1989), 79 - 93.

[283] F. de THÉLIN: Résultats d'existence et de non-existence pour la solution positive et bornée d'une elliptique non linéaire, Ann. Fac. Sci. Toulouse, 8 (1986/87), 375 - 389.

[284] F. de THÉLIN: Positive solutions of an elliptic equation with strongly nonlinear lower order terms, Revista Matematica Univ. Madrid 2 (1989), 271 - 287.

[285] P. TOLKSDORF: Regularity of a more general class of quasilinear elliptic equations, J. Differential Equations 51 (1984), 126 - 150.

[286] H. TRIEBEL: Mapping properties of non-linear operators generated by $\Phi(u) = |u|^p$ and by holomorphic $\Phi(u)$ in function spaces of Besov--Hardy-Sobolev type. Boundary value problems for elliptic differential equations of type $\Delta u = f(x) + \Phi(u)$, Math. Nachr. 117 (1984), 193 - 213.

[287] WAN SE KIM: Boundary value problem for nonlinear telegraph equations with superlinear growth, Nonlinear Analysis T.M.A. 12 (1988), 1371 - 1376.

[288] J. R. WARD: Existence theorems for nonlinear boundary value problems at resonance, J. Differential Equations 35 (1980), 232 - 247.

[289] J. R. WARD: Periodic solutions for systems of second order differential equations, J. Math. Anal. Appl. 81 (1981), 92 - 98.

[290] J. R. WARD: Asymptotic conditions for periodic solutions of ordinary differential equations, Proc. Amer. Math. Society 81 (1981), 415 - 420.

[291] J. R. WARD: Existence for a class of semilinear problems at resonance, J. Differential Equations 45 (1982), 156 - 167.

[292] J. R. WARD: Perturbations with some superlinear growth for a class of second order elliptic boundary value problems, Nonlinear Analysis T.M.A. 6 (1982), 367 - 374.

[293] J. R. WARD: A boundary value problem with a periodic nonlinearity, Nonlinear Analysis T.M.A. 10 (1986), 207 - 213.

[294] J. R. WARD: A note on the Dirichlet problem for some semilinear elliptic equations, preprint.

[295] M. WILLEM: Topology and semilinear equations at resonance in Hilbert space, Nonlinear Analysis T.M.A. 5 (1981), 517 - 524.

[296] S. A. WILLIAMS: A sharp sufficient condition for solution of a nonlinear elliptic boundary value problem, J. Differential Equations 8 (1970), 580 - 586.

[297] G. T. WHYBURN: *Topological Analysis*, Princeton, Princeton University Press 1958.

[298] F. ZANOLIN: Remarks on multiple periodic solutions for nonlinear ordinary differential systems of Liénard type, Boll. Un. Mat. Italiana 1-B (1982), 683 - 698.

Subject index